SELECTED BOTANICAL PAPERS

PRENTICE-HALL BIOLOGICAL SCIENCE SERIES

William D. McElroy and Carl P. Swanson, *Editors*

BIOCHEMICAL SYSTEMATICS,* by Ralph E. Alston and B. L. Turner
CLASSIC PAPERS IN GENETICS, by James A. Peters
EXPERIMENTAL BIOLOGY, by Richard W. Van Norman
MECHANISMS OF BODY FUNCTIONS, by Dexter M. Easton
MILESTONES IN MICROBIOLOGY, by Thomas D. Brock
PRINCIPLES OF BIOLOGY, by Neal D. Buffaloe
SELECTED BOTANICAL PAPERS, by Irving W. Knobloch
A SYNTHESIS OF EVOLUTIONARY THEORY, by Herbert H. Ross

CONCEPTS OF MODERN BIOLOGY SERIES

BEHAVIORAL ASPECTS OF ECOLOGY,* by Peter H. Klopfer

FOUNDATIONS OF MODERN BIOLOGY SERIES

ADAPTATION, by Bruce Wallace and A. M. Srb
ANIMAL BEHAVIOR, by Vincent Dethier and Eliot Stellar
ANIMAL DIVERSITY, by Earl D. Hanson
ANIMAL GROWTH AND DEVELOPMENT, by Maurice Sussman
ANIMAL PHYSIOLOGY, by Knut Schmidt-Nielsen
THE CELL, by Carl P. Swanson
CELLULAR PHYSIOLOGY AND BIOCHEMISTRY, by William D. McElroy
HEREDITY, by David M. Bonner
THE LIFE OF THE GREEN PLANT, by Arthur W. Galston
MAN IN NATURE, by Marston Bates
THE PLANT KINGDOM, by Harold C. Bold

* These titles are also in the Prentice-Hall International Series in Biological Science. Prentice-Hall, Inc.; Prentice-Hall International, United Kingdom and Eire; Prentice-Hall of Canada, Ltd., Canada; Berliner Union, West Germany and Austria.

SELECTED
BOTANICAL PAPERS

edited by

Irving William Knobloch
Professor of Botany
Michigan State University

Prentice-Hall, Inc.
Englewood Cliffs, N. J.

PRENTICE-HALL INTERNATIONAL, INC., *London*
PRENTICE-HALL OF AUSTRALIA, PTY., LTD., *Sydney*
PRENTICE-HALL OF CANADA, LTD., *Toronto*
PRENTICE-HALL FRANCE, S.A.R.L., *Paris*
PRENTICE-HALL OF INDIA (PRIVATE) LTD., *New Delhi*
PRENTICE-HALL OF JAPAN, INC., *Tokyo*
PRENTICE-HALL DE MEXICO, S.A., *Mexico City*

Third printing ....June, 1965

Library of Congress Catalog Card Number: 63–14908

Printed in the United States of America

C—76087

PREFACE

The roots of botanical inquiry reach back into the misty past. The first human being was probably surrounded on all sides by vegetation of one sort or another and no formal education was involved in his trial and error methods of ascertaining which plants were suitable for food, which were unpalatable, and which were definitely poisonous. The second generation of mankind profited to the extent that the parents were available as teachers. Life has thus proceeded, learners becoming teachers. At some point in Man's history, the teaching profession became established, partly as a means of making a livelihood and partly as a method of satisfying an urge to open up the wonders of the universe to the uninitiated.

Botanical instruction has been given to millions of students during the course of hundreds of years. Many of these students have responded to the "call" and have carried the torch of learning forward by becoming great teachers or by making significant contributions to knowledge or by doing both.

For the most part, the emphasis in botanical instruction has been on straight factual matter. In the last one hundred years or so the pace of factual accumulation has gradually accelerated to the point where each teacher begins to know "more and more about less and less." The sum total of knowledge is so great that more careful selection has to be made in the classroom. Much important material has to be omitted or passed over hurriedly. In some schools only really important "blocks" of knowledge are considered, with the "gaps" bridged over by a few well-chosen words.

In the general botany course, we also have to consider what type of students we are teaching and ask ourselves—why are they taking botany? William James once said "The natural enemy of any subject is the professor thereof." Judging by the course content of many freshman botany courses, it seems apparent that teachers have assumed that the course in question must lay a fundamental background for the more advanced courses. Many botanical philosophers have pointed out the error of this thinking. C. Stuart Gager pointed out that the first course will be the *last* course for most students. Barzun, in a study of large freshman enrollments in midwestern colleges, showed that 50 per cent of those taking Chemistry I, 60 per cent of those taking Geology I, 73 per cent of those taking Physics I, 75 per cent of those taking Biology I, and 82 per cent of those taking Botany I *never* go further into these subjects. Note the figure for Botany! This may be a sad commentary on our ability to interest students in the field. While we do not intend to make botanists out of a majority of our freshman students, yet we should expect to interest more than we do in the cultural and aesthetic aspects of the subject.

The first course in almost any subject should be made rich in cultural, aesthetic, and philosophic phases. Memorization of factual material should not obscure the important development of thinking ability. Botany can offer much to make the free time of people worthwhile and meaningful.

This book has been compiled with the hope that it will serve a purpose in aiding to fulfil many of the objectives of a modern course in botany.

Most of the classical selections will point up the states of knowledge and the methods of inquiry existing in the earlier days of the subject. The more modern writings, for the most part, pass over the minute details and stress the developmental background, the modern ways of attacking problems, the implications for modern man, the ramification of the subject and the philosophic aspects, as a whole.

By a wise selection of subject matter from textbooks and readings from this book, the author hopes that students in botany will emerge from their course with a broader perspective, with an aroused interest, and with a strong desire to pursue further work in botany.

The writer's thanks are expressed to the many botanists who have expressed an interest in this type of endeavor and have encouraged me in one way or another.

Acknowledgments are also due to many writers and publishers who have kindly contributed selections. Such acknowledgments are made at the appropriate place. It is regrettable that our effort to obtain a broad spectrum of botanical thought has necessitated leaving out some important passages from all of the articles. It is our hope that students will be stimulated to read the original article in its entirety and go on from there into other areas.

IRVING WILLIAM KNOBLOCH

TABLE OF CONTENTS

PART FOUR

PHYTOGEOGRAPHY AND EXPLORATION 43

PART FIVE

SYSTEMATIC BOTANY 65

PART SIX

ANATOMY AND MORPHOLOGY 81

PART SEVEN

PHYSIOLOGY 95

PART SIXTEEN

PART SEVENTEEN

PART EIGHTEEN

INTRODUCTION

Botany is a very diverse subject if one includes all of the branches which have sprung from it. Algology (study of algae), Mycology (study of fungi), Plant Pathology (diseases of plants), Bryology (mosses), Pteridology (ferns), Anatomy (structure), Histology (tissues), Technique, Physiology (function), Cytology (cells), Genetics (study of heredity), Economic Plants, Poisonous Plants, Taxonomy (classification), Phytogeography (distribution of plants), Seed Testing, and Weed Control are usually considered as strictly botanical subjects. In addition to these, there are many botanical subjects which are taught in separate departments, largely because they have become so specialized. Included in this category are Bacteriology (soil, dairy, general, medical, physiological, taxonomic), Virology (viruses), Farm Crops, Plant Breeding, Forestry, Wood Technology, General Horticulture, Pomology (fruits), Floriculture (flowers), Olericulture (vegetables), and possibly others.

Many thousands of trained people are teaching botanical subjects throughout the world and hundreds of thousands of students are being taught. The study of plants serves many purposes. Many take courses in botany because they enjoy the beauty of the plant world, while others realize the paramount importance of plants in the past, present, and future and wish to have some knowledge of this phase of learning. Others regard botany as a stepping stone to some career in the same or a related subject.

From the aesthetic viewpoint, the higher plants have an advantage over the animals in that they are not only more colorful but they are sedentary. One can usually be sure of continuous enjoyment since the same plant or its progeny will be in about the same place in woods or garden, year after year. There is something about a beautiful fern or flower that strikes a responsive "chord" in the human brain. Artists and poets alike draw inspiration from the detail and beauty of plants, not to mention engineers. Along with the beauty, comes a desire to preserve it for our posterity. Sound conservation practices must be stepped up to keep pace with the destructive forces.

The majority of students taking botany are simply interested in the world of plant life *per se*, although it would be difficult to separate this group from the preceding one. The contacts one has with botany start early in the morning with coffee, bread, and cereals and continue in one way or another throughout the day. From infancy to old age one sees, hears about, feels and tastes plants or their products. The bulk of man's shelter (wood, fiber-board), food (cereals, fruits, vegetables, condiments) and clothing (rayon, cotton, linen) comes from the plant world.

Almost everyone realizes that animals are dependent upon green plants for food, directly or indirectly, in the marvelous though not completely understood process of photosynthesis. It is not always emphasized that the oxygen by-product is very important in maintaining this element in the atmosphere for animal use.

Many students are familiar with the drugs derived from plants such as belladonna, digitalis, morphine, and strychnine. Not as many are aware of the fact that the "wonder drugs" penicillin, aureomycin, streptomycin, and chloromycetin are products of the lowly molds. The sale of antibiotics products in the United States reaches hundreds of millions of dollars each year. It is surprising to some to learn that bacteria are plants and, more astounding still, to find out that most species of bacteria are harmless and not a few definitely beneficial.

When a person speaks of plants seeking the light, roots searching for water, and flowers blooming in the spring to avoid being shaded later by the trees of the forest, they are being teleological—they are ascribing human attributes to organisms which do not think or feel as human beings do. In a book on plant physiology we find the statement: "Man's knowledge that water and light are essential to plants is not evidence that plants are similarly aware of these facts." The knowledge of plant hormones (auxins) and their functions is being put to work to dispel much of this type of thinking.

Through faulty training in their earlier years, students come to the botany course with a ridiculous idea about respiration. It is difficult in many cases to fix the notion that all living plants and animals respire all the time and when they cease this activity, they are dead. They confuse cellular respiration with breathing.

Sex, being the number two driving force in the human being, is always of interest to students. Plants are very "sexy" albeit unemotional or, more properly, emotionless. This latter characteristic need not detract from the fact that plants possess many wonderful devices and structures designed for reproductive purposes. Botany brings home, or can, the similarity of pattern pervading much of the biological world in regard to sex. Ignoring the few exceptions, we find that the higher plants and animals all have sex cells or gametes, fertilization takes place and, in a moist medium, a zygote results; and from this zygote the embryo, and subsequently the adult, will develop.

Enough has been written to show that great benefits can result from the study of botany. The articles to follow will amplify what has been said and delve deeper into the relationships of modern man and modern botany.

PART ONE

THE IMPORTANCE OF PLANTS

In a world preoccupied with thoughts of the destructive power of the atom and hydrogen bombs, with the equally deadly population explosion, with the rise and fall of governments, and with monetary crises, it seems almost trivial, at first glance, to talk about the importance of plants. However, it is not really an inappropriate topic if one recalls that before he goes to work at Los Alamos, *the physicist eats his breakfast, possibly packs his lunch, and is glad to return home to dinner. These three meals, repeated day in and day out, are composed of plant products or of animal proteins made from grass leaves.*

Then too, our physicist friend arrays himself in the morning with cotton clothes made from the plant genus Gossypium *or in wool made from grass-eating sheep. Some of the newer fibers are made from cellulose, the principal ingredient of plant cell walls. One cannot overlook the additional fact that wood from trees is one of the primary building materials of the world. Many other plant products have never been successfully synthesized.*

It is not generally realized that food plays a part in world politics and the balance for power. If the communist countries were as well-fed and prosperous as we are, they might well become more aggressive than they are and create a great deal more world tension. Food, often overlooked in our thinking, is still man's basic need.

William J. Robbins

The Importance of Plants

Reprinted with the permission of the author and publishers from Science **C**: Nov. 17, 1944 and Ann. Rept. Smith. Instit. for 1945: 305–312, 1946.

Plants are the basis upon which all other life depends. In the last analysis they supply us with all the food we eat, they maintain the oxygen content of the air and they are the primary source of those important accessory foods, the vitamins. Without plants we would starve to death, die of suffocation, and expire from a combination of deficiency diseases. In addition, plants are the chief means by which the energy of the sun is and has been in ages past caught and stored for us in usable form. Without plants fire would be unknown because there would be no wood or coal or petroleum to burn, and electricity—except as a natural phenomenon—would be at most limited to areas freely supplied with water power.

The essential relation of plants to the food we eat, the air we breathe, and the energy we dissipate with such reckless abandon is based on two of their characteristics. These are their ability to store the energy of the sun's rays in sugar, starch, cellulose, oils, fats, and other constituents of the plant body, and their ability to construct from simple and elementary substances types of chemical compounds necessary for the existence of animals, including ourselves.

The first of these powers, limited from a practical standpoint to plants which possess the green pigment chlorophyll, is the familiar process of photosynthesis in which the plant transforms water obtained from the soil and gaseous carbon dioxide from the air into sugar and oxygen. In the course of photosynthesis, the first part of which occurs only in the light, energy from the sun is stored in the product sugar and in the starch, wood, oils, and fats, or other organic substances constructed by living things from this sugar. The energy we obtain by burning coal, lignite, peat, and petroleum was stored by the activity of plants in the dim past. It represents our capital stock of usable energy and once dissipated cannot be recovered. The energy in wood, sugar, plant and animal oils and fats released by burning or by the metabolism of living things is that part of the sun's energy stored in our time. This can be regenerated within a reasonable period by the activity of plants now growing. Other sources of power, water power, wind power, power from the tides, are minor in comparison with the energy which has been and is being stored by the photosynthesis of plants.

The major features of this essential process were discovered and elaborated by Joseph Priestly, Ingenhousz, Boussingault, and others over a period of about 100 years beginning in 1771 and are taught in every course in botany and biology. The details of how chlorophyll works are, however, still unknown, and the basic and essential character of the process is not yet a part of our national thinking. If it were, the small group of men who are attempting to discover how photosynthesis occurs—that is, how plants store the sun's rays—would receive more encouragement and assistance than they do, and in the discussions of the future of synthetic rubber made from petroleum we would see some consideration given to the wisdom, from the long view, of using petroleum in quantity to make something which can be produced from the air and water by the activity of plants.

Perhaps the significance of photosynthesis for our mechanical age could be more clearly grasped if it were possible to prepare a balance sheet on the world's store of available energy and the rate at which it is being dissipated. This cannot be done. We can say that the coal and petroleum burned annually represents a net loss of potential energy, and we can also say that in time, though not in what time, we will have to depend upon the energy fixed annually by plants unless some other source at present not at our command, for example, atomic energy, is discovered and methods for its utilization devised.

How much energy is fixed annually by plants? Abbot has estimated that the energy given off by the sun amounts to the equivalent of 4×10^{23} tons of coal annually, of which the earth intercepts a small fraction, the equivalent of 2×10^{14} tons of coal. According to Berl, plants fix each year 2.7×10^{11} metric tons of carbon, which is the equivalent of somewhere near 3×10^{11} tons of coal. If these figures are approximately correct, then about 0.15 percent of that part of the sun's energy which falls on the earth is caught annually and stored by plants.

Riley has estimated that photosynthetic efficiency of the world as a whole to be 0.18 percent and that of the land areas 0.09 percent.

Another set of data leads to somewhat the same conclusion. Transeau calculated that 1.6 percent of the sun's energy was utilized by a field of corn in Illinois during the 100 days of its growing season. Since for much of the rest of the year a cornfield lacks vegetation it would appear that something less than 1 percent of the sun's energy annually reaching corn land in Illinois is fixed. In some parts of the Tropics and other sections of the world where vegetation is active the year round this proportion would be larger; on the other hand, in the Arctic and in deserts it would be much less. We may be justified, therefore, in assuming that the annual energy fixation of plants approximates the equivalent of 3×10^{11} tons of coal.

This astronomical figure is at first sight quite comforting, particularly when we learn that in energy value it is over 200 times the coal and oil burned in 1938. The difficulty is that most of this annal income is not used. Wood, alcohol produced in fermentation, and plant waste play but a minor part in furnishing heat or mechanical energy because of their inconvenience, expense, or lack of adaptability to modern machinery. We depend at present upon coal and petroleum, the world's capital stock of available energy, to supply the amount required for this mechanical age.

Berl has reported a method by which motor fuel equal in many respects to petroleum can be produced from cellulose, starch, sugar, and other carbohydrates, thus offering the possibility of replacing our stock of usable stored energy by utilizing part of the current day-to-day income. Carbohydrates only can be used by Berl's method; lignin, protein, oils, and fats are unsuitable as crude materials. However, if all the carbohydrates in all the plants were used as Berl suggests, and this is obviously impracticable, we would have but 6 times the present annual consumption of petroleum and less than 2 times the equivalent of the annual world consumption of petroleum and coal. If all the world used coal and petroleum as we did in this country in 1942, the total energy fixed by plants would be but 25 times that dissipated and all the carbohydrates made each year would yield about one-third the amount the world would need. We can only guess what these figures would be if we knew the energy consumption for the war years of 1944 and 1945.

Two years ago the National Science Fund asked a representative group of outstanding scientists to list the problems with which scientific research should be concerned in the postwar era and on which special emphasis should be placed. Future sources of energy stood third on the list. Its importance was surpassed, in the judgment of these men, only by the analysis and study of human behavior and the general field of medical problems.

I shall not linger long on the second characteristic of plants so necessary for the existence of other life on this planet; that is, their ability to construct from simple and elementary substances types of chemical compounds essential for animals. Their capacity for making sugar from carbon dioxide and water, constructing amino acids from inorganic nitrogen and organic-carbon compounds, and for synthesizing vitamins enables us to live. Plants are able chemists and there is no substitute for them.

PLANTS AND RESEARCH IN SCIENCE

It would seem perhaps appropriate to terminate a discussion of the importance of the plant kingdom after having pointed out the essential relation of plants to our sources of energy and the dependence of all life on their existence. However, plants do more than fill our stomachs, warm our bodies, and help us to go quickly from here to there. For example, plants are useful for the investigation of problems in science. For this purpose they have certain advantages. They can be grown in large numbers, and we have no compunction in destroying them in quantity if it is desirable for the purposes of the research. Their firm, well-delineated cell walls, general structure, and methods of reproduction make them well adapted to the investigation of certain kinds of problems, and their infinite variety in morphology and physiology offers opportunity to select an organism best fitted to serve as experimental material for attack on a particular question.

The study of plants played a major part in the development of our knowledge of cells and the formulation of the cell theory. Cells were first described by Robert Hooke in 1665 from charcoal, cork, and other plant tissues. The discovery of the nucleus is generally ascribed to Robert Brown, botanist, who made his announcement in 1831. The first careful description of cell division we owe to the botanist Hugo von Mohl, who introduced the term "protoplasm" in its present sense. Chromosomes were figured by the botanist Anton Schneider in 1873 and first adequately described by Strasburger in 1875.

In many other directions we find that research with plants has led to fundamental discoveries. The investigations of Payen and Persoz in 1833 on the diastatic activity of germinated barley opened the door to the field of enzymes. Mendel's laws, the foundation of our understanding of heredity and genetics, were discovered by experimenting with peas. The idea of hormones was first presented by the botanist Sachs in 1880. The essential nature of the so-called minor essential mineral elements, for example, manganese, copper, and zinc, was demonstrated by Bertrand and his coworkers for the black mold *Aspergillus niger* considerably before their importance in animal nutrition was recognized. The discovery of the nature of virus diseases to which belong the agents responsible for smallpox, yellow fever, influenza, poliomyclitis, virus pneumonia, foot and mouth disease, hog cholera, rabies and many other afflictions of man, animals, and plants began with experiments by Iwanowski in 1892 on the mosaic disease of tobacco and was completed by Stanley in 1935 by the isolation from tobacco afflicted with mosaic of the active agent as a nucleoprotein of high molecular weight. The influence of day length on reproduction was demonstrated for plants by Garner and Allard some years before the correlation of reproductive activity in animals and day length was investigated.

Perhaps nowhere is the importance of work with plants for scientific objectives of general application demonstrated better than that which has been carried on with yeast. Pasteur's investigations on fermentation contributed in a major way to the germ theory of disease and to his later discoveries in the field of medicine. Investigations on the chemical changes induced in carbohydrates by yeast have had an immense influence on our knowledge of respiration and the intermediary metabolism of carbohydrates in animals, including man. At least two vitamins, pantothenic acid and biotin, were discovered from a study of yeast.

Many other examples could be cited illustrating the importance of research on plant material. What I have said, however, will suffice to show that the study of plants has given us in the past, as it will in the future, concepts of general significance in biology, a knowledge of principles applicable to other living things, including ourselves.

RECREATIONAL VALUE OF PLANTS

I scarcely need call your attention to the recreational value of plants. The opportunity to enjoy flowers, shrubs, and trees acts as an antidote for the artificiality and tension of city life relieves the drabness and monotony so frequently associated with existence in a small town or in the country, and satisfies a deep-seated desire in all of us. It cannot be expressed in units of value, though it has been recognized in art, poetry, architecture, and design since the beginnings of recorded history.

Someone has said that gardening and a love of gardens are essential components of a full, sane, and rounded life, and traffic with the soil and the green things that grow from it is one of the noblest and most healthful associations man may adopt. To own a bit of ground, dig it with a spade, plant seeds and watch them grow is a most satisfying thing, and fondness for such activity often comes back to a man after he runs the round of pleasure and business. As Henry Ward Beecher once wrote, every book which interprets the secret lore of fields and gardens, every essay that brings us nearer to an understanding of trees and shrubs and even weeds is a contribution to the wealth and happiness of man.

A garden gives the possessor fruit, vegetables, and flowers; it also teaches patience and philosophy, pacifies and heals the body and the mind. This is recognized in the employment of gardening in occupational therapy by hospitals and prisons, a practice which has been used successfully and is increasing. This was not always so. Oscar Wilde, writing of his own experience in an English jail, said:

> But neither milk-white rose nor red
> May bloom in prison air
> The shard, the pebble and the flint
> Are what they give us there
> For flowers have been known to heal
> A common man's despair.

May I add a word of caution. We need nothing but our senses to enjoy the beauty of flowers, but the deeper satisfaction of knowing them and growing them requires a breadth of knowledge and experience surprising to the uninitiated. So long as any man out of employment is considered to be a capable gardener, and seed catalogs are looked upon as adequate texts, gardening is likely to be a series of disappointments which only the persistent will survive. Gardening as a profession requires training, practice, and a body of special information, as other professions do, and the amateur, whether individual or corporate does well to look to the professional for guidance and for help. The Royal Botanic Gardens at Kew and at Edinburgh as well as similar institutions on the continent have long recognized gardening as a profession and have conducted courses of instruction in theory and practice. In this country few institutions have as yet concerned themselves with this aspect of education, though in the postwar period there is going to be a considerable need for it.

ECONOMIC IMPORTANCE OF PLANTS

Everyone recognizes the economic importance of the common field crops, wheat, oats, and corn, of the vegetables and fruits, and of lumber. These are items in our everyday living. Not everyone realizes, however, how many other products are obtained from plants. They are the source of linseed oil, corn, and coconut oil, turpentine, lacquer, varnish, and resin, coffee, tea, and other beverages, perfumes, flavorings, and spices, drugs and insecticides, paper, cordage, and clothing, cellulose for artificial silk, and a hundred other useful products. The plant-extractives industry alone, including drugs and flavorings, probably amounts in the United States to between 100 and 160 million dollars annually. It took a war, a war which cut us off from normal supplies, to make us appreciate how much our economy and our comfort and convenience depend upon many of these plant products from distant places. Rubber and quinine are two of the most generally known, but there are many others, for example, the sponge of the luffa gourd, the insecticide pyrethrum, chicle for chewing gum, the drug ergot, agar agar, and cork. And yet in spite of the varied materials we now obtain from plants the potentialities of the plant world are but partially explored. What might be called economic botany is largely an inheritance from our untutored ancestors who obtained their information over the centuries by trial and error. Very little systematic effort has been made to explore the plant kingdom with the idea of exploiting products as yet unknown or unused. The wide contacts brought through this war to hundreds of thousands of our young men, many of them already trained in science, may result in new and important uses for plants. The opportunity exists because not only are familiar plants incompletely investigated, but there are considerable areas of the earth botanically unexplored and thousands of species of plants still unknown to science. Any one of them might become as important to us as *Penicillium notatum.*

I cannot close this discussion of the economic aspects of plants without referring to their importance in disease and decay. It is not my intention, however, to discuss bacteria, yeasts, and molds as causes of disease in other plants and in animals and man, nor to elaborate on their relation to decay except to call attention to the importance of the fungi in rotting wood and cloth, molding food, short-circuiting electrical instruments, and deteriorating optical equipment in the Tropics. Although those of us who live in the Temperate Zone are acquainted with the fungus rots of telephone poles, railroad ties, and house timbers and the minor losses from mildewed curtains or moldy food, we have little conception of the destructiveness of molds in the moist Tropics. Their control is a matter of major concern.

Another way in which plants contribute to our economic system is through the association of microorganisms in the formation of various products, for example, cheese which depends upon the activity of the lactic acid and other bacteria and various molds; beer, wine, and other fermented liquids produced by yeast; sauerkraut, vinegar, soy sauce, and many others less well known or desirable. Bacteria, yeasts, and molds as we learn to know them better are increasingly used for producing specific chemical compounds which are beyond the skill of the laboratory worker or which can be made more cheaply by the microorganism. Alcohol, acetic acid, acetone, glycerine, citric acid, gluconic acid, and riboflavin are some of these compounds. The most famous and illustrious addition to this list is, of course, penicillin.

"Botany," said Thomas Jefferson, "I rank with the most valuable sciences whether we consider its subjects as furnishing the principal substances of life to man and beast, delicious varieties for our tables, refreshments from our orchards, the adornment of our flower-borders, shade and perfume of our groves, materials for our buildings or medicaments for our bodies."

Jefferson wrote these words in 1814. Priestley had but recently demonstrated that plants produce oxygen; the uniqueness and importance of photosynthesis was still to be recognized; coal and petroleum were still to be developed; vitamins and amino acids, the relation of plants to them and their importance in animal nutrition were unknown; rubber was a plaything; the relation of bacteria and molds to disease and decay was still to be discovered and penicillin was a long way in the future. Thomas Jefferson estimated the importance of plants on the basis of the knowledge about them available in 1814. What would he have said today?

QUESTIONS

1. Justify the statement: "Plants are the basis upon which all other life depends."
2. Define or explain the process of photosynthesis.
3. What is the relationship of coal and oil to photosynthesis?
4. What are said to be the three most important subjects for scientific research?

5. What group of scientists were first responsible for the investigations on cells, nuclei and on cell division?
6. For what are each of the following men noted: Robert Hooke, Robert Brown, Gregor Mendel, Payen and Persoz, and Stanley?
7. What plant did Louis Pasteur do a lot of work on and what was he investigating?
8. List fifteen important plant products.
9. Name some beneficial aspects of the activities of microorganisms.

Elmer Drew Merrill

Plants and Civilizations

Reprinted with permission of the publisher from Scientific Monthly **43**:430–439, 1936.

"All flesh is grass," an ancient scriptural saying, is essentially true, for as all herbivorous animals are directly dependent on plants, so, once removed, are carnivorous animals dependent on the vegetation, even as is man. To a very large degree our present civilization is based directly or indirectly on plants, and its continuance, in ultimate analysis, is definitely dependent on the plant kingdom. These evident truths are merely stated to explain or at least to justify the caption, "Plants and Civilizations."

There is an interesting corollary between the development of the various types of vegetation in past geologic times and the types of animals characteristic of each geologic period. In the past, as now, the animals of each epoch were dependent on the available food supply, and at all times the vegetation was the primary source. It was not until after the modern types of vegetation were developed, in the Cretaceous and in the Eocene of the Tertiary, that the mammals, the highest group of animals, could become dominant, although they appeared in geologic time some millions of years earlier. Previous to the development of the grasses, the chief type of plant that will thrive under constantly heavy grazing, the food supply of the herbivorous mammals was distinctly limited. The Eocene, the oldest period of the Tertiary, commonly designated "the dawn of the recent," was the dawn of the recent only in so far as the animal life was concerned. Most of the modern types of flowering plants were even then extant and widely distributed, many of them having originated in the Cretaceous.

One can hardly say just how long man has been present, but there is clear evidence that he existed as a very primitive individual in the Tertiary. It was not, however, until some time during the Pleistocene that he commenced to become a dominant factor, and even here the term dominance is relative. . . . As long as he remained in the primitive stage of nomadism, having no fixed place of abode, dependent for his daily food entirely on hunting, fishing and such edible portions of wild plants as were available to him, little definite progress was possible. Thus dependent on nature for his daily food, he must, of necessity, follow a nomadic existence, for such a food supply is not constant, varying from season to season, involving the necessity of moving from place to place in search of it. It was only well after agriculture had become a definitely established art that anything approaching what we call civilization was possible, for agriculture is and always has been basic to advanced cultures in all parts of the world. . . .

The claim is frequently made that astronomy is the oldest of the sciences, but this may be challenged if we admit that agriculture and a wide knowledge of the economic uses of plants are sciences. Before even the most primitive agriculture could be developed, man must have acquired a vast fund of knowledge about plants, their properties and uses; botany, if you will, or at least economic botany. Essentially this knowledge must have been empirical, acquired in part by the method of trial and error, in part by direct observation, but it was cumulative. This applies to plants yielding edible fruits, seeds, tubers, vegetative parts and even flower-buds and flowers; to those yielding poisons, medicines, fibers, gums and resins; and even to those yielding timbers adapted to this or that particular need. It was only on the basis of a very wide and intensive empirical knowledge of plants, their products and their uses, that primitive man could possibly develop even the beginnings of agriculture, and these beginnings must have antedated anything that we should recognize as civilization by many thousands of years.

Ethnologists recognize various periods in man's development from a thoroughly primitive nomad through various stages to what we call modern civilization. For several million years little progress was evident. . . .

For most of this million years upward progress was very slow. Beginning perhaps between 20,000 and 30,000 years ago, but probably earlier, more definite advances were made. The use of fire, the construction of shelters, the use of clothing and bodily ornaments, the practice of various ceremonies, primitive sculpture, formal burial of the dead, are some of the factors involved in a very slowly unfolding civilization.

Then came an economic revolution of the greatest significance for the future of the human race. Possibly between 10,000 and 15,000 years ago, but probably earlier, although some authorities allow only 8,000 to 10,000 years, agriculture became an established art, and the primitive civilizations based on this early agriculture became an established way of living. This primitive agriculture was merely the successful domestication of certain basic food plants in certain parts of the world, followed later by the successful domestication of certain animals. This step or these steps thus supplied the pioneers of civilization with the advantages of a permanent and dependable food supply. Thus sedentary life became possible, and a certain amount of leisure resulting from the division of labor enabled those individuals endowed with the proper mental capacity the opportunity to devote time and thought to other than the previously dominant factor of providing the necessary daily food.

The probability is that the actual cultivation of plants preceded the domestication of animals, for animals under close domestication must be provided with food. Possibly in some parts of the world man did follow his flocks and herds before he actually commenced tilling the soil, but it was the actual planting and care of crop plants that definitely removed man from the nomadic class and provided the basis on which higher civilizations could be developed. . . .

* * * * * *

If, however, there be any single factor that has permitted or encouraged the development of civilization over and above all others, it is probable that agriculture should be given this credit. Just when agriculture was first practiced we do not know, but we can approximate the places where its development first became manifest. Just how the discoveries were made that certain food plants could be profitably grown is immaterial—they were in any case unquestionably accidental. Agriculture is not the invention of any one man or any one people, but numerous individuals in the dim past and among diverse peoples in various parts of the world have contributed to it, now in this direction, now in that. Let it be emphasized here that modern man has not added a single basic food plant or domesticated animal to the long list of those selected and tamed by prehistoric man, for every important species was already in domestication somewhere in the world at the dawn of recorded history.

In tracing the origin of cultivated plants many factors are involved. Plants long in cultivation have by selection and hybridization frequently assumed strikingly different and reasonably fixed forms, as indicated by such common vegetables as the cabbage, kohlrabi, Brussels sprouts, kale and cauliflower, all derived from the native European *Brassica oleracea* Linn. It is therefore sometimes difficult to prove that this or that feral type is really the parent form of this or that cultivated plant. Were such distinct forms as those of the *Brassica* mentioned above found in nature as wild plants, most botanists would unhestitatingly accept them as distinct species. Convincing evidence is that provided when we find the parent species growing in its native habitat and can positively prove that it is the wild prototype; but here one must constantly be on guard, because cultivated plants introduced into remote regions even in modern times have frequently become naturalized in their new homes and from their present occurrence appear quite or almost as though they were indigenous species in their new homes. The wild ancestors of nearly all cultivated plants are now known and we can with confidence state that this species is a native of that region and that that species comes from Mexico or Asia Minor or China, as the case may be. Even when we do not actually know the wild parent of such important cultivated plants as tobacco, maize and the common garden bean, we can with confidence state that they originated in some part of North or South America, and that the coconut came originally from some part of the Old World tropics.

* * * * * *

A brief survey of the approximate places or origin of cultivated plants and of domesticated animals emphasizes the striking fact that most of the plants and animals, and all the really important ones, came from certain restricted areas in North and South America and Eurasia. These regions are essentially the highland of Mexico and contiguous areas in North America; of Peru, Bolivia and Chile in South America, and in Eurasia certain parts of China, northern India, Central Asia, Asia Minor and perhaps Abyssinia.

* * * * * *

It should be noted that the centers of origin of agriculture and of civilization are in general characterized by an equable type of climate, without great extremes of heat and cold, and in general with a restricted rainfall. They are to be classed as subtemperate or subtropical, rather than as temperate or tropical, presenting from the standpoint of primitive man neither the rigors of the colder temperate regions nor the equally evident disadvantages of the deep tropics.

Even more impressive is the fact that those centers in which ancient civilizations developed, whether in the Old World or in the New, are the same as those wherein our basic cultivated food plants and domesticated animals originally occurred as feral species. There is thus a very close correlation between the places of origin of cultivated plants and domesticated animals and the places of origin of early civilizations. . . . Thus in Mexico may be listed as basic species maize, beans and the sweet potato; in Peru the potato, maize and beans; in Central Asia, Asia Minor and perhaps very limited parts of the Mediterranean basin certain cereals, including rye, barley, wheat and oats; in India and China rice and perhaps millet and sorghum. . . .

* * * * * *

The number of described species of plants is probably in excess of 350,000. Most of these are of no particular economic value. The number of cultivated agricultural plants, even including strictly forage plants, is relatively small, a few hundred at most, while what might be called the food plants basic to civilization are limited to a few score.

A brief consideration of the strictly American species of cultivated plants will give us some graphic idea of the important contributions of early man in America to modern agriculture. It should be kept in mind that in the following long and rather impressive list not a single species was known in Europe or in Asia until the close of the fifteenth century. America produced but one cereal, but that one the most important maize or Indian corn. Other important food plants were the potato, sweet potato, cassava, all varieties of field and garden beans, as well as the lima, scarlet runner, tepari and yam beans, tomato, pepper, sunflower, Jerusalem artichoke, squash, pumpkin, arrowroot, peanut, chayote, papaya, avocado, pineapple, custard apple, soursop, cherimoya, guava, cacao, cashew, sapote, white sapote, sapodilla, star apple and mamei. These are now widely cultivated in appropriate regions in both hemispheres, some being strictly tropical, others also extensively planted in temperate regions. Particularly in South America, a number of other native species were and are still grown for food, but which have not become of importance in other regions. They include the ulluco (*Ullucus*), oca (*Oxalis*), anyu (*Tropaeolum*), yautia (*Xanthosoma*), llacou (*Polymnia*), arracacha (*Arracacia*), achira (*Canna*), jataco (*Amaranthus*) and quinoa (*Chenopodium*). In Peru alone it is estimated that about 70 native species had been domesticated in pre-Columbian times, although some of these were not food plants, including cotton, tobacco and various ornamental and medicinal species. Yet there is much evidence that leads one to believe that Mexico and Central America are more important as an original source of food plants than are the South American centers.

American contributions to domesticated animals were comparatively few, the llama, alpaca, muscovy duck and guinea pig in South America, and in Mexico the turkey, exhausting the list.

Eurasia, particularly Asia as contrasted with America, yielded a very much larger number of cultivated food plants and domesticated animals. Among the latter may be mentioned cattle, the horse, sheep, goat, swine, water buffalo, yak, camel, goose, duck, hen, guinea hen and pigeon. With the exception of maize all the true cereals are of Eurasian origin, including wheat, barley, rye, oats, millet, Italian millet, pearl millet, sorghum, rice, teff, ragi and coix, while for convenience buckwheat may be placed here, although it is not a true cereal. Among the vegetables are the turnip, cabbage, rutabaga, rape, chard, mustard, radish, beet, parsnip, carrot, onion, leek, garlic, shallot, spinach, eggplant, lettuce, endive, salsify, celery, asparagus, globe artichoke, pea, soybean, cow-pea, chickpea, pigeon-pea, lentil, broad, hyacinth and asparagus beans, taro, yam, sugar cane, sesamum and various others. Among the fruits the apple, pear, plum, cherry, wine grape, apricot, peach, prune, olive, fig, almond, persimmon, quince, pomegranate, jujube, melon, watermelon, cucumber, and in the warmer regions the banana, coconut, orange, lemon, pomelo, lime, date, mango, breadfruit, jak fruit, rambutan, litchi, longan, mangosteen and various others. Practically all the cultivated forage crops, including the hay grasses, clovers and alfalfa, are also of Eurasian origin.

In modern times, with steadily improving intercommunication between various parts of the world, man has become the most important single factor in the actual dissemination of plants. It can not, however, be too greatly overemphasized that it was not until after the discovery of America in 1492 and the succeeding period of European colonial expansion that there was any important distribution of cultivated plants as between Eurasia and America and *vice versa*. This fact has a very striking bearing on certain persistent claims that are made over and over again regarding the origins of pre-Columbian civilizations in America, and may be accepted as reasonably good evidence that no ancient contacts between the two continents existed. The early dissemination of cultivated plants within the limits of the eastern or of the western hemisphere is in itself an excellent illustration of diffusion, but a diffusion limited by barriers in the form of broad seas that early civilized man could not pass. Pioneer advanced civilizations, whether in Eurasia or in America, failed to keep pace with the spread of early agriculture even within the limits of the one hemisphere or the other. The botanical, zoological and agricultural evidence is wholly in support of the idea that pre-Columbian civilizations in America were autochthonous, gradually developed here over a period of many centuries, quite as parallel early civilizations were developed in Eurasia, the one having no influence on the other until after the period of European expansion following the Middle Ages.

QUESTIONS

1. Why are not nomads good agriculturists and what connection is there between nomadism and agriculture?
2. How did agriculture get started?
3. What reason is there for believing that the domestication of plants preceded the domestication of animals?
4. What are considered to be the places of origin of the majority of cultivated plants? What general climate prevails in these areas?
5. Name 10 plants of strictly American origin.

Harry J. Fuller

The Role of Botany in a Liberal Education

Reprinted by permission of the author and publisher from Plant Science Bulletin 3(1):4–6, 1957.

I assume that all or most members of this audience are on my side at the outset, that they share my conviction that our science has an important role in liberal education. Thus my function is neither that of devil's advocate nor of a salesman facing a sales-resistant group. My function, as I interpret it, is to inquire into and to evaluate the contributions which botany can make to true education.

Discussion of the role of any discipline in education presupposes some conception of the functions of education. If all the words which have been written on this subject were laid end to end, this would be a good thing or a colossal nuisance, depending upon where the laying was done. I do not propose to examine into this topic in detail or in a frustratedly philosophical manner, but I want to emphasize that two functions loom large on the lists of educational objectives prepared by most American educators. One of these stated objectives is the acquisition of a skill or set of skills or professional training (call it what you will) which enables the educational product to work gainfully with his mind. The other is the development of a set of values, of attitudes, of behavioral traits which make of the educational product a completely social being, that is, one who is an affable, cooperative, well-adjusted, civic-minded, healthy, and (above all) happy extrovert. According to this latter view of educational aims, a major function of education is the improvement of society through the effects of education on the behavior and attitudes of individuals as members of a group. The liberal studies—the humanities, the fine arts, the pure sciences—are supposed to help in achieving this social objective, but pronouncements concerning their efficacy in such achievement are in general only vaguely pious.

I do not argue against good citizenship, emotional stability, roseate health, jihads against pathogenic bacteria, or happy extroversion. I should like merely to indicate that there are reasons for regarding such virtues with some restraint. Repeated and perhaps undiscriminating emphasis upon the social functions of education and upon human beings as units of society often leads to excessive veneration of conformity (at which the bees and ants have done rather well) and to a corresponding suspicion of or deprecation of individualism or unorthodoxy. Great creations in music, painting, literature, and pure sciences have in considerable degree been creations of highly individualistic, often socially maladjusted introverts possessed of little social consciousness or little civic virtue. I do not advocate that we strive in education to produce skittish introverts but that we should place more emphasis upon the growth of individual minds, that we teach botany in an effort to stimulate individual minds and outlooks, and that we cease worrying about the possible social justification or social utility of what we teach.

Frequently linked with the view that education should concentrate on the production of good citizens is the thesis that the teaching process should be based upon, and should proceed from, the background of a student, that is, his experience. There are 2 corollaries of this doctrine: 1. It is perhaps educationally unwise to plunge a student into a completely new kind of experience, one in which he has no background, one which constitutes, in other words, a completely new kind of knowledge; 2. Education should answer the "felt needs" of student. But these attitudes overlook the thrill, the mental excitement, the sense of wonder, awe, and beauty which may result when the student mind, perhaps for the first time, encounters facts and ideas of which it has had no forewarning. If the needs of students are to be the major criteria of what we teach, one wonders how he might justify the initiation of students into the Ode on a Grecian Urn, into Christopher Marlowe's Dr. Faustus, into the writings of Thomas Wolfe or Arnold Toynbee or Joseph Conrad, or into the study of the great nature cycles or of organic evolution, topics which, I feel certain, most students are not aware of needing. To teach a kind of botany which neglects the presentation of new intellectual horizons, of unexpected and unappreciated facts and principles in favor of a kind of botany which emphasizes foundation plantings, or the care and feeding of petunias or what to do about the bagworms on the Pfitzers, is not really to teach botany at all and is clearly not to be effective in providing other than a utilitarian and mundane (although probably socially significant) education in the ways of plants.

Time for a summary of what I have said this far. If we are to grant botany an important place in liberal education, we must be cognizant of two things: 1. We must teach botany in an effort to stimulate and nourish individual minds, without compulsion to assess the value of our teaching on the yardstick of social utility; 2. We should emphasize the value of opening the minds of students to entirely new facts, ideas, and experiences and we should do what we can to enhance the individual intellectual pleasure and understanding which a student may gain from his contemplation of these entirely new vistas. To create a new need in students, the need to know ever more, is more desirable than to cater merely to those needs which students possess before they enter our classes.

Now the question of what specific contributions botany can make to liberal education; these relate largely, I believe, to the pleasure and intellectual stimulation which come from "being in on the know":

1. Recognition and appreciation of beauty in the plant world, not as a separate kind of unit, but rather as derivative of studying plant structure: *Spirogyra*, diatoms, microscopic sections of woods, cleistothecia of powdery mildews, flowers, for example. It is an entirely legitimate and a desirable activity of scientists to emphasize beauty wherever it may be found in nature, but such emphasis is only infrequently given, since, in large segments of American science, to mention the word "beauty" is seemingly considered not quite manly.

2. Making known to students that satisfaction which comes from possessing accurate knowledge, from detecting and rejecting misinformation and superstition. Such satisfaction may arise in large degree from the flattering of the ego, certainly a legitimate function of education, if that flattery is derived from intellectual growth. The erasure from student minds of superstitions and misconceptions about plants (e.g., that spontaneous generation accounts for the appearance of molds on stale foods, that yeast is a chemical, that plants lose their nutritive value if they do not receive "organic fertilizers," that plants poison the air at night, that oaks, poplars. willows, and walnuts do not have flowers, that one may distinguish between edible and poisonous mushrooms by placing a silver coin against a fresh slice of the sporophore and observing the color change), commonly leads to a kind of intellectual pleasure, the delight of being "in on the know."

3. Understanding the interdependence of living organisms, as this may be appreciated through the study of the carbon and nitrogen cycles, of the relationships between flowers and pollinating insects, of parasitism and symbiosis, of nutritional checks and balances, of ecological phenomena. Such study will broaden and deepen a student's conception of the operations of nature, will create or reinforce the idea of order and of symmetry in the world.

4. Demonstration that the scientific method is not an esoteric technique peculiar to white-coated gents testing mouthwashes or adding numbers to toothpastes, but that it is basically the method of common sense. Such demonstration may be achieved by having students propose, discuss, and criticize real or hypothetical experiments. The acquisition of some skill in scientific thinking may lead to the development of less emotional, more objective, more calculating methods of viewing controversial questions and problems, to the detection of spurious claims in advertising, to generally more objective modes of thinking.

5. Appreciation of the interrelationships among the sciences and the connections of the sciences with other fields of human thought. The relation between plant production and soil science, that between plant functions and chemistry, that between tree rings and meteorology, and especially that among botany, archaeology, philology, radiation physics, human history, an-

thropology, geography, and plant breeding in the solution of problems concerning the origins of cultivated plants are topics which illustrate a phase of interdisciplinary cooperation and reinforcement, an appreciation of which should be a part of the intellectual equipment of every truly educated person.

6. Awareness that the practical applications of the sciences in human life are outgrowths of basic research in the pure sciences. Teaching botanists have many opportunities to emphasize this dependence of applied science upon pure science in the treatment of such topics as plant hormones in relation to the horticultural applications of growth regulators, photoperiodism in relation to the control of flowering, mineral nutrition in relation to fertilizers, basic genetics in relation to crop improvement, ecology in relation to conservation, soil control, reforestation, etc.

7. Student understanding of the true nature of botany. Laymen in general regard our science as primarily the study of diseases of cultivated plants and of the management of cultivated plants and of gardens and fields. Our students should certainly recognize clearly as they study botany that the management of cultivated plants, the learning of names of ornamental and truck-garden plants, and the study of landscaping do not constitute the core of botany, that they are only indirectly related to the central purpose of our science.

8. Organic evolution and its implications, which are so obvious that they do not require further comment.

The questions which now arise are these: How shall we proceed to teach general botany so that we may achieve these desirable results in liberal education? What techniques shall we use? What subject matter should be emphasized? I shall not attempt to answer these questions, because I know no absolute and specific answers to them. The achievement of these important educational aims is, after all, a function of the teacher and of his background, his personality, his enthusiasm for working with young minds and for botany. As the late Neil Stevens wrote in a paper in the *Journal of The American Society of Agronomists* in 1944, "Teaching may be a little like love-making. If the available literature is to be believed, many techniques have been successful in this field, but there appears to be no written record of a successful lover who was not interested in his subject." Thus, the methods and techniques of teaching toward the liberal education ends which I have listed are, I suspect, as numerous and as varied as are teachers of botany. One thing is certain about teaching botany in such fashion as to render it contributory to sound liberal education, and that is that the teachers of general botany must be broadly educated in their science.

QUESTIONS

1. What may be called the two major objectives of American education?
2. What are the dangers, according to Fuller, of having a population consisting of well-adjusted, affable and cooperative people?
3. Will satisfying the felt needs of students produce well-educated citizens? Explain.
4. List the 7 contributions made by botany to a liberal education.

PART TWO

THE DEVELOPMENT OF BOTANY

The automobile, the jet airplane, and the television set, among others, have histories. Likewise academic disciplines of all kinds have their histories, some going back into the distant past. Some fields have split into smaller fragments and new disciplines are appearing. Genetics, formerly taught in botany or zoology departments, is now in its own department. Likewise bacteriology, forestry, and horticulture have broken off from botany. New fields like electron microscopy, radiation biology, and space biology have sprung up.

Botany did not originate in the New World, of course, but abroad. The first botanists were amateurs, collecting seeds, bark, leaves, and roots for food, medicine, poisons, and so forth. Formal agriculture followed the aimless plant gathering of the nomads of the past, and plant classification was a subsequent development to make order out of the thousands of plants known. Other disciplines followed in response to some need. Anatomy and then physiology followed rapidly. Plants serve man and botanists "interpret" plants for man's use. The first phases were oriented to the practical side of plants and this is still with us. However, pure science became started—the search for knowledge for its own sake—and this has furnished answers to the practical people. Modern botany retains the best of the old knowledge and combines it with the new. Isotopes, electron microscopes, and chromatograms are common sights in modern botanical laboratories. The last chapter in botany is yet to be written.

John M. Coulter

Development of Botany in the United States

Reprinted with the permission of the author and publisher from Proceedings American Philosophical Society **66**:309–318, 1927.

The period covered by the present article includes the whole history of the origin and development of botany in the United States. In outlining this history I shall not include citations from bibliography, for the names of investigators who have made important contributions to our botanical progress are numerous, and a selection would be difficult. I shall attempt, therefore, only to present in outline the development of the subject, from its start in this country to its present status.

At the beginning of the period we are considering, botany was represented only by the random collection of plants from a virgin flora. At first these collections were not studied or published in this country, for there were no botanists trained sufficiently for this work. The plants were sent or taken chiefly to England and France, and described and published in those countries.

This first phase of botany is known as taxonomy, and it was the only phase for many years in this country. This was natural, for our flora was being explored for the first time, and the enormous extent of the territory to be covered led to the organization of many exploring expeditions, each securing a wealth of new material. At that time, therefore, botany in the United States consisted only of the collection and naming of plants. It was in this period that our manuals of botany began to be published, registering the current knowledge of the conspicuous flora of various regions. This phase of our subject may be defined as the assembling of material for subsequent investigation.

It must not be supposed that taxonomy stopped its development when other phases of botany started. It calls for more critical work now than ever before, for the accumulating body of morphological data is constantly shifting classification. Taxonomy must include the last expression of our knowledge of plants, so that taxonomists are engaged in keeping their phase of botany up to date.

The next phase of botany to begin its development was morphology, the study of structures. This start was made under the influence of European contacts. In those days botany was progressing rapidly in Europe. The American botanists visited European laboratories, and returned to this country equipped for a new kind of investigation. Morphology should probably be regarded as the most fundamental subdivision of botany, for it treats the structures of plants and their development, and upon these data taxonomy must build. At first morphology dealt only with the forms of mature plants and their organs.

Gradually another phase of morphology began to develop. Instead of studying mature structures alone, their development began to be investigated, following much earlier investigations in certain European laboratories. In this work, the life histories of plants began to be traced, from the egg to maturity.

This development of morphology began the segregation of botanists that increased rapidly. Botanists were grouped as taxonomists and morphologists, and neither group shared in the work of the other. In fact, at that time the college courses in botany were chiefly morphology, and attention to taxonomy began to decline.

The next segregate in botany was physiology. This phase of work was also introduced into this country through contact with European laboratories. Nothing was known of the activities of plants except what had been learned through agricultural and horticultural operations. The functions of the different plant organs were gradually discovered, and a new technique of plant investigation became established. Plants were not merely observed, as in the case of taxonomy and morphology, but were put under experimental control, and their various activities evoked. The important general functions which engaged physiological research were the absorption of material and of energy from the outside world; the transfer of water through the plant body; transpiration, by means of which water is lost from the plant surface; photosynthesis, by which carbohydrates are manufactured; digestion and assimilation; respiration, by means of which energy is liberated for the activities of the body; growth; and movement.

Next in historical succession, ecology emerged, with its interest in the effect of environment on plants. This is really a phase of plant physiology. This phase of botany is about 53 years old, but it has had a very rapid and extensive development. Three rather distinct lines of investigation have been developed. One deals with the reactions of plants, tissues, and organs to their environment, a phase of the subject called physiologic ecology. A second line of ecological investigation has to do with the origin, development, and life relations of the plant communities, often called plant societies, and is called physiographic ecology. The third line of investigation is concerned with the great forest, grass, desert, and other formations of the earth in relation to climate, and is called geographic ecology.

The next segregate of the botanical field was plant pathology, which deals with plant diseases, chiefly those inflicted by other plants. In the meantime bacteriology had developed because of its relation to human diseases, and was hardly considered as a part of botany. When plant pathology began to develop, however, as a distinct field of investigation, bacteria were inevitably included, at least so far as bacteria are related to plant diseases. It is of importance to note that plant pathology, as first developed, was interested solely in the parasites inducing disease, discovering them and investigating their life histories, but really paid little attention to the patient whose diseased condition belonged to physiology.

Finally, the last segregate, which really began with the present century, was plant breeding, which in its scientific aspects is known as genetics. As in the case of the other segregates, breeding was carried on with most complex material, with little knowledge or appreciation of the structures involved.

All of these phases of botany developed independently. As a result, not only were the phases of botany segregated, but the botanists also. Taxonomists, morphologists, physiologists and ecologists represented distinct and too often rival groups. The prominent advantage of this segregation of subjects was the development of the technique of each field. One had to be a comparatively narrow specialist to develop technique to its limit. The disadvantage of the segregation of botanists was the lack of cooperation. Taxonomists did not know morphology or physiology. Morphologists cared nothing about either; and so on down the list of segregates. This segregation was for a time very complete, so that the interests of one group would not have been affected if none of the other groups had existed. This may be called the monastic phase of botany.

The transformation of botany from a list of segregates to a synthesis of all the sciences was hastened by our experience during the First World War. In that emergency every phase of botany was called upon to contribute information. It was a revelation to discover that every phase proved to be useful.

As a natural result of our experiences in two world wars and of the importance of our agriculture, one of the features of botanical research today is to attack problems that are fundamental in connection with some important practice. In the older days, botany was regarded as the most impractical of all the sciences. It was really regarded as a pastime rather than a profession. The outstanding illustration, of course, is the increasing attention given to the problems that underlie agriculture; but there are many other practices also which are bedded in botanical investigation. It is so strong at present that I do not believe it will ever subside, but it should be understood. The great objective of research, of course, is to extend the boundaries of knowledge. The tendency to which I refer merely means that experience developed in connection with an important practice has suggested fundamental problems. In fact, among our most fundamental problems are those that have been suggested by experience. It must be confessed that certain botanists still resent the inclusion of what they call practical problems among our research problems. It is very common to distinguish the two groups of problems as pure and applied science. The fact is that pure science is often immensely practical, and that applied science is often very pure science. Between the two there is no dividing line. Practical problems are not a detriment to botanical science. In fact they incidentally strengthen its claim on public interest as a science that must be promoted. It will develop a far greater opportunity for research than has been possible heretofore.

A second feature that characterizes botany today, and which I regard as more important than the preceding feature, is the increasing realization of the fact that botanical problems are synthetic. Around each bit of investigation, with its single point of view and single method of attack, there is developing a perspective of other points of view and other methods of attack. We realize now that plants are synthetic, and that is quite a notable advance from the distant time when we thought of them only as objects subservient to laws of nomenclature.

A third feature that is becoming increasingly prominent is a recognition of the fact that structures are not static; that is, inevitable to their last detail. This is so fundamental in connection with the future development of botany that I wish to emphasize it by a few illustrations.

The old method of morphology in recording the facts observed in connection with the development of the embryo of seed plants, was to record not only every cell division, but also the plane of every cell division. The conception back of such records was that the program of ontogeny was fixed to the minutest detail. It is probably true that such a structure is about as uniform in its development as any structure can be; but it has now become evident that many of the details recorded were not significant. Instead of recording them as of equal value, we are now trying to distinguish those that are relatively fixed from those that are variables.

Perhaps the greatest mass of details has been accumulated by the cytologists, in connection with their examination of the machinery of nuclear division and nuclear fusion. In no other field has the conception of rigidity of the structures involved become more fixed, even to the minutest variation in form and position. The time has come when even the recorded facts of cytology are being estimated on the basis of relative values; that is, the inevitable things are being differentiated from the variable.

In considering these illustrations of the tendency to recognize that facts are not all pigeonholed and of equal value, it is becoming more and more obvious that our botanical problems are in general the application of physics and chemistry to plants; that laws, when we really discover them, are by definition static, but that their operation results in anything but static structures. In other words, structure must respond to law, but the particular law that is gripping the situation may be one of many.

Until recently the scientific and practical phases of botany were completely divorced. As a consequence, the science was not practical, and the practice was not scientific. At last it came to be recognized that practice by itself is sterile, and that it needs a continuous discovery of new knowledge to apply. This new botanical perspective, therefore, might be described as practice based on science, and science that illuminates and extends practice.

It should be recognized also that practice makes its contribution to progress, for under the pressure of necessity it is practice that suggests the problems. In this way the cooperation of botanical science and practice become established.

In conclusion, I may give what may be called the modern creed of botany. I shall put it under three articles, in the order of what I conceive to be their relative importance. The service of botany today is (1) to understand nature, that the boundaries of human knowledge may be extended; this may be called pure science; (2) to apply this knowledge to the service of man, that his life may be fuller of opportunity; this may be called applied science; and (3) to use the method of science in training man, that he may solve his problems and not be their victim.

QUESTIONS

1. The collecting and naming of plants is generally the first botanical endeavor in a new region. Was this true of botany in the United States?

2. What was the second field of botany to be exploited in this country?

3. What is the connection between taxonomy and morphology?

4. Name some other fields of botany which developed rather rapidly.

5. Explain the relationship existing between pure and applied science.

6. What is meant by the "synthetic" method of research?

7. What does Dr. Coulter say is the "Modern Creed of Botany"?

PART THREE

ECOLOGY

The interactions of the environment and organisms encompass far more than the superficial examination of organisms in water, field, and forest. Ecology is a growing field of increasing complexity involving statistics, chemistry, and physics. Some of the topics found in a modern ecology text would startle an older ecologist; such as strontium 90 in plant food, range management, paleoecology, and biogeochemical cycles. The older topics are not neglected for we still lack information in such areas as parasitism and the relation of color of flowers to insects. The present work on the tropical rain forests, deserts, and arctic slopes may well be of later service to man. The reason for this is that man has had to spread out into regions formerly thought unsuitable. Either the areas will have to be modified or man will have to learn to adapt himself to them.

Man is not merely an animal but more than an animal. He is the only animal which consciously tries to understand and control his environment. His own progress and development is intertwined with the quality of his cerebral cortex.

For more information on ecology, read Adaptation *by B. Wallace and A. M. Srb.*

Francis Ramaley

The Growth of a Science

Reprinted with the permission of the University of Colorado Press from the University of Colorado Studies 26(3):3–14, 1940.

As any field of human knowledge is cultivated it broadens far beyond its original confines. While Aristotle, twenty-four hundred years ago, could encompass all learning of his day, and even Albertus Magnus, many centuries later, could be looked upon as a man who knew everything, it is now but the veriest commonplace that no one can be master of more than a small part of any serious discipline. I propose to trace for you briefly the growth, not of one of the main fields of knowledge, but of a small part of one of these—the development of old-time natural history into the ecology of the present day.

You will forgive me, if, as an old teacher, I remind you that the word ecology (e-c-o-l-o-g-y) is akin, in origin, to the word economy, and hence has reference to the house or household. It has to do with the habits of animals, the kinds of houses or shelters which they make use of, their food, their neighbors, and the inorganic and organic worlds in which they find themselves. And so also of plants—columbines and orchids do not grow on arid plains, nor do buffalo grass and prickly pears inhabit the rain-blessed mountains. Animals and plants are environed by climate, by lakes, rivers, mountains, and deserts, and by competitors for a place in the sun. Animals have enemies seeking them for food, but other creatures, especially of the plant kingdom, afford them food or give shelter. In like manner one kind of plant will "help" another. Without the shade of trees where would be the livid green of mossy banks and the delicate odor of sweet fern?

But here we must remind ourselves that while we human beings are able to modify our environment, as when we construct a house, build a fire, or put on an overcoat, there is very little that plants and animals can do to alter theirs, save by migration. It is an all too simple statement that "plants and animals adapt themselves to their surroundings," that beavers put on a thick coat of fur against approaching winter, or that a tree sheds its leaves in autumn to keep from having them frozen, and that peach blossoms burst forth in beauty to attract bees to carry pollen. The kindergarten child is delighted to hear how "the dear little bean plant" pushes its roots downward into the soil to get the "life-giving water" or sends its stem upward for "heaven's sunlight." As a matter of fact, if beans are sprouted in an ink-black closet the stems grow straight upward, although there is no light above, and the roots grow down even if the soil below is as dry as chalk dust. It is easy, even for the trained ecologist, to lapse into anthropomorphisms, as I have seen in manuscripts submitted to me as editor of a journal devoted to ecology. Thus an author writes of the Douglas fir as a "virile" and "aggressive" species, or relates that roses "prefer" a sunny situation or "rejoice" in plentiful sunshine; or he ascribes to animals a foresight which would do credit to a "seventh son of a seventh son"—or is it a daughter?

Ecology as a separate branch of biology arose in the eighteen-nineties, and I have seen its growth from the rather simple "natural history" of two generations ago to its present expanded state wherein the ecologist, who is an outdoor man, may have comparatively little in common with his biological colleague of the laboratory, and may even speak a different language from that of his brother ecologist who works in some other field than his own.

It is plain that the discipline which treats of the relation of organisms to their environment must be the very foundation of agriculture and stock-raising; and so it is for horticulture, forestry, grazing, and soil conservation. The disciple of ecology looks to both the past and to the future. What were the environmental conditions which brought about the formation of coal, or of oil? Why did dinosaurs become extinct? What has caused the development of oak woods in Britain where alders and willows grew in the Stone Age? What sort of forest will there be in Oregon when the Forest Service shall have prevented fires for two hundred years? What will become of waterfowl if we continue to destroy their breeding grounds by drainage of swamps and bayous? If the war on coyotes and snakes and birds of prey continues shall we have to live in a rodent-dominated world?

* * * * * *

While it is true that ecology as a science arose near the close of the last century, there have always been a few naturalists interested to some degree in environmental relations. The philosopher Theophrastus, long-time friend and associate of Aristotle, may well be called the first ecologist in history, for he wrote, and quite sensibly too, of the communities in which plants are associated, the relation of plants to each other and to their lifeless environment. He recognized the features of water plants, plants of swamps and marshes, plants of dry and arid plains. Sometimes, but not often he falls into mild anthropomorphisms, as in a statement in his *Inquiry into Plants*:

> All trees grow fairer and more vigorous in their proper positions, . . . some love wet and marshy ground, . . . as the white poplar and willow, . . . some love exposed and sunny positions, some prefer a shady place.

Aristotle, who was more zoologist than botanist, hardly takes a place in ecology, although he did study the habits of animals to some extent. Animals are less influenced by circumstance than are plants. Aristotle was a believer in a final, or formal, cause for animal structure—as we should say now, heredity—but he recognized that modifications occur in animal structure. He believed that animals so develop that they are suited to their surroundings. For example:

> An eye the animal must have of necessity (for the fundamental idea of the animal is of such a kind), but it will have an eye of a particular kind, of necessity in another sense.

He believed that there is a purpose back of all development, although he does not maintain that it is the purpose or desire of the individual animal which causes a particular kind of development. Aristotle was evidently a believer in teleology, so would hardly feel at home with modern animal ecologists. And he did not have the idea of natural selection, which holds that environment eliminates those individual plants or animals which are unfit for the particular environment in which they are placed.

Pliny, in his *Natural History*, which is, in its best parts, a rewriting of Theophrastus, Aristotle, Cato, and others, offers much material of simple ecological sort, as when he considers the purchase of farm land, or the relation of crops to soil and climate, or of insect pests to garden plants. Quoting, indirectly from Cato, he says:

> Do not be too eager in buying a farm. A bad bargain is always a cause for repentance. Those who are about to purchase land should have an eye to the water, the roads, and the neighborhood. . . . Where land is good the people will look well-conditioned and healthy.

Continuing our survey of Pliny for ecological material, certain facts come to light which only recently have been generally recognized as of consequence:

> A soil that is adorned by tall and graceful trees is not always a favorable one except, of course, for those trees. What tree, indeed, is taller than the fir? Yet what other plant could exist in the same spot? Nor are verdant pastures so many proofs of richness of soil. What is there that enjoys a greater renoun than the pastures of Germany? But they are a mere thin layer of earth with sand underneath.

Here it may be stated that ecologists now recognize the native plants on a piece of land as "indicators" of agricultural possibilities. But the person employing such indicators for land classification, as now practiced in the United States, must needs have a much more complete knowledge of native plants than Pliny had.

* * * * * *

Following the Greek and Roman period, writers on zoology and botany show little interest in ecology. Their work is a description of individual kinds of animals and plants, with little thought of environmental relations. Foundation facts for the development of ecology were lacking.

And yet the teachings of Theophrastus were not entirely forgotten; a glimpse of ecological thinking now and then may be obtained, as when Albertus Magnus refers to the plants of streamsides and marshes, or discusses the quality of different kinds of wood and the usefulness of these different woods for building purposes depending upon the conditions under which they grew. The notion of transmutation, i.e., the change of one plant to another under special conditions of the environment, was widely held. Even the Greek philosophers, who should have known better, gave mild assent to it; be it said, however, that Theophrastus in mentioning change of wheat into rye on poor soil suggests some doubts of the phenomenon.

To return to our main theme, the growth of the science of ecology: by the close of the nineteenth century the various natural branches of biology as we now know them had become recognized, and specialists had taken the place of the all 'round students of a former day. There appeared men and women devoted to form and structure —especially the finer microscopic structure—of living things (these people we call morphologists); others, the physiologists, studied life processes. Physiology in the early part of the nineteenth century had lagged far behind morphology for lack of sound organic chemistry on which to build. The German chemist Wöhler, however, in his epoch-making synthesis of urea, in 1828, threw into the discard the old notion that organic compounds are always the result of life processes. He produced, it will be remembered, from ammonium cyanate of inorganic origin, the well-known substance urea, a characteristic animal product—and soon organic chemistry began its wonderful growth which continues to the present day.

Besides the morphologists and the physiologists there were the taxonomists, or classifiers. They were not a new group, for they were disciples of the great Linnaeus, most renowned naturalist of the times just preceding Darwin. But besides continuing their former work of mere describing and classifying, the taxonomists now became interested in geographical distribution and, following Darwin, interested also in the history of life—evolution. Taxonomists are the great conservators of knowledge—we must classify, else all is confusion.

With the opening of the twentieth century a trend toward synthesis became manifest, the subjects of genetics and ecology acting to bring together diverse interests. It is seen that biology agreed with other sciences in having first a period of general accumulation of facts. The second period in biological development was one of specialization into narrow fields, each research group working without thought of others, and only the evolution doctrine of Darwin to draw them together.

* * * * * *

One of the foundation conceptions of ecology is that of zonation, illustrated in simple form by a freshwater pond or lake, and its environs. Within the water are fishes and pondweeds; near the shore are sandpipers, frogs, salamanders, snails, cat-tails, and bulrushes; around the pond is an encircling zone of marsh grasses and sedges with meadow-mice and mosquitoes, then another circum-area of flowering herbs, grasshoppers, meadow grass, and meadowlarks. Such ecological zones, or belts, or associations are usually named for the dominant plants in each; so this pond exhibits a pondweed zone, a bulrush zone, a marsh zone, and a meadow zone. The ecologist, in his study of zonation, is not content merely to list these communities. He wants to know why they exist, and so he studies the climate, the soil and its temperature and moisture-content, the physiographic features, as slope and exposure. But zonation is not limited to the plants and animals around a frog pond. Zones depending on differences in climate are recognized in our mountain country, where there is a basal zone of grassland, higher up a montane zone of forest, and at the top an alpine zone of grassland again—albeit a different grassland from that at the base of the mountains, for in the alpine zone the vegetation is sparse, and flowering herbs are more conspicuous than grasses.

Related to zonation, since all ecological facts are related, is the process of succession. The history of the fresh-water pond or lake is the story of succession. Whether the pond originated as an ox-bow cut from a meandering stream, or whether it fills a depression hollowed out by wind, or by a glacier, or is dammed by a terminal moraine or a land slump it has had a history influenced by water and wind and plant life. Once the pond was larger than now; unless natural processes are interfered with by man it will continue to shrink in size. As filling continues, in place of pondweeds and open water there are bulrushes and cat-tails, for these have extended into the former lake. The plant remains of the bulrush and cat-tail zone change soil conditions so that the soil becomes more suitable for marsh grasses; marsh grasses no longer can live in their former place, for they have rendered it too dry, so meadow grasses and flowering herbs take their place; finally the short grass or the spruce trees or the oak chaparral follow into where meadow recently flourished. With the disappearance of open water there was no place for pondweeds; as drying continued the bulrushes and cat-tails were crowded out by marsh plants, and the marsh plants gave way to meadow plants—all of these changes part of a definite and, as it might appear, a pre-arranged succession.

With changes in plant population the animal population likewise is bound to change: fishes disappear, then frogs, salamanders, and sandpipers. The fauna soon consists of animals fitted to the new conditions. Those animals which do not fit the new conditions either die or go elsewhere; the animals which find the environment now well suited to their life activities multiply, and other animals from outside come in to become a part of the animal population.

Subjects for research in ecology are many and varied; they may engage the general zoologist or botanist or such specialists in biology as entomologists, ornithologists, grazing experts, foresters, agronomists or, again, geographers, geologists, and psychologists. All of these make use of the fundamental sciences: mathematics, astronomy, physics, and chemistry. Ecology can be just as abstruse as other sciences, for it uses a complex terminology, employs graphs, formulae, and tables of variance—from all of which I spare you. The ecologist is much interested in theoretical matters, yet he is not one to "sit apart and reason high." He travels to the wilds of Africa and to the tundra of Siberia. He carries on laborious and time-consuming studies in field and laboratory, spends hours and hours in watching the behavior of animals or in testing them experimentally. His long-time experiments in forestry run beyond the life experience of any one man, and are so planned that they must be finished by others.

* * * * * *

Before ecology had become recognized as a discipline deserving a place and name of its own those who carried on research in plant and animal relations published their results in the established journals. Perhaps some titles of research papers may be cited to suggest the kinds of investigation carried out by ecologists. I do not cite any which are primarily devoted to agriculture; there are hundreds of these published every year, for, as already suggested, agriculture is essentially applied ecology. And now, for a few of the subjects culled from periodicals:

Native grasses for erosion control; Tree rings and chronology in the Southwest; Present-day vegetation compared with that of the Glacial period; Spawning of red salmon; Altitudinal range of rattlesnakes; Rodents in over-grazed grassland; Reforestation of sub-marginal lands; Nature and man illustrated in the North American Indian; Influence of long and short days on flowering and fruiting; Hydrogen-ion concentration and the distribution of fishes; Relations of dust to humanity; Minnows as mosquito destroyers; Problems of nature protection.

But why do people engage in such studies? What is the true motive for their research? Does it add marmalade to our bread and butter, or ease our tired feet, or give us better and cheaper homes, or enable us to have a pleasanter summer vacation? Yes, research does just these, and more; but the primary urge to research is intellectual curiosity. We study for the sake of finding out. He who knows little is likely to be satisfied with that little, he who knows much wants to know more. Intellectual curiosity pushes beyond recorded knowledge into the unknown. For the larger and fuller life let us hope that intellectual curiosity may ever grow and not be stifled, that the creative mind shall have full play to express itself.

QUESTIONS

1. What is one difference between plants and animals when both are confronted by an unfavorable environment?
2. Give several examples of anthropomorphic thinking.
3. Who was the first recorded ecologist, Theophrastus or Linnaeus?
4. The ancients believed in the transmutation of plant species. What does this refer to?
5. What was the significance of Wöhler's synthesis of urea?
6. Give the important steps in the succession of a common habitat such as a lake.
7. What is said to be the primary urge back of research?

Frederic E. Clements

The Nature and Role of Plant Succession

Reprinted by permission of the Carnegie Institute of Washington from News Service Bulletin 3(30):241–244, 1935.

Darwin once said that every traveler should be a botanist, since plants furnish the chief embellishment of all landscapes. Today it may be asserted with equal warrant that the traveler should be an ecologist if he is to understand the changes wrought by nature and by man upon the countenance of Mother Earth.

Even the everlasting hills are not ageless, for they are worn down by wind and water; lakes are filled, rivers grow old, and swamps become dry land subject to the plow. Intimately connected with these changes, hastening or retarding them and in turn being modified by them, are the populations of living things, interacting in a maze of causes and effects to render the mantle of life a veritable kaleidoscope.

Most responsive of these is the plant cover, forming the pattern of a complex community in which animals and primitive man in particular find shelter and homes and from which they draw food and materials. Every such community is essentially an organism, of a higher order than an individual geranium, robin, or chimpanzee, but possessing structure and development, and a coordination of functions and parts similar in many respects. Like them, it is a unified mechanism in which the whole is greater than the sum of its parts and hence it constitutes a new kind of organic being with novel properties.

Communities arise, grow, mature, attain old age and die from natural causes or by accident. They regularly reproduce themselves after partial destruction by fire, lumbering, clearing, or other disturbance, regenerating new parts, not altogether unlike the process by which a lobster grows a new claw or a lizard a tail. The final or adult community is termed a climax, by reason of the fact that it is the highest type of social organism capable of growing in a particular climate, and its process of growth is known as succession, from the series of transient populations that pass across the scene.

The driving force behind succession is climate, operating directly or more often indirectly through soil or terrain. Like the individual plant, the community is acted upon by the environment and in turn reacts upon the latter, modifying such ruling factors as water, light and temperature. The associated animals are affected less immediately by these, but find their chief relations with plants as the source of food, materials and shelter. Man has modified or evaded physical conditions to a large degree, but even he is much controlled by differences of climate, soil, raw materials and food.

PLANTS INDICATE CONDITIONS

The significant outcome of these relations is that both species and communities serve as measures or indexes of conditions and hence are known to the ecologist as indicators. In connection with land classification, agriculture, forestry, grazing, erosion, flooding, and water supplies, the use of indicators furnishes a method of primary importance.

They indicate not merely the present features of climate and soil, but they also possess the clairvoyance of forecasting future changes and the possibility of controlling them, as well as of deciphering past events. Thus, climax and succession have not only great practical applications, but also provide the open sesame by which traveller or nature-lover may unlock the pages of nature's book and read the past and present of every landscape, and likewise its further story.

The primary indications have to do with climate and soil and the outstanding changes of the past, but woven into this pattern is the infinite variety wrought by man, directly through fire, settlement, logging, cultivation and so forth, or indirectly by grazing, erosion, flooding, draining. Each of these processes has its own indicator communities, and its major effects can be read with almost as much certainty as though recorded on the spot by an eye-witness. [Lately, the effect of atomic radiation on plants and animals demands serious attention—Ed.]

THE GREAT PLANT CLIMAXES

Everyone is familiar in a general way with the great climaxes of our country and especially with the two most extensive, the eastern forest of beech, maple, chestnut and oaks, and the prairies of many kinds of grasses. In addition to these are the great transcontinental forest of spruce and fir to the northward and the Barren Grounds of sedge and lichen stretching along the Arctic Circle from ocean to ocean.

Related to these and hence of single interest as seeming far out of place are the alpine tundras of Mount Katahdin, Mount Washington, and of Pikes Peak, Mount Whitney, Mount Rainier, and other high summits of the Rocky Mountains, Sierra Nevada, and the Cascades, all survivals of a distant time of glacial advance when the arctic tundra moved far to the south.

Each of these great communities consists of certain dominants, a ruling class drawn usually from trees or grasses and best fitted to the climate concerned, and of various subordinate groups, among which the flowering herbs of woodland and prairie are the most conspicuous and familiar. Each climax is the product of its particular climate and hence the indicator of it, and thus serves as the point of departure for all the disturbances brought about by man and for all projects of utilization, restoration and rehabilitation under way or projected in the present national program.

KINDS OF SUCCESSION

Examples of the growth of climaxes, of their childhood and adolescence are to be found everywhere within the corresponding climate. Most frequently seen are those due to disturbances caused by man, but others with a much longer lifespan occur in pond and lakelet, on rocky ridge and cliff, in sand dunes and bad lands, on the exfoliating domes of Yosemite and in the sinter and diatom basins of Yellowstone geysers.

Wherever an area is bare or is denuded by natural agencies or by man and his animals, development begins, progressing slowly or rapidly in accordance as the site is water, rock or actual soil, and passing through a series of communities to end finally in the climax proper to each climate.

Primary successions on granite may require a thousand years or more between the pioneering crustlike lichens and the climax forest of oak or pine, and hundreds of years to fill a lakelet to the point where meadow or woodland can flourish on the humus soil. By contrast, secondary successions following fire or cultivation may take no more than a half-century for the complete cycle, and an abandoned field in the prairie may be reclaimed by the grasses in a decade or two.

SUCCESSION IN WATER AND ON ROCK

Probably the most familiar kind of succession is that found in standing water, with its communities of pond-lilies, cat-tails, bulrushes and sedges. The pioneer colony of this series is founded by submerged stoneworts, pondweeds, hornworts and the like in water up to about 20 feet.

As these grow and decay, the pond is gradually filled to the level at which floating plants can push in and take possession. These then rule as conquerors for a while, but likewise bring about their own downfall by shallowing the water so that bulrushes, cat-tails, wild rice and reed-grass can invade, usually in this order. The remains of these accumulate even more rapidly and in a few decades the pool may become a wet meadow covered with sedges, which in their turn yield to grasses and afterwards to shrubs, or in some cases to the latter directly.

When the ruling caste of woody plants is once established in a forest climate, trees of small demands and rapid growth overshadow the shrub stage, and later yield to the invading phalanx of climax trees of slower growth but greater permanence. In the prairie region, the succession terminates with a community of drouth-resisting grasses, since the rainfall is not sufficient to permit the development to continue to forest.

On rocky ridges, mountain peaks, lava fields and boulders everywhere, the course of succession is quite different. By contrast with water plants, the chief task of the pioneers is to convert rock into soil and to increase the water rather than diminish it. In the miniature deserts of rock-surfaces only the humblest plants can thrive, such as lichens and mosses which are capable of enduring desiccation for months.

The first settlers are crustlike lichens, which etch the surface and slowly produce a thin layer of dust. After many years leafy species gradually invade and carry the task forward, yielding to mosses as a thin soil appears in crack and crevice. As the soil increases in depth, tiny saxifrages and other "rock-bearing" herbs enter, and these are followed after an interval by grasses. From this stage, the general course is the same as that in succession from water, inasmuch as grasses are followed by shrubs and these by trees in the case of a forest climate.

SUCCESSION IN SOILS

Succession on sand dunes takes place more rapidly and dramatically since soil of a sort is already present and the major problem is to fix the shifting sand and enrich it with plant remains. To be a sand binder, a plant must not only be well-anchored and hold sand, but it must also be able to catch the load borne by the wind and even more important, to keep its "head" above the sand as the latter heaps up about it.

The early invaders are lowly annuals of small requirements, which gradually stabilize small areas for the entrance of an ascending series of perennials, either herbs or grasses. In the prairies, grasses of progressively higher demands replace each other in forming a permanent cover, while in forest regions the grasses yield ultimately to shrubs and trees.

The reconstruction of the adult community is a simpler and still more rapid process where fire or clearing has destroyed the climax. The soil usually is neither removed nor impaired, and in the case of fire is often enriched by the minerals liberated.

Mosses and liverworts appear almost at once, and during the first full season a complete cover of annual herbs and grasses may be formed. Many perennials and shrubs survive the fire and their root sprouts soon appear in large number, gradually overtopping the herbs, reducing the light and taking the lion's share of the water in the soil.

The herbs are conquered by bushes and low shrubs; these are succeeded by taller shrubs, and trees then begin to straggle into the copses, or take more or less complete control by means of sprouts. After a few decades a young climax forest is again in possession.

A somewhat similar course is followed in cultivated fields that are allowed to "go back," the term itself indicating some popular appreciation of the process of succession. Annual weeds dominate for a few years, and the usual communities of perennials, grasses, and shrubs gain successively a short period of mastery, and return to forest or prairie often requiring but two or three decades.

FORCES CONCERNED IN SUCCESSION

Succession depends for its opportunity upon the production of bare or denuded areas, but the driving force back of it is climate, each succeeding community becoming less controlled by soil or terrain and more by climatic factors until the adult stage or climax is attained.

The actual growth of the community is regulated by certain processes or functions by means of which soil and climate produce their effects. The initial processes are aggregation and migration, by which individuals are brought together to form communities. These react upon the soil and then upon the local climate to render conditions at first more favorable to themselves and later to the invaders that are to replace them, the actual conquest being brought about by the outcome of the competition for water, light, and minerals especially.

Within each community there is likewise a certain amount of cooperation, as seen in the reaction that produces shade, increases the organic matter in the soil, minimizes the effect of wind, or augments the moisture of the air. The plants and animals of the community also exhibit many essential interactions, in some of which the mutual benefit is striking, as in the pollination of flowers by insects and hummingbirds. When man enters the situation, such relations become much more varied and important, especially in the hunting, pastoral, and purely agricultural stages of human society.

SUCCESSION OF RACES AND CULTURES

It is obvious that human communities are subject to the control of climate and soil—to what have often been called geographic influences. They exhibit aggregation and migration, reaction upon the environment and increasing control of it. Competition has been rife between and within them, and out of this has gradually emerged a new function, cooperation, first within the family and then spreading to larger and larger units under a slow but inevitable compulsion.

Succession has been less clearly perceived in human communities, though everywhere prevalent in prehistoric and ancient times, while modern rivalries disclose certain aspects of it. The first recorded succession is that of Chellean, Achulean, Mousterian, Solutrian and Magdalenian peoples in Europe, while the most complex has been the sequence of races in Mesopotamia, from Sumerian to Akkadian, Amorite, Babylonian, Assyrian, Chaldean, Persian, Macedonian, Mongol, Tatar and Turk.

Better known to us is the series of invasions that have swept over England, involving Pict, Goidel, Brython, Roman, Angle and Saxon, Dane, and Norman. A similar succession on our own continent is illustrated by the Maya, Toltec, Aztec and Spaniard in Mexico, by various Pueblan cultures of the Southwest, and by the trapper, hunter, pioneer, homesteader, and urbanite in the Middle West.

SUCCESSION AS A TOOL

The applications of succession to human problems and natural industries are manifold. They are exemplified in all the disturbances wrought by man in the vegetation of the globe, as already suggested in the case of fire and clearing.

Succession is invoked for its benefits in the rotation of crops, and it lies at the root of systems of forest management, and particularly of afforestation and reforestation. It is indispensable to land classification, and hence to regulated grazing and the utilization of the public domain. It is the chief tool in the control of run-off, erosion and floods, and the conservation of water supplies for irrigation and urban use, as in the maintenance of all surface natural resources, including game.

How varied is its service may be shown by the appeal to it in the litigation between Texas and Oklahoma over the location of boundary formed by the Red River in which millions of dollars in the Burkburnett oil field were involved. The decision of the United States Supreme Court in favor of Texas was based upon the evidence obtained from succession studies made possible by the researches of the Carnegie Institution of Washington.

QUESTIONS

1. Define and illustrate a climax community.
2. Define and illustrate succession.
3. What determines, largely, the type and speed of succession?
4. Name some of the factors comprising the environment of plants.
5. What are the two most extensive climaxes in the United States?
6. Describe the main events in any one prominent type of succession.

F. O. Bower

Parasitism in Flowering Plants

Reprinted from Chapter 23 of Plants and man. London, Macmillan Company, 1925 with the permission of the representatives of the late Dr. Bower.

In human society a brigand is not merely regarded as a moral delinquent; he is held to be an enemy of the State. The foundation for this lies ultimately in Man's consciousness and volition. It is from his possession of these powers that the social order which recognizes public and private rights has sprung. In plants there is no evidence of either consciousness or power of volition, nor consequently of moral sense. In a crowded flora there is ruthless competition for any suitable nourishment that may be available, and the prize naturally falls to the plant that has the strongest absorptive powers. Consequently parasitism, or physiological brigandage, may follow at any point where contact results from overcrowding, provided that one of the organisms in contact has more power to retain it. Such opportunity is general; very naturally, therefore, the origin of parasitism does not appear to have been restricted to any definite place or period. Nor is it restricted to any one group of organisms. It is true that the most typical instances of the habit are found among the Fungi, plants probably of Algal origin, which have existed from very early times. But many genera of Flowering Plants belonging to divers families show it; and this in itself suggests that in them the habit has been relatively recently acquired. Parasitism being thus a phenomenon of sporadic origin, it is difficult to speak of it effectively in general terms. It will be better to study concrete examples: and for simplicity of description to choose them first from Flowering Plants.

The Convolvulaceae provide a good instance of the way in which a climbing habit may lead to full parasitism. The common Bind Weed or *Convolvulus* is a spiral climber, whose thin whip-like stem twines round its support, so that its living tissue comes into very close contact with the outer surface of the host. But the advantage it derives is merely mechanical; it is well able to nourish itself by its large green foliage leaves, and by supplies of salts brought up from the soil by the roots. But the genus *Cuscuta*, the Dodder, which is referred to the *Convolvulus* family because its flowers are of that type, comprises plants whose whip-like stems are almost leafless, and in colour are sometimes pink, sometimes very pale green or white. Since chlorophyll is almost absent, and there are no foliage leaves but only a few minute scales, these plants cannot nourish themselves; moreover, the adult plants are not rooted in the soil. Nevertheless they flower freely in dense clusters, and produce large well-stored seeds. Examination of the surface of contact between this root-less climber and the support that it clasps, will show that numerous suckers from the former have penetrated the tissue of the host, so as to establish a series of physiological bridges between the two. It is believed that these suckers represent highly specialized roots. Their position appears to be determined by contact. The method of attack in *Cuscuta europaea* is that first a flat adhesive disc projects from the stem of the parasite, attaching itself by broadly spreading hairs to the surface of the host. An active growth from within then bursts through the superficial tissue, just as a young root does, and, like a borer, it penetrates the tissue of the host, sinking into its tissue softened by a process of digestion. Long rhizoid-like tubes then spread radially out from it, applying themselves especially to the wood and to the pith. Both the conducting tracts and the storage region are thus tapped, and the parasite is put into intimate relation with the supplies of its victim. No wonder then that it has need neither of foliage leaves nor of normal roots. In accordance with the general principle of economy these otherwise essential parts are abortive.

It has been seen that the dodder seeds profusely; but how does the seedling of the parasite initiate the attack? The well-stored seed is able on germination in the soil to start the seedling off in a form suited for success, for its seed-leaves are rudimentary and it produces only a simple taproot. Almost all the reserve food is used in forming a long whip-like stem, that moves in the air in wide circles, so as to bring about contact with any living shoot within reach. As soon as this is achieved it promptly becomes a parasitic twiner like the parent. If the food supply runs out before the contact is made, it dies; but if contact be made the root dries off, and the plant continues its life in the degraded form shown by the adult. But the degradation is only vegetative; the flowers are normal, though small. The effect of this parasitism on the host is just what one might expect. It may be seen in any clover field infected by dodder. The clover is stunted in growth, but it is not otherwise altered unless the parasite actually smothers it.

Though the adult dodder is thus isolated from the soil, it starts its germination in the ordinary way. But the evergreen mistletoe is an epiphyte from the first, and germinates where it grows, attached to the branches of trees. The viscid white berries, which are one of the sources of bird-lime, are greedily eaten by birds, which wipe their bills on the branches on which they perch to rid them of the sticky seeds. The seeds stick to the twigs, and are thus widely sown. The green embryo, on germinating, protrudes its root, which turning from the light, forms first an attachment disc, from the center of which a root plunges into the tissue of the host. It passes to the level of the cambium, and there establishes with the wood a close relation, which is permanently retained. Other roots arising from it run horizontally through the cortex, and they may give rise to fresh shoots, often at a considerable distance from the main shoot. This, which springs direct from the plumule of the seedling, develops a forking habit, the pale green stem bearing the well-known pairs of yellowish leathery leaves and spikes of minute greenish flowers and ultimately the white berries.

The green of its shoot, though pale and golden, proves its ability for self-nourishment by photosynthesis. But for water and a supply of the necessary salts, it is dependent upon tapping the transpiration stream carried by the wood of the host. This is secured at once on germination, and it is maintained throughout life. An absorption of organic food also is by no means excluded; possibly the plant does not depend wholly upon the activity of the imperfectly developed pigment. Mistletoe stands thus in an intermediate position as a green parasite which has not dispensed with its own powers of self-nutrition.

Another quite distinct family of flowering plants is addicted to root-parasitism, which has clearly taken its origin from the contact of roots matted in the soil. While the majority of the snapdragons lead an ordinary independent life, the group of genera that center round the eyebright (*Euphrasia*) present above ground pale and livid colouring of the green shoot, and this goes along with the fact that their roots fix themselves by suckers essentially similar to those of the dodder upon the roots of other plants, such as grasses and clovers. They are, in fact, root parasites. The yellow rattle is perhaps the most injurious, and its effect on the meadow can be easily noted from a distance by the stunted appearance of the crop where the parasite is present in quantity. The plants of this family, the snapdragons, show a very interesting progression towards complete parasitism and the loss of the chlorophyll function altogether. Starting with the fully self-nourishing types, such as the mullein and foxglove, there is nothing to remark beyond the fact that they represent a family with rather advanced floral characters. But the eyebright, bartsia, cow-wheat, louse-wort, and the yellow rattle are root parasites with a pale or livid aspect of their vegetative shoots. Finally, the tooth-wort (*Lathraea*) is a full parasite, with its scaly and branched shoot blanched underground, and attached to the roots of the hazel.

Examples of still further reduction of the vegetative system, accompanied by flowers some of which are the largest in the vegetable kingdom, are seen in the fully parasitic family of the *Rafflesiaceae*, and these may be held to mark an acme of the parasitic habit in flowering plants. It includes genera and species which share a most remarkable character, for the vegetative system is completely enclosed within the tissues of the host. A small form, *Pilostyles,* which grows on various *Mimoseae,* has been fully examined, and the vegetative system of the parasite has been found to consist of fine filaments like fungal threads which perforate the cells of the host, and traverse its conducting column. The attack is exactly along the same lines as that of a parasitic fungus. But the proof that this greatly reduced body is really a flowering plant appears when it forms buds that burst through the skin of the host plant, as flower buds. Though these have a curiously specialized structure, their features are unmistakably those of a flowering plant.

To the same family, to which the genus gives its name, belongs that most wonderful object, *Rafflesia,* first discovered on the island of Sumatra by Dr. Arnold. Its flowers are "a full yard across," of a livid red colour; they smell like carrion, and are pollinated by carrion-flies. This is again the flower of a parasite. Its vegetative system develops within the tissues of the root of a vine, and is, like that of *Pilostyles,* of a degraded type. The flower buds borne upon it burst through the tissues of the host. The flower itself is not only large, but also complex in its structure, and the seed production is prodigious.

A general parallel may be drawn between such parasitism in plants and that in animals. The general similarity of the effect of the habit upon organisms so diverse as *Rafflesia* and a tape-worm or a liver-fluke may be held as demonstrating the biological principles that underlie it in either kingdom. In both the phenomenon is sporadic, a fact which indicates that it arises in relation to opportunity rather than by any definite evolutionary trend. Parasitism brings with it the easy acquirement of food without the obligation of gathering or acquiring it by individual exertion. So far it is a direct advantage to the organism that adopts it. But the habit brings also two natural consequences. The first is a reduction or even abortion of parts. The disused organs—and in particular the leaves and roots of plant parasites—not being necessary, are partially or wholly aborted; while in flowering plants developed as parasites the whole vegetative system may in extreme cases be represented by filaments no more elaborate than are the filaments of a fungus. The second consequence is an enormous production of seeds. Any parasite that has wholly desisted from self-nourishment stakes all its chances of existence upon finding the peculiar conditions of its supply. The chances of its doing so are the more remote the more peculiar they are. The germs of a parasite that is successful only on one host must find that host or perish. The risk of not doing so is met by the immense output of seeds, which is specially marked where the parasitism is of an advanced type. It is seen in the large seed-output of the tooth-wort, which is parasitic on hazel roots, or of *Rafflesia* parasitic on those of certain vines. If we turn from such examples to animal parasites, we shall see in the liver-fluke and in the tape-worm conditions of simplified or indeed degraded bodily structure, and of high fecundity, which may be read as similar responses to biological conditions that rule for parasitism in either kingdom. They provide indeed some of the widest possible examples of homoplasy: that is, the similar reaction of unrelated organisms to like conditions of life. It appears, then, that the result of parasitism may be stated quite generally for any living type, including even man himself: once the individual reaches maturity, physiological dependence and degradation tend to go hand in hand.

QUESTIONS

1. Do scientists generally believe that aborted organs arise *because* the organ was not needed? Explain.
2. Does the theory of Bower sound like Darwin's, Lamarck's or DeVries' Theory?

Oakes Ames

Pollination of Orchids through Pseudocopulation

Reprinted with the permission of the Botanical Museum of Harvard University from Leaflet V(1), 1937.

Within comparatively recent years, biologists have been made aware of a peculiar relationship between certain orchids and the hymenopterous insects which pollinate them. A wholly unexpected trend in biological behavior has been revealed and it has been proved that the motives leading to pollination are much more complex than formerly had been supposed. It is now known that certain insects are attracted by orchids for a purpose wholly apart from the search for food and that there are aspects of pollination presenting new and practically unexplored fields for research.

Scolia ciliata is a member of the *Scoliidae,* a family of burrowing hymenoptera, whose burrows are made in sandbanks exposed to the sun. The males emerge from the burrows about a month earlier than the females, usually in March. The females lead an almost subterranean existence and leave the burrows chiefly in search of food. While waiting for the females to make their appearance (mating takes place only in the open air), the males may be seen exploring in sinuous flight the ramparts of Algerian fortifications and exposed railroad embankments. And it is just such places as these for which the plants of *Ophrys speculum* exhibit a predilection. The flowering season of the orchid coincides with the appearance of the males of *Scolia ciliata* and during the long wait for the coming of the females, the male insects visit the orchid flowers, seeming to find in them a compelling attraction. There were questions here demanding deep thought. In the first place, why the indifference of the females? And in the second place, what attributes peculiar to *Ophrys speculum* were of a nature to attract one sex and not the other of an insect seeking food?

Pouyanne established beyond any doubt that the flowers of *Ophrys speculum* are not visited for nectar or edible tissues, because when the males of *Scolia ciliata* enter a flower the suctorial apparatus is not used and the proboscis of the insect does not come in sustained contact with any part of the labellum of the orchid. The insect assumes a position lengthwise of the labellum with the head directed toward the column, just beneath the rostellum, and inserts the tip of the abdomen among the reddish-yellow or maroon colored hairs that form a fringe near the apex of the labellum. While in this position, peculiar movements of the insect's body take place; the pollinia of the orchid are dislodged and are affixed to the insect's head. After the usual hygrometric behavior of the pollinia the pollen masses are in a position for coming in contact with the stigmas of the next flower visited. Pouyanne observed the action of the insect after the tip of the abdomen had been inserted among the hairs of the labellum and described it as follows: "Le bout de l'abdomen est alors agité, contre ces poils, de mouvements désordonnés, presque convulsifs, et l'insecte tout entier se trémousse; ses mouvements, son attitude paraissent tout à fait semblables à ceux des insectes qui pratiquent des tentatives de copulation."

Seeking to explain the behavior of the males of *Scolia ciliata*, Pouyanne conducted a series of experiments that might prove enlightening. He cut off the labellum of some of the flowers, leaving the sepals, petals and column intact. Flowers so mutilated were neglected; the insects became quite indifferent to them. If single flowers were taken from a raceme and placed on the ground, they were immediately approached. But when the separate flowers were inverted with only the under side of the labellum exposed, the insects still came to them, yet with lessened interest. If a bouquet of flowers was held in the hand, the males of *Scolia ciliata* came to it in numbers, contending with each other for the possession of a labellum. If, however, such a bouquet was forced on the attention of the females, they exhibited indifference, and if pressed too insistently flew away as if from something repugnant to them. If flowering specimens of the orchid were concealed under sheets of newspaper and thus hidden from view, the males of *Scolia* would approach, as if trying to reach the concealed flowers, attracted, it would seem, by some odor too faint for perception by human nostrils, because *Ophrys speculum* is described as being without scent. Pouyanne refers to the metallic, violet-blue patch of color on the labellum of *Ophrys speculum* as resembling the metallic blue of the female of *Scolia ciliata* when, at such times as the insect is at rest or crawling on the ground, the wings are half crossed. It is then that the insect, if the sun is shining, exhibits a metallic lustre, an iridescence, similar to that of the labellum of *Ophrys speculum*. Even though the resemblance between the female of *Scolia ciliata* and the labellum of the orchid is hardly of a nature to deceive our eyes, Pouyanne reminds us that the vision of insects is myopic and less keen than ours and that, moreover, in addition to even a faint resemblance that might not in itself deceive the males of *Scolia ciliata*, there is some subtle scent that completes the deception and induces the sexual phenomena he has so convincingly described.

From Pouyanne's experiments and from the behavior of the insects there was every reason to believe that *Ophrys speculum* and the males of *Scolia ciliata* are biologically adjusted for purposes mutually advantageous, although if the purposes are purely sexual, as is evident, then the orchid alone seems to be biologically benefited by the association and, according to human standards, the insect seems to be sadly hoodwinked.

We may wonder how the brief time between the emerging of the males and the females of *Scolia ciliata*, about thirty days each year, was turned by the plant through the ages to such advantage to itself, because in seasons when the orchids are late in flowering or the females of *Scolia ciliata* emerge from their burrows earlier than usual, the orchids are neglected and yield few if any seeds. And once the females of *Scolia ciliata* appear, the males apparently lose interest in the orchid flower and pseudocopulation is no longer performed. Here indeed is a circumstance that is rather amazing. It forces us to assume gradual change and a series of slow modifications through a prodigiously long period of time before the male insect and the orchid became biologically adjusted. Is it not true, that in contemplating the action of Natural Selection as Darwin propounded the doctrine, we think of modifying influences as being prolonged or in constant operation on the affected organism? And yet the direct stimuli associated with pseudocopulation that have affected the flowers in the case of *Ophrys speculum*, have been confined in their action to the brief flowering period, to the duration of anthesis, and under certain circumstances, in exceptional seasons, may operate for a very limited time.

Since 1916 when Pouyanne's observations were published, pseudocopulation has been recorded for at least six species of *Ophrys* and for four species of *Cryptostylis*.

It may be that those who would reject the evolutionary approach to an understanding of life and who prefer to regard the world as the product of Special Creation will lean a little more lightly on human weakness when they discover moral turpitude among the insects. And it may be that entomologists, who see for insect societies parallels in human institutions, will become Freudian in their outlook when discussing the sexual vagaries revealed by symbiotic phenomena and introduce such terms as *Lissopimplan behavior* or *Ophrydean complex*. Perhaps even the poet will have to reconsider whether "Only man is vile."

QUESTIONS

1. What is meant by the term "pseudocopulation"?
2. Is this relationship of mutual relationship to both insect and orchid? Explain.
3. Speculate how such a relationship could have come about solely through Natural Selection.

PART FOUR

PHYTOGEOGRAPHY AND EXPLORATION

Who among us has not been excited by tales of strange places and people? Even the Sunday afternoon drive attests to man's desire to get away from it all. Those of us who have read of the incredible journeys of men in search of the cinchona tree for its malaria-curing bark, of the bringing back of the breadfruit tree and the subsequent mutiny on the Bounty, and of the start of the East Indian rubber plantations from seeds "smuggled" out of South America, have wished that we might have been able to take such journeys. Some people feel that the last frontier has been crossed and there is really nothing new to see. Actually, there are many places in this hemisphere that have never had a white man visit them.

Our four explorers, to follow, are (or were) scientists who go to far-off places for a purpose. We still thank Humboldt for his pioneer work on curare, an arrow poison now used to relieve some types of paralysis. Professor Gray not only showed the similarity of two floras but he made deductions as to why they were similar, thereby solving a problem of long standing. Dr. Maguire's work in South America and Dr. Polunin's work in the Arctic will be of value to future generations. The United States Government also sends out explorers for new plants, more resistant strains, for new oils, and so forth. Exploration, in short, is finding out more about the planet upon which we live and making it a pleasanter and safer abode for Homo sapiens.

Asa Gray

The Similarity Between the Flora of Japan and that of the United States, Epecially the Atlantic Side

Reprinted with the permission of the publisher from Darwiniana. New York, D. Appleton Co., 1889.

If we now compare, as to their flora generally, the atlantic United States with Japan, Manchuria, and northern China—i.e., eastern North America with eastern North Asia, half the earth's circumference apart—we find an astonishing similarity. The larger part of the genera of our own region, which I have enumerated as wanting in California, are present in Japan or Manchuria, along with many other peculiar plants, divided between the two. There are plants enough of the one region which have no representatives in the other. There are types which appear to have reached the Atlantic States from the south; and there is a larger infusion of subtropical Asiatic types into temperate China and Japan; among these there is no relationship between the two countries to speak of. There are also, as I have already said, no small number of genera and some species which, being common all round or partly round the northern temperate zone, have no special significance because of their occurence in these two antipodal floras, although they have testimony to bear upon the general question of geographical distribution. The point to be remarked is, that many, or even most, of the genera and species which are peculiar to North America as compared with the Californian region, are also represented in Japan and Manchuria, either by identical or by closely similar forms! The same rule holds on a more northward line, although not so strikingly. If we compare the plants, say of New England and Pennsylvania (latitude 45°–47°), with those of Oregon, and then with those of northeastern Asia, we shall find many of our own curiously repeated in the latter, while only a small number of them can be traced along the route even so far as the western slope of the Rocky Mountains. And these repetitions of east American types in Japan and neighboring districts are in all degrees of likeness. Sometimes the one is indistinguishable from the other; sometimes there is a difference of aspect, but hardly of tangible character; sometimes the two would be termed marked varieties if they grew naturally in the same forest or in the same region; sometimes they are what the botanist calls representative species, the one answering closely to the other, but with some differences regarded as specific; sometimes the two are merely of the same genus, or not quite that, but of a single or very few species in each country; in which case the point which interests us is, that this peculiar limited type should occur in two antipodal places, and nowhere else.

It would be tedious, and, except to botanists, abstruse, to enumerate instances; yet the whole strength of the case depends upon the number of such instances. I propose therefore, if the Association does me the honor to print this discourse, to append in a note a list of the more remarkable ones. But I would here mention certain cases as specimens.

Our *Rhus Toxicodendron*, or poison-ivy, is very exactly repeated in Japan, but is found in no other part of the world, although a species much like it abounds in California. Our other poisonous *Rhus* (*R. venenata*), commonly called poison dogwood, is in no way represented in western America, but has so close an analogue in Japan that the two were taken for the same by Thunberg and Linnaeus, who called them both *R. vernix*.

Our northern fox-grape, *Vitis Labrusca*, is wholly confined to the Atlantic States, except that it reappears in Japan and that region.

The original *Wistaria* is a woody leguminous climber with showy blossoms, native to the middle Atlantic States; the species, which we so much prize in cultivation, *W. sinensis*, is from China, as its name denotes, or perhaps only from Japan, where it is certainly indigenous.

Our yellow-wood (*Cladrastis*) inhabits a very limited district on the western slope of the Alleghanies. Its only and very near relative, *Maackia*, is confined to Manchuria.

The hydrangeas have some species in our Alleghany region: all the rest belong to the Chino-Japanese region and its continuation westward. The same may be said of *Philadelphus*, except that there are one or two mostly very similar species in California and Oregon.

Our May-flower (*Epigaea*) and our creeping snow-berry, otherwise peculiar to atlantic North America, recur in Japan.

Our blue cohosh (*Caulophyllum*) is confined to the woods of the Atlantic States, but has lately been discovered in Japan. A peculiar relative of it, *Diphylleia*, confined to the higher Alleghanies, is also repeated in Japan, with a slight difference, so that it may barely be distinguished as another species. Another relative is our twin-leaf (*Jeffersonia*) of the Alleghany region alone: a second species has lately turned up in Manchuria. A relative of this is *Podophyllum*, our mandrake, a common inhabitant of the atlantic United States, but found nowhere else. There is one other species of it, and that is in the Himalayas. Here are four most peculiar genera of one family, each of a single species in the atlantic United States, which are duplicated on the other side of the world, either in identical or almost identical species, or in an analogous species, while nothing else of the kind is known in any other part of the world.

I ought not to omit ginseng, the root so prized by the Chinese, which they obtained from their northern provinces and Manchuria, and which is now known to inhabit Korea and northern Japan. The Jesuit Fathers identified the plant in Canada and the Atlantic States, brought over the Chinese name by which we know it, and established the trade in it, which was for many years most profitable. The exportation of ginseng to China probably has not yet entirely ceased. Whether the Asiatic and the atlantic American ginsengs are to be regarded as of the same species or not is somewhat uncertain, but they are hardly, if at all, distinguishable.

There is a shrub, *Elliottia*, which is so rare and local that it is known only at two stations on the Savannah River in Georgia. It is of peculiar structure, and was without near relative until one was lately discovered in Japan (*Tripetaleia*), so like it as hardly to be distinguishable except by having parts of the blossom in threes instead of fours—a difference not uncommon in the same genus, or even in the same species.

Suppose *Elliottia* had happened to be collected only once, a good while ago, and all knowledge of the limited and obscure locality were lost; and meanwhile the Japanese form came to be known. Such a case would be parallel with an actual one. A specimen of a peculiar plant (*Shortia galacifolia*) was detected in the herbarium of the elder Michaux, who collected it (as his autograph ticket shows) somewhere in the high Alleghany Mountains, more than eighty years ago. No one has seen the living plant since or knows where to find it, if haply it still flourishes in some secluded spot. At length it is found in Japan; and I had the satisfaction of making the identification. A relative is also known in Japan; and a less near one has just been detected in Tibet.

Whether the Japanese and the Alleghanian plants are exactly the same or not, it needs complete specimens of the two to settle. So far as we know, they are just alike; and, even if some difference were discerned between them it would not appreciably alter the question as to how such a result came to pass. Each and every one of the analogous cases I have been detailing—and very many more could be mentioned—raises the same question, and would be satisfied with the same answer.

These singular relations attracted my curiosity early in the course of my botanical studies, when comparatively few of them were known, and my serious attention in later years, when I had numerous and new Japanese plants to study in the collections made, by Messrs. Williams and Morrow, during Commodore Perry's visit in 1853, and especially, by Mr. Charles Wright, of Commodore Rodgers's expedition in 1855. I then discussed this subject somewhat fully, and tabulated the facts within my reach.

This was before Heer had developed the rich fossil botany of the arctic zone, before the immense antiquity of existing species of plants was recognized, and before the publication of Darwin's now famous volume on the "Origin of Species" had introduced and familiarized the scientific world with those now current ideas respecting the history and vicissitudes of species with which I attempted to deal in a moderate and feeble way.

My speculation was based upon the former glaciation of the northern temperate zone, and the inference of a warmer period preceding and perhaps following. I considered that our own present vegetation, or its proximate ancestry, must have occupied the arctic and subarctic regions in Pliocene times, and that it had been gradually pushed southward as the temperature lowered and the glaciation advanced, even beyond its present habitation; that plants of the same stock and kindred, probably ranging round the arctic zone as the present arctic species do, made their forced migration southward upon widely different longitudes, and receded more or less as the climate grew warmer; that the general difference of climate which marks the eastern and the western sides of the continents—the one extreme, the other mean—was doubtless even then established, so that the same species and the same sorts of species would be likely to secure and retain foothold in the similar climates of Japan and the atlantic United States, but not in intermediate regions of different distribution of heat and moisture; so that different species of the same genus, as in *Torreya*, or different genera of the same group, as redwood, *Taxodium*, and *Glyptostrobus*, or different associations of forest trees, might establish themselves each in the region best suited to the particular requirements, while they would fail to do so in any other. These views implied that the sources of our actual vegetation and the explanation of these peculiarities were to be sought in, and presupposed, an ancestry in Pliocene or earlier times, occupying the higher northern regions, And it was thought that the occurrence of peculiar North American genera in Europe in the Tertiary period (such as *Taxodium*, *Carya*, *Liquidambar*, *Sassafras*, *Negundo*, etc.) might be best explained on the assumption of early interchange and diffusion through North Asia, rather than by that of the fabled Atlantis.

The hypothesis supposed a gradual modification of species in different directions under altering conditions, at least to the extent of producing varieties, sub-species, and representative species, as they may be variously regarded; likewise the single and local origination of each type, which is now almost universally taken for granted. The remarkable facts in regard to the eastern American and Asiatic floras which these speculations were to explain have since increased in number, especially through the admirable collections of Dr. Maximowicz in Japan and adjacent countries, and the critical comparisons he has made and is still engaged upon.

I must refrain from all enumeration of the angiospermous or ordinary deciduous trees and shrubs, which are now known, by their fossil remains, to have flourished throughout the polar regions when Greenland better deserved its name and enjoyed the present climate of New England and New Jersey. Then Greenland and the rest of the north abounded with oaks, representing the several groups of species which now inhabit both our eastern and western forest districts; several poplars, one very like our balsam poplar or balm-of-Gilead tree; more beeches than there are now, a hornbeam, and a hop-hornbeam, some birches, a persimmon, and a plane tree, near representatives of those of the Old World, at least of Asia, as well as of atlantic North America, but all wanting in California; one *Juglans* like the walnut of the Old World, and another like our black walnut; two or three grapevines, one near our southern fox grape or muscadine, another near our northern frostgrape; a *Tilia*, very like our basswood of the Atlantic States only; a *Liquidambar*; a magnolia, which recalls our *M. grandiflora*; a *Liriodendron*, sole representative of our tulip-tree; and a sassafras, very like the living tree.

Most of these, it will be noticed, have their nearest or their only living representatives in the Atlantic States, and when elsewhere, mainly in eastern Asia. Several of them, or of species like them have been detected in our Tertiary deposits, west of the Mississippi, by Newberry and Lesquereux. Herbaceous plants, as it happens, are rarely preserved in a fossil state, else they would probably supply additional testimony to the antiquity of our existing vegetation, its wide diffusion over the northern and now frigid zone and its enforced migration under changes of climate.

Concluding, then, as we must, that our existing vegetation is a continuation of that of the Tertiary period, may we suppose that it absolutely originated then? Evidently not. The preceding Cretaceous period has furnished to Carruthers in Europe a fossil fruit like that of the *Sequoia gigantea* of the famous groves, associated with pines of the same character as those that accompany the present tree; has furnished to Heer, from Greenland, two more Sequoias, one of them identical with a Tertiary species, and one nearly allied to *Sequoia Langsdorfi*, which in turn is a probable ancestor of the common Californian redwood; has furnished to Newberry and Lesquereux in North America the remains of another ancient sequoia, a *Glyptostrobus*, a *Liquidambar* which well represents our sweet-gum-tree, oaks analogous to living ones, leaves of a plane-tree, which are also in the Tertiary, and are scarcely distinguishable from our own *Platanus occidentalis*, of a magnolia and a tulip-tree, and "of a sassafras undistinguishable from our living species." I need not continue the enumeration. Suffice it to say that the facts justify the conclusion which Lesquereux—a scrupulous investigator—has already announced: that "the essential types of our actual flora are marked in the Cretaceous period, and have come to us after passing, without notable changes, through the Tertiary formations of our continent."

According to these views, as regards plants at least, the adaptation to successive times and changed conditions has been maintained, not by absolute renewals, but by gradual modifications. I, for one, cannot doubt that the present existing species are the lineal successors of those that garnished the earth in the old time before them, and that they were as well adapted to their surroundings then, as those which flourish and bloom around us are to their conditions now.

Such ideas as these, though still repugnant to some, and not long since to many, have so possessed the minds of the naturalists of the present day that hardly a discourse can be pronounced or an investigation prosecuted without reference to them. I suppose that the views here taken are little, if at all, in advance of the average scientific mind of the day. I cannot regard them as less noble than those which they are succeeding. An able philosophical writer, Miss Frances Power Cobbe, has recently and truthfully said:

> It is a singular fact that, when we can find out how anything is done, our first conclusion seems to be that God did not do it. No matter how wonderful, how beautiful, how intimately complex and delicate has been the machinery which has worked, perhaps for centuries, perhaps for millions of ages, to bring about some beneficent result, if we can but catch a glimpse of the wheels its divine character disappears.

I agree with the writer that this first conclusion is premature and unworthy—I will add, deplorable. Through what faults or infirmities of dogmatism on the one hand, and skepticism on the other, it came to be so thought, we need not here consider. Let us hope, and I confidently expect, that it is not to last; that the religious faith which survived without a shock the notion of the fixity of the species which inhabit it; that, in the future even more than in the past, faith in an *order*, which is the basis of science, will not—as it cannot reasonably—be dissevered from faith in an *Ordainer*, which is the basis of religion.

QUESTIONS

1. Mention a few plants which are found both in eastern Asia and eastern North America.
2. What parts did glaciation, migration and climate play in developing the peculiar type of vegetational distribution referred to by Asa Gray?

Alexander Von Humboldt

The Curare Poison

Reprinted from Personal narrative of travels to the equinoctial regions of America during the years 1799–1804, Vol. 2. London, Henry B. Bohn, 1852.

Esmeralda is the most celebrated spot on the Orinoco for the preparation of that active poison, which is employed in war, in the chase, and singularly enough, as a remedy for gastric derangements. The poison of the *ticunas* of the Amazon, the *upas-tieute* of Java, and the *curare* of Guiana, are the most deleterious substances that are known. The missionaries, Gumilla and Gili, had not been able to penetrate into the country where the *curare* is manufactured. Gumilla asserts that "this preparation was enveloped in great mystery; that its principal ingredient was furnished by a subterranean plant with a tuberous root, which never puts forth leaves, and which is called specially 'the root' (raiz de si misma); that the venomous exhalations which arise from the manufacture are fatal to the lives of the old women who (being otherwise useless) are chosen to watch over this operation; finally, that these vegetable juices are never thought to be sufficiently concentrated until a few drops produce *at a distance* a repulsive action on the blood."

When we arrived at Esmeralda, the greater part of the Indians were returning from an excursion which they had made to the east to gather *juvias*, or the fruit of the bertholletia, and the liana which yields the *curare*. Their return was celebrated by a festival. The women had prepared a quantity of fermented liquor, and during two days the Indians were in a state of intoxication. We were fortunate enough to find an old Indian more temperate than the rest, who was employed in preparing the *curare* poison from freshly-gathered plants. He was the chemist of the place. We found at his dwelling large earthen pots for boiling the vegetable juice, shallower vessels to favor the evaporation by a larger surface, and leaves of the plantain trees rolled up in the shape of our filters, and used to filtrate the liquids, more or less loaded with fibrous matter. The greatest order and neatness prevailed in this hut, which was transformed into a chemical laboratory. The old Indian was known throughout the mission by the name of the poison-master (amo del curare). He had that self-sufficient air and tone of pedantry of which the pharmacopolists of Europe were formerly accused. "I know," said he, "that the whites have the secret of making soap, and manufacturing that black powder which has the defect of making a noise when used in killing animals. The *curare*, which we prepare from father to son, is superior to anything you can make *down yonder* (beyond sea). It is the juice of an herb which kills silently, without anyone knowing whence the stroke comes."

This chemical operation, to which the old man attached so much importance, appeared to us extremely simple. The liana (bejuco) used at Esmeralda for the preparation of the poison, bears the same name as in the forests of Javita. It is the *bejuco de Mavacure*. Although the bundles of *bejuco* which we found in the hut of the Indian were entirely bare of leaves, we had no doubt of their being produced by the same plant of the strychnos family which we had examined in the forest of Pimichin. The mavacure is employed fresh or dried indifferently during several weeks. The juice of the liana, when it has been recently gathered, is not regarded as poisonous; possibly it is so only when strongly concentrated. It is the bark and a part of the albumum which contain this terrible poison. Branches of the mavacure four or five lines in diameter are scraped with a knife, and the bark that comes off is bruised, and reduced into very fine filaments on the stone employed for grinding cassava. The venemous juice being yellow, the whole fibrous mass takes that colour. It is thrown into a funnel nine inches high, with an opening four inches wide. This funnel was, of all the instruments of the Indian laboratory, that of which the poison maker seemed to be most proud. It was the leaf of the plantain-tree rolled up in the form of a cone, and placed within a stronger cone made of the leaves of the palm-tree. The whole of this apparatus was supported by slight frame-work made of the petioles and ribs of palm-leaves. A cold infusion is first prepared by pouring water on the fibrous matter which is the ground bark of the *mavacure*. A yellowish water filters during several hours, drop by drop, through the leafy funnel. This filtered water is the poisonous liquor, but it acquires strength only when concentrated by evaporation, like molasses, in a large earthen pot. The Indian from time to time invited us to taste the liquid; its taste, more or less bitter, decides when the concentration by fire has been carried sufficiently far. There is no danger in tasting it, the *curare* being deleterious only when it comes into immediate contact with the blood. The vapours, therefore, which are disengaged from the pans are not hurtful, notwithstanding all that has been said on this point by the missionaries of the Orinoco.

The most concentrated juice of the *mavacure* is not thick enough to stick to the darts, and therefore, to give a body to the poison, another vegetable juice, extremely glutinous, drawn from a tree with large leaves, called *kiracaquero*, is poured into the concentrated infusion. At the instant, it blackens, and coagulates into a mass of the consistence of tar, or of a thick syrup. This mass is the *curare* of commerce.

The Indians consider the curare, taken internally, as an excellent stomachic. At the Orinoco the *curare de raiz* (of the roots) is distinguished from the *curare de bejuco* (of lianas, or of the bark of branches). We saw only the latter prepared; the former is weaker, and much less esteemed. Scarcely a fowl is eaten on the banks of the Orinoco which has not been killed with a poisoned arrow, and the missionaries allege that the flesh of animals is never so good as when this method is employed. Indians who have been wounded in battle by weapons dipped in the *curare* feel congestion in the head, vertigo, and nausea. They are tormented by a raging thirst, and numbness pervades all the parts that are near the wound.

QUESTIONS

1. Why did the Indians think curare was superior to gunpowder?
2. What part of the plant contains the poison?
3. Can the poison be taken internally?
4. How is curare used to kill game?

Bassett Maguire

Exploration

Reprinted with the permission of the author and publisher from A.I.B.S. Bulletin 7(5): 14–17, 1957.

"Exploration" is a term of broad concept and application. Historically, great voyages and travels have sought to establish trade routes, to acquire land possessions, to open up new territories, to obtain new sources of basic materials, and to seek out new geographical and scientific knowledge. Perhaps the time of classic exploration marked by such heroic episodes as the travels of Marco Polo, Columbus, the transcontinental journey of Lewis and Clark, and the voyage of the H.M.S. Beagle are completely gone. Yet today there remain ever increasing demands for more refined field procedure in natural history, and surely there has never been keener competition in exploration for new sources of raw materials, petroleum, metals, and plants of economic promise than there has been in the past decade. Exploration will remain for some time to come an important tool of modern society.

. . .

In the conduct of exploration, two primary general requisites precede organization and preparation for the expedition, viz., a well considered and selected objective, and an adequate background knowledge of the country or region to be visited, viz., its geology, geography, biological history, language and social customs. The general physical characters of the selected region would predetermine the kind of problems to be met, and hence the requirements of equipment, supplies and foods. Obviously, if an expedition were to be sent to the Arctic, the types of clothing, camp equipment, etc., would be greatly different from those required for an expedition to the tropics.

As it happens, this piece is being written aboard a 300 ton, twin-engined, diesel powered passenger ship, now about 600 miles inland, plowing upstream to the head of large river-craft navigation at Puerto Ayacucho, the capital city of the Territory, built at the foot of the great rapids of the Orinoco in Amazonian Venezuela. Preparation for this trip has been going on for some time. Organization is still in progress. An outline in some small detail, giving the background, objective, organization and preparation of the present trip, may serve to typify one kind of exploration.

BACKGROUND

A hundred and twenty years ago, Robert Schomburgk, while performing a geographical commission for the Royal Society in London, doing general exploration for the Colony of British Guiana, and collecting large series of plants and animals to be studied and distributed by the Royal Botanic Gardens, Kew, and the British Museum, Kensington, crossed the Tacutú River to visit the old fort of San Joaquim, which lay at the confluence of the Araricuera and Tacutú where the Rio Branco, one of the principal tributaries of the Amazon is formed. Traveling northward from Joaquim, Schomburgk traversed rugged terrain dominated by crystalline rocks of the Guayana Shield and intrusive granites. Some fifty miles south of the present Venezuelan-Brazilian frontier, he encountered series of sandstone sediments and associated sedimentary volcanics, and was thus the first European of record to set foot on the eastern region of the Roraima Formation (Martius some years earlier collected on sandstone areas in Colombian Amazonas). Further to the north he reached a chain of exceedingly high sandstone block mountains, the most prominent of which was called by the Indians "Roraima." Schomburgk's descriptions of the terrain and collections from the slopes of Roraima and the surrounding sedimentary plateau, together with material collected on his visit four years later, aroused much interest in England and on the Continent. Subsequently, a succession of European biologists visited the Roraima area, the last of whom was Ernst Ule, circa 1912.

In dugout and on foot during his first visit to the sandstone regions of Guayana, Robert Schomburgk, still under commission of the Royal Society, traveled westerly for some four hundred miles until he made contact on the

Orinoco at Esmeralda with the point visited by Humboldt and Bonpland nearly forty years earlier. Schomburgk recognized the sediments of the western mountains of Marahuaca and Duida to be similar to those of the lofty Roraima and its neighbors. Near the beginning of the present century, other travelers, most notably the anthropologist Köch-Grünberg, traversed Guayana, and the geographer Hamilton Rice skirted its periphery. By about 1940 the Venezuelan Government had concluded a geological survey of the Gran Sabana, and Felix Cardona, geographer for the Venezuelan Government, was well progressed in his remarkable career of exploration of Guayana. The American Museum expeditions to Mount Roraima near the eastern periphery, Cerro Duida on the Upper Orinoco, and lastly to Auyan-tepuí on the Gran Sabana, from which drops the spectacular Angel Falls, led by the late G. H. H. Tate, had been completed. All of this pioneer work in biology, geology and geography laid a background which defined one of the major physiographic and coincident phytogeographic provinces of northern South America. . . .

OBJECTIVE

Early botanical work had demonstrated conclusively that the sedimentary region of Guayana, considered to be of Cretaceous or earlier origin by most contemporary geologists, is the seat of a remarkable self-contained flora of extremely high endemism. . . .

The New York Botanical Garden in 1944 reactivated its interest and began a second series of explorations to this fascinating region for the purpose of doing plant reconnaissance throughout as much of Guayana as is practical to reach. The resulting inventory of the plant resources of the region has become the basis for a continuing series of technical reports, and is expected to become the basis for the floristic treatment of the province. . . .

ORGANIZATION

Exploration is a costly operation. If the individual or institution planning an expedition has sufficient money, one of the major problems is at the outset obviated. Most planners of exploratory field work are not so fortunate, however, and must develop additional sources of financial support. Given an adequate work plan which sets forth the objectives to be achieved, the adequacy of the proposed program, and demonstrates the principal's background preparation and ability to carry the work through to completion, financial support may not be difficult to achieve. Many foundations, research institutions, industrial organizations are prepared to give assistance to the well-conceived project. And, of course, individual friends and private donors often are the most sympathetic sources of support.

. . .

Given assurance of financial security, the next step may well be obtaining official authorizations from the concerned government department or agencies of the country or countries to be visited. Naturally, the requirements of law must be met, and it is well to conclude such necessary understandings and authorizations considerably before any planned departure. The consular offices or the national institutions of common interest with the objectives of the expedition are usually the best sources of advice and instruction. For botanical work in Venezuela it is necessary to obtain passport visa and authorization to enter the country from the Venezuelan Consul. Authorization to do botanical collecting is to be had from the Director of the Botanical Service of the Ministry of

Agriculture and Animal Husbandry. To enter into and conduct study within regions where there are protected Indian populations, authorization must be obtained from the Ministry of Justice. And, finally, on entry, one must register with the Security Officers to facilitate travel and transport within the country. It is exceedingly helpful to present a carefully prepared list of all equipment and supplies that are to be used on the expedition for approval by the Consular Office—in our instance, the Consulate-General in New York, who will issue, on agreement, a stamp of approval or "Visto Bueno" for it. . . .

PREPARATION

Details of preparation for an expedition cannot be too precisely or meticulously done. Major categories in preparation are as follows: 1. immunizations, medical and drug supplies; 2. personal clothing and effects: 3. instruments and equipment for scientific work; 4. camp equipment; 5. photographic equipment; 6. clothing and useful articles for guides and porters if the expedition has such requirements; 7. food; and 8. facilities for transport.

1. *Immunizations, medical and drug supplies.*

Ordinarily, any applicant for a U.S. Passport is given a card of "International Certificate of Inoculation and Vaccination as approved by World Health Organization and The Pan American Sanitary Organization," upon which record of inoculations and vaccinations should be entered. For travel in most American tropical countries, the more important immunizations are those against smallpox, typhoid, yellow fever, and tetanus. Inquiry should be made as to whether typhus and cholera vaccines would be advisable for the country to be visited. For our present purposes, except for the last two diseases, all members of our party have received updated inoculations, and in addition, because of the present danger of epidemic or pandemic Oriental influenza, have obtained before leaving New York anti-flu vaccine. . . .

A carefully prepared and stocked medical kit is essential to the success of an expedition. With the exercise of moderate judgment and care, travel in tropical areas is as safe as living in any city. If one is stricken with malaria or is handicapped by the stricture of dysentery, it is because of his own carelessness. There are a number of effective anti-malarials now on the market. The New York Botanical Garden has successfully used for the entire personnel of its expeditions for a period of ten years the Parke, Davis & Co. anti-malarial Camoquin. As a result of the use of Camoquin as a prophylactic, in only one instance has malaria broken through, and then only of brief and mild occurrence. More recently Camoform with Neomycin and Bacitracin added has successfully been used as an anti-amoebic. Anyone contemplating exploratory work in tropical areas should inform himself very carefully about medical and drug requirements.

Danger from wild animals, particularly poisonous snakes, is minimal in most parts of the American Tropics. Poisonous snakes do occur, but we have encountered them so seldom during the fifteen years of our present tropical program, that we have not considered it necessary to provide ourselves with anti-venoms. We have felt that the ordinary snakebite kit providing tourniquet, lancet and pump is all that is necessary. We have never had occasion to use this equipment.

Biting insects, bete rouge, ticks, etc., are often very abundant and can cause considerable personal discomfiture. The best of repellents seem to be inadequate but should be provided. We have found the Parke, Davis product Caladryl most effective in ameliorating the effect of insect stings and bites, and alcohol sponge most soothing and preventive of infection. . . .

2. *Personal clothing and effects.*

More often one is oversupplied than undersupplied with clothing for tropical field work. In low altitude rainforests we have found that the best footwear is the stoutest basketball shoes that can be obtained. Where one is wet much of the time and is frequently wading up or across streamcourses, leather shoes or boots are not practical, whereas canvas shoes with thick rubber soles give adequate protection, will permit water to drain off quickly, and are not so subject to mildew. Sturdy khaki or denim pants and shirts, substantial socks, and a cloth hat or cap which will shed rain and dry out quickly complete the essential garb. Some travelers prefer woolen shirts—we have not found them useful. At higher elevations, jackets, sweaters and flannel shirts are most comfortable in the evenings. We do not use raincoats. All such gear is most conveniently carried in a duffel bag. It is desirable to have two or three changes of shirts and trousers, an extra pair of basketball shoes, a pair of comfortable camp shoes or slippers, and cotton or dacron pajamas. Many more sophisticated travelers shave regularly in the bush. We do not do so for two practical reasons. A heavy beard protects the face against insect molestation and exposure. In one's personal kit it is convenient to have always available a small bottle of antiseptic such as merthiolate, band-aids, a small bottle of rubbing alcohol, a small container of desenex or some suitable anti-fungal powder. Dental floss, where much bush game is to be used, is an essential.

Shelter in rain-forest bush is best provided by canvas tarpaulins, the size to be determined by the number of occupants. A 16′ × 18′ tarpaulin will provide ample shelter and working space for four individuals. The best bed is a hammock, preferably a woven cotton string of Indian fabrication, and least of all a canvas hammock. A cotton or light wool blanket is useful at low altitudes. Mosquito nets should be ample and completely protective. Such nets prevent objectionable bed companions such as ants, spiders, mosquitoes, etc., from molesting one, and will even provide a refugium if in the daytime the biting flies become excessively severe.

At high altitudes, where the temperature may be depressed to 45°F. or less, we use tents, cots and sleeping bags.

3. *Instruments and equipment for scientific work.*

Obviously the most effective equipment is that with which any party or individual can obtain the best results. For collecting and drying plant specimens much has been written by various competent people, showing the bias of their own procedure. Ours is as follows: we press and dry all specimens in a standard press made up of alternating units of aluminum corrugated driers and two drying felts or blotters. A full press contains 120 units, therefore will hold that many full specimens. The press when full is approximately 36 inches long, and is placed for drying over a folding rectangular drying frame made of light 3-ply pine stock, with sides 18 inches high, elevated on short legs, within which is placed a single burner Coleman Speedmaster gasoline stove. Most specimens will dry completely within eight hours. Succulents, of course, take longer.

All the presses, pressing paper, manila wrapping paper, cordage, etc., and general supplies are packed in lightweight plyboard boxes or telescoping fibre-board boxes of suitable size to hold the collected plant specimens for return shipment. Pliofilm or other plastic sheeting that may be purchased by the yard has been found to be extremely useful in wrapping packages of plants, to prevent absorption of moisture and wetting.

It is presumed that records of ordinary weather data will be maintained, so that standard maximum-minimum thermometers, etc., will be needed. Suitable rain gauges can be improvised from powdered milk tins or others of proper size. A Brunton compass and Taylor, or Short and Mason, altimeters are dependable. We have found Coleman gasoline lamps to be preferable to kerosene lanterns.

4. *Camp equipment.*

At higher altitudes, particularly in sites where forest cover is not available, tents with canvas floors and zippered net fronts are most comfortable. Water-proofed canvas tents are practical if problems of transport are not serious. Otherwise, where weight is a factor, tents made of Egyptian cotton or treated nylon are best, although they are expensive.

Naturally, the size of the party will determine the kind of kitchen gear that is used. Our expeditions usually comprise some twenty to thirty individuals, including porters. Large heavyweight aluminum pots of 12 and 16 quart capacity have been found to be most practical. We do not have separate cooking for principals and porters. Along with the ordinary utensils it is good to provide an eggbeater to prepare milk from the dehydrated concentrate, and a good, sizable meatgrinder. Much of the bush game is tough.

5. *Photographic equipment.*

Photographic records are an essential part of exploration. Our own equipment consists of a 16 mm. Bolex moving picture camera, a 3¼ × 3¼ Rolleiflex for black and white film, and two 35 mm. cameras, a Leica and Exakta for kodachrome film. On expeditions of several months' duration, it is well to transport cameras and particularly film in tight boxes that can be sealed, into which may be introduced packets of silica gell to maintain a reduced humidity.

6. *Clothing and useful articles for guides and porters.*

In many parts of tropical America it is necessary to employ porters for the transport of goods and equipment during the final stages of expeditionary travel. More often Indians, who from small boyhood are trained to carry heavy loads through the forests, provide the best labor. Second to keeping the Indians well and feeding them well, it is necessary to provide them with adequate footwear and clothing, particularly for high altitudes where it is cold at night. Standard supplies, on our expeditions, for each porter consist of a pair of heavy basketball shoes, two pairs of stout denim pants, two denim shirts, a web belt, a sweatshirt, a stout denim jacket, a blanket, a mummybag bedroll, and a machete. . . .

7. *Food*

Ordinarily, and particularly on extended tours of exploration, it is important to make food requirements both simple and acceptable to all participating principals and porters alike. Staples, such as rice, beans, tinned meats, sardines, coffee, sugar, dehydrated milk, cheese and salt, and in much of tropical America the products of the tubers of manihot known in Venezuela as casabe (in English-speaking areas cassave-bread) and manioco, form the basic foods. For the principals oatmeal and cream-of-wheat for breakfast, a limited amount of marmalade and butter, provide the maximum luxury that transport can afford. Onions, if obtainable, and fresh native fruits supplement the fare. In Venezuelan rivers an abundance of fish is usually to be caught, and in the more remote places a reasonable amount of game can be found.

With such a table there are usually no dietary problems, and seldom are vitamin supplements necessary. We have found that dehydrated foods, with the exception of milk and eggs, are usually not practicable. It is especially essential that food in ample quantity be on hand for all members of the expedition. On the present expedition, based on needs for 2400 man-days, we are providing quantities much as follows: tinned meat, corned beef and ham, 1000 tins; sardines and salmon, 1000 tins; rice, 500 pounds; beans, 300 pounds; refined sugar, 200 pounds; brown sugar 120 pounds; coffee, 50 pounds; dehydrated milk, 150 pounds; salt, 250 pounds; oil, 10 gallons; casabe, 1000 pounds; manioco, 1500 pounds; cheese, 100 pounds; oatmeal, 50 pounds; cream-of-wheat, 50 pounds; onions, 100 pounds; dried prunes, apricots, and raisins, 100 pounds. These staples will total some 4900 pounds, which together with the few special things, will exceed more than 5000 pounds of food which must be transported nearly 1000 miles of river travel and travel in bush by foot. . . .

8. *Transportation.*

On the present expedition, when we leave Sanariapo at the head of the great rapids of the Orinoco, we will have, as indicated above, nearly 1000 miles more of river travel to accomplish in our own boats. To move the 5000 pounds of food and equal weight of gear and equipment, and total of 20 members of the expedition, a large "falca" (dugouts some 50 feet long with built-up sides) powered by a 35 horsepower Johnson outboard motor, a small "falca" powered by a Johnson 10 horse motor, and four dugout canoes, will make up our flotilla. . . .

. . .

COLLECTION OF PLANT SPECIMENS

Field practice is as variable as are the natures of the collectors. Some competent practitioners have written rather excoriatingly about the use of vascula. We have used collecting cans successfully. Others preserve collected material in formaldehyde or alcohol, to await later pressing and drying. We feel that the preparation of plants can best be done in the field. We do not use hand presses, except in the confines of our boats during river travel, but prepare our materials as neatly and effectively as possible under the more efficient protection and facilities of well-made camps. Collections are obtained in large series, numbered, wrapped in cloth or large leaves, chiefly of monocotyledonous plants, and carefully packed and transported in large canvas bags, each to be returned to camp in a protected carrying basket by a porter. Attempt is made to collect in series of 5–10 specimens, so that distribution may effectively be made to principal herbaria.

An expedition of the character now mounted should yield for a period of three effective months in the field some 2000 to 2500 collection numbers, with a total of 20,000 or more sheets. It should be pointed out most emphatically that an expedition should not be considered terminated with the successful transport of collected materials back to the home institution. Rather is the project completed only when the material has been studied and reported upon, and the specimens distributed throughout the world.

QUESTIONS

1. What are some of the primary requisites before planning an expedition of a scientific nature?
2. What are the 8 details which must be checked after one's visas are granted?
3. Describe the procedure used in collecting and caring for plant specimens.

Nicholas Polunin

Aspects of Arctic Botany

Reprinted by permission of the author and publisher from American Scientist **43**(2):307–322, 1955.

The Arctic regions have long attracted the adventurous, and latterly have become relatively easy and safe to visit. Of special interest is the plant life of these regions, largely because of its limitation by harsh environmental conditions, so that in recent decades it has been more and more actively investigated. During this time, and particularly in the quarter-century of my own participation, certain trends in the research within the wide bounds of arctic botany have been evident. It is chiefly these modern aspects, their origins, and some of the main results of the latest investigations, that I propose to discuss in this paper.

But first we should be clear as to just what arctic botany comprises. The days when it merely involved the assembling and working out of plant collections are now well past; the bounds have extended enormously, so that arctic botany nowadays includes at least some consideration of almost all of the twenty or more disciplines which are included in modern plant science. With this broadening of the scientific horizon, there has come an increased need for clarity as to what we understand the Arctic to include—a need necessitated by persistent laxity in citing plants and animals as "arctic" when they are merely boreal in range. It is accordingly suggested that the Arctic should comprise those regions of land

and water lying to the north poleward of an imaginary line delimiting it from the subarctic regions, and which, as astronomical lines of division fail, seems best based on a set of biological as well as climatological criteria. This arctic-subarctic boundary may for the present be drawn along whichever of the following means of separation lies farthest north in each narrow sector of the northern hemisphere: (1) a line 50 miles north of the northern limit of coniferous forest, or at least of more or less continuous *taiga* (that is, terrain of sparsely scattered trees); (2) north of the present limit of microphanerophytic growth (that is, of trees 2–8 meters in height, but disregarding straggling bushes in unusually favorable situations); or (3) north of the Nordenskiöld line, which is based upon the mean temperature of the warmest and coldest months of the year and is arrived at by using an empirical formula.

ARCTIC FLORISTIC BOTANY AFTER 1900

Among the tendencies aiding research that have been growing in recent years, especially with the post-war easy transportation, has been the admirable urge of specialists to visit the Arctic regions themselves. Thus nowadays all sorts of qualified men are available who can expertly collect and describe the many species. For example, in the study of the lower plants, such as Algae, Fungi, Mosses, and Lichens, specialists in particular groups work in the field investigating the various members properly.

Meanwhile there has long been an increasingly urgent need for a synthesis of the taxonomic and phytogeographical knowledge of the higher plants inhabiting Arctic regions. Previous attempts, most notably Ostenfeld and Gelert's *Flora Arctica*, have been largely abortive; moreover, recently our knowledge has grown enormously. Accordingly, for the past 15 years or so, I have been gathering material for an illustrated circumpolar treatment of all the *species* of seed plants and ferns, etc., which are known to live in any arctic area. It does not profess to be exhaustive, for I do not think a critical arctic flora should be attempted without more Russian materials than are at present available in the herbaria of America and western Europe. Included are about 900 species belonging to 229 genera in 65 families. Doubtless further collecting, especially near the southern boundary of the Arctic, will add considerably to these figures.

ARCTIC ECOLOGY AND VEGETATION

Let us next consider the ecological and allied fields which are entering more and more into the studies of arctic plant life. Whereas the *flora* of an area is made up of all the different kinds of plants inhabiting it, the *vegetation* is concerned largely with the question of the relative abundance of these various kinds, and is the total display made by the plants collectively, while their *ecology* is their relationship to the environment in which they live. The environmental conditions in the Arctic are usually especially rigorous, so that the inhabiting species tend to be few, the individuals reduced in stature, and the ecological relationships frequently critical.

Ecological studies have come well into their own in recent years, so that we now have available numerous and widespread accounts of different arctic vegetation types. Much the same is true of plant sociology, the study of the composition of the communities that collectively form vegetation. Many more accounts await the tedious study in herbaria and work in laboratories to support the field observations. Unfortunately, the study of the ecology of individual forms has not been stressed in the Arctic, so that we still know very little about such important biological aspects in arctic types as perennation and dispersal mechanisms, propagation except in obvious ways, reaction to the almost continuous summer illumination, and the maturation of fruits and seeds.

The apparent youth of the plant communities and of soil formation are noticeable. Also it will be found that the plant associations are often mixed and jumbled in a complicated, puzzling way. To what extent they are climax types is problematical, though such mixtures are often loosely called "polyclimax." For, unlike the situation in regions of more genial climate, it is evident that, at least in the high-arctic, plants rarely take sufficient hold of the surface to control even the immediate soil environment. Instead we have a situation in which they live anywhere they can, and the vegetation is very largely an expression of habitat differences.

Where the local changes are so endless and drastic as in the Arctic, with its extreme microrelief and microclimatic aspects, the complications of frost-heaving, snowdrift, and snowmelt phenomena, and of a relatively small or at best highly impotent plant life, induce or anyhow allow almost endless vegetational change from spot to spot. Nevertheless, competition and struggles for food and space undoubtedly exist among arctic plants, and so do some kinds of successional tendencies. This last point should be emphasized in view of the denial by some enthusiasts, who apparently have not worked in the real Arctic, that plant succession occurs there.

STUDIES ON CRYPTOGAMS

Before we leave the realm of the taxonomic and ecological, some analysis should be attempted of the degree to which the various cryptogamic aspects have been investigated. The bacterial floras of the Arctic have been little studied, and the same is unfortunately true of the Fungi, in spite of their many and diverse species. The Algae and the Lichens, on the other hand, have been quite extensively studied in Arctic regions—especially the Lichens and the microscopic freshwater Algae, such as the Desmids and Diatoms, and the marine planktonic plants. Numerous publications are available on arctic Mosses and Liverworts, and also on the few arctic Ferns and other Pteridophyta, but there is considerably more to be done.

PHILOSOPHY OF DISCIPLINES

At one time there was considerable interest in Scandinavian centers and particularly in Copenhagen, where plant material from Greenland was being studied, in the form and general biological attributes of arctic plants. This investigation might be expected to increase as a fertile field of study, particularly with regard to the question of plant reactions to the harsh arctic environment. Research in this field, however, seems to have decreased or rather to have had its place taken by cytology. Cytotaxonomic and genetical studies of arctic plants, or of plants which reach the Arctic, have recently been appearing in a broadening stream. These are indeed welcome but it is to be wished there were more simple transplant experiments. Such are necessary to determine whether specific instances of the very numerous dwarf and other plant forms that are found in the Far North are genetic types worthy of higher taxonomic rank, or are merely ecological forms (ecads) that result from the impress of the environment on the one generation. Certainly some of these modified types are of the latter nature, but probably others are not.

Genetics and physiology lie very close to ecology and in fact are apt to overlap. To a considerable extent ecology and genetics are complementary, as an organism is what it is and does what it does largely because of the interaction of environment and heredity—both fields are necessary for the continued existence of the organism, neither being more important than the other. Even closer is the relationship between ecology and physiology, both of which deal with functions, though generally at different levels of organization.

This brings me to a further point, more directly concerned with plant geography. Study on a full circumpolar basis of the vascular plants known to reach the Arctic, and of some species throughout their range on earth, which I contend should be considered wherever possible, has convinced me that many of the entities commonly upheld as species should really be united. Frequently, these so-called species stand out as distinct races that possibly should have the rank of subspecies. These forms often hybridize freely where their ranges overlap, and also show clines of gradual change from area to area. But when sufficient material is examined, the types are seen to vary—in many cases similarly or in parallel fashion even in different areas involving different subspecies. In this connection, it is good to see the modern tendency to "lump" together many arctic types in the interest of scientific understanding and practicability.

DIVERSITY FACTORS

Now what is the reason for arctic plants being so notoriously plastic and difficult to treat taxonomically? Only a very bold man would hazard more than a guess, but it does seem that different factors are operative in different cases and that sometimes several factors may act together. One of the beliefs most widely held is that, following the last glacial retreat, plants long isolated came together in the North and hybridized, and have continued this process ever since. Doubtless this has happened to some extent, though how widely and pertinently it is difficult to gauge. Then again, the ecological amplitude, the tolerance to a range of conditions, of many species is very wide in the Arctic, and this fact practically demands a morphological plasticity which might be expected to be further emphasized by differing environmental impress. Another possibility would seem to be that the rigorous arctic climate is conducive to the production of mutants and polyploids as well as of various genetical or transient "ecological" forms. Yet another possibility is that the low degree of biotic competition and the multiplicity of micro-habitats permit all sorts of biotypes to persist.

GENETICS AND AEROBIOLOGY

Furthermore, there is another factor which may be contributing to the complexity of some wind-pollinated plant-groups in the Arctic, namely, the dispersal of genes and subspecific characters over great distances by the wind. In this connection it should be recalled that even a single pollen grain finding its stigmatic billet in a millennium might serve to establish a subspecies, genetically speaking, in an entirely new region. For it is now known that, under suitable conditions, a wide range of pollen grains, as well as fungal spores, bacteria, etc., can remain viable for months with almost unimpaired germination and fertilization potentialities. During this time pollen grains could, like the dust of Krakatau, travel around the world and more. I have become confident of this from aerobiological studies recently pursued to the highest latitudes where a considerable range of such microscopic airborne particles is often to be found, some at least being in a viable condition.

PLANT PHYSIOLOGY

Let us dwell for a moment on this last important discipline, physiology. There is a great need for far more plant physiological work in the Arctic, where the extreme conditions often offer attractive possibilities, but relatively little has yet been attempted, some lines have been entirely neglected so far.

Plant growth rates in the Arctic are generally reduced far below those typical of temperate regions—possibly owing in part to the slowness of protein synthesis as well as to reduced cell elongation at low temperatures. Also, growth is subject to unusually great depression by locally unfavorable conditions of soil or climate in the Arctic. The low growth-rates result in an accumulation of sugars and probably also of soluble nitrogenous compounds, and, in turn, the high sugar levels are supposedly responsible for some of the low rates of assimilation which have been observed. On the other hand, conversion into anthocyanins may possibly lead in the opposite direction, and their prevalence in the Arctic may effect an increase in the absorption of radiant energy and, conceivably, result in higher rates of transpiration and metabolism. It is certain that in the Arctic, given suitable conditions of light and temperature, which rarely persist there for long, photosynthesis may be rapid. However, transpiration appears in general to be rather feeble.

Photosynthesis has, however, been shown in some plants to proceed throughout the twenty-four hour arctic day; and it may be recalled that bacterial activity is now known to continue at temperatures down to at least 7°C., while there are claims of algal activity in brine down to −15°C.

There is some evidence of a lack of available combined nitrogen in most arctic land habitats, owing perhaps to the low activity of soil microorganisms, but this question requires detailed investigation. Also pregnant with possibilities of explanation of plant ranges would be an investigation of the photoperiodic and night-temperature responses of arctic plants—such as have recently been discovered to be of great importance farther south.

PHYTOGEOGRAPHY

Before concluding I should like to return to phytogeography for two special items, the first of which is intriguing rather than important. In 1937 I found, growing around Old Norse ruins in southwestern Greenland, the descendants of plants which had almost certainly been introduced by the Vikings from continental North America. The known but restricted ranges of these plants, in some cases barely overlapping on the American Atlantic seaboard, give strong suggestions as to where they originated. Their detailed study should tell us where to search for the ruins—the only evidence which the more cautious archaeologists, who are unconvinced by all earlier claims, will accept as the final corroboration of ancient sages (and current belief) that these shores were known to European civilization centuries before the time of Columbus.

The other item of phytogeography concerns the persistence of plants on ice-free areas of the North. Having practically witnessed the colonization of plants on recently bared tracts in various parts of the Arctic, and marvelled at the luxuriant vegetation that in some places may now be seen growing alongside or actually over ice, I have reason to believe that many plants can, and through parts at least of the Pleistocene ice-age did, persist on various unglaciated areas. But, in this connection, I cannot help recalling how plants of supposed isolation or disrupted distribution have frequently appeared in intermediate positions, where their supposed absence was their previous claim to fame! Also, it is to be noted how many of these so-called relict plants have exacting habitat requirements—for example, in being markedly lime-loving or, very frequently, open soil plants, for which suitable situations are lacking between their known stations.

I shall not deal here with more of the subjects that spring to mind under the general theme of arctic botany, hoping only to have given in proper perspective some idea of its development and scope, and of what is being done at this stage of its evolution.

QUESTIONS

1. How may the "flora" of a country be distinguished from its "vegetation"?
2. What does Polunin think about the relative importance of heredity and environment?
3. What feeling is expressed here regarding the lumping versus the splitting of species?

PART FIVE

SYSTEMATIC BOTANY

Malaria is probably one of the most prevalent diseases in the world. Up until recently, the only cure for it was cinchona bark extract and the cinchona trees are native to the Andes Mountains. Seeds of the South American trees were used to start plantations in Ceylon, Java, and India and when our supply of cinchona was cut off by the Japanese, it became necessary for the United States Government to send men to South America to locate supplies of this tree for use by the troops. Since there are about 40 species of the genus Cinchona, *what type of man would have the best chance of finding the right one? Naturally, systematic botanists were chosen. Systematists also identified food plants, lumber plants, plants for rubber, essential oils, and so forth. They write identification manuals such as Gray's Manual, Hitchcock's Manual of the Grasses of the United States, and dozens of others. People use these books to identify wild flowers, grasses, and weeds.*

Actually no scientific work on an organism can be done unless one knows the exact scientific name of the creature. Results without this assurance are not acceptable. There are about 414,000 species of plants known, and new species are coming to light each year. Linnaeus, whose word is law for many names, is famous for popularizing the binomial system, certainly a better system than using only a long description.

Dr. Gleason discusses the reasons why botanists use Latin or Greek, and Dr. Camp demonstrates the value of a herbarium, a study collection of dried plants. Arboreta and botanic gardens feature live plants. Such places may be as important as herbaria although only adaptable plants can be grown. They have a special appeal to gardeners and plant lovers of all kinds.

The modern systematist uses all of the tried and true approaches but in recent years has added cytotaxonomy, paper chromatography, and other techniques to his arsenal. The naming of plants will always remain one of the foundation stones of botany.

For more information on this topic, read The Plant Kingdom *by Harold C. Bold.*

Carolus Linnaeus

Excerpts from the Critica Botanica

Reprinted with the permission of the Ray Society from *Critica Botanica,* translated by the late Sir Arthur Hort and revised by Miss M. L. Green, 1938.

What difficulty has been caused to botanists from the revival of the sciences down to the present day by the invention of new names, is known to everyone who has handled the subject: accordingly, when at the beginning of the last century the invasion of barbarism threatened by the vast horde of names in use was stemmed by C. Bauhin, by the general consent of botanists anyone who should in the future dare to introduce new names was stigmatized with a black mark, and this was well advised, since in the circumstances, the stage of learning which the science had at that time reached did not make it possible to frame better names.

When at length the commonwealth of Botany had been brought by Morison under an ordered constitution, and an eternal law, taken from Nature's book, had been promulgated, any who should offend against or transgress this law were branded as ignoramuses. No exception was then allowed: all specific names which did not suit the genus in question were to be banned by an inexorable decree of fate.

However citizens of the commonwealth never ceased to bring in every day new supplies from foreign lands, to distinguish them as they arrived with more suitable names, to restore what was lacking, to repair previous disasters, to become wiser and to devise better counsels, and to provide for the general well-being of the commonwealth, though not one of them took upon himself to introduce a complete reformation of its constitution or to bestow new names. Nevertheless by slow and almost imperceptible steps more new names have crept in than were ever bestowed at the bidding of any dictator. It is fated that botanists should impose wrong names so long as the science remains an untilled field, so long as laws and rules have not been framed on which they can erect as on firm foundations the science of Botany:

and so botanists have, under pressure of necessity, corrected most wisely the faulty names given by their predecessors.

As I turn over the laborious works of the authorities, I observe them busied all day long with discovering plants, describing them, drawing them, bringing them under genera and classes: I find, however, among them few philosophers, and hardly any who have attempted to develop nomenclature, one of the two foundations of Botany, though that a name should remain unshaken is quite as essential as attention to genera. That they can find no rules given by the ancients for the bestowal of names, no demonstrations or settled principles, is the complaint of novices and equally of men practised in the science. For any rules of nomenclature which botanists have brought in from time to time are too specialized for any certain conclusion to be drawn from them. Again there is so much disagreement between the authorities that the reader can hardly determine to which in preference to the others he should give his allegiance, since satisfactory principles are not everywhere to be seen. Wherefore it is not surprising if, when the novice has developed into a mature botanist, he in his work makes mistakes over nomenclature and so comes to burden Botany with wrong names.

Wherefore we can never hope for a lasting peace and better times till botanists come to an agreement among themselves about the fixed laws in accordance with which judgment can be pronounced on names, that is to say, good names can be absolutely distinguished from bad ones, the good ones maintained and the bad ones banished without any exception, so that Botany firmly built on immoveable principles may remain a fortress inviolable and unshaken.

Before botanists can admit such laws, it is necessary that someone among them should take upon himself to offer proposals to be examined by other botanists, so that, if they are good they may be confirmed, if unsound, they may be convicted of unsoundness and abandoned, while something better is put in their place. But, so long as botanists refuse to make this beginning, so long also will they remain in doubt and uncertainty, and false names will accumulate every day to burden Botany. Now as hitherto no one has thought fit to undertake this self-denying task, I have determined to make the attempt: for, if a citizen in a free commonwealth may speak his mind, it will be at least allowable for me to state my principles among botanists. I have not reached such an extreme of hardihood as to believe that all my reasoning is so firmly based but that someone else may propound reasoning much more mature: still mine will be true until some other principles are shown to be truer. To you, my dearly-beloved botanists, I submit my rules, the rules which I have laid down for myself, and in accordance with which I intend to walk. If they seem to you worthy, let them be used by you also, if not, please propound something better.

If anyone should distinguish precisely all the plants in the world according to the characters stamped on them, and yet bestow no names on the plants themselves, he would be keeping his learning entirely to himself. Even a rustic knows plants, and so maybe does a brute beast, but neither can make anyone the wiser: hence in the words of Isidorus, "If you know not the names, the knowledge of things too is wasted."

The names bestowed on plants by the ancient Greeks and Romans I commend, but I shudder at the sight of most of those given by modern authorities: for these are for the most part a mere chaos of confusion, whose mother was barbarity, whose father dogmatism, and whose nurse prejudice.

Only when plants have been classified under genera, and not before, should names be assigned to them. Hence no names that have been assigned to plants must be adopted if they do not fit the genera. Where a single genus is concerned, there shall be but one name.

Again the foundation of all classification of plants depends on genera and species: let those things which agree in genus or species come under the same generic or specific name: and let the converse of this rule hold.

Further it is required of the botanist that he should use judgment in assigning names, and not merely assign the first that occur to his mind. We do reverence to the omnipotence of the Creator, and to his sublime mysteries as discerned in plants: but we do not admit those names which have a religious significance.

All those plants which belong to one genus must be designated by the same generic name. All those plants which agree in their method of fruiting should be united in one genus. Generic names compounded of two entire Latin words are scarcely to be tolerated. Hybrid generic names, namely, those made from a Greek compounded with a Latin word, and the like are not to be recognized. Generic names which have not a root derived from Greek or Latin are to be rejected. Long ago the learned men of Europe met and chose the Latin language as the common language of learning. Few of the leading botanists, all of whom have, to their great credit, learned to speak Latin, have departed from it, and in naming plants hardly any Greek generic names must inevitably be tolerated, since the science of plants was first of all built up by the Greeks, or at least it was among the Greeks that it began to lift its head.

Generic names should not be misused in order to perpetuate the memory of Saints and men distinguished in some other branch of learning, or to secure their favor. The man who has in a later age obtained a glorious and honourable commemoration of his name among posterity, has I maintain, obtained the highest honour that mortal man can desire.

Generic names which have been bestowed without harm to Botany should, other things being equal, be allowed to pass. A large number of generic names were bestowed by the Fathers of Botany centuries ago, and throughout the centuries have been accepted in common use. I think that these names, so long familiar, should be retained among botanists.

Those generic names are best which show the plant's essential character, or its appearance: *Helianthus*, or "Flower of the Sun." Who can see this plant in flower without admiring the handsome flower modeled on the sun's shape?

A plant is completely named when it is furnished with a generic and a specific name. The specific name should distinguish the plant from all others of the genus. Size does not distinguish a species. All plants growing in barren exhausted dry soil are smaller. All plants in the Alps are small. Any comparative degree of size is erroneous. Colour, varying as it does in the same species, is strangely sportive: hence it is of no value as a distinguishing character. Hairiness is a distinguishing character which may very easily become misleading, since it often disappears under cultivation.

The position of the fruit affords the best distinguishing character. The generic name should be attached to every species of the genus. The specific should always follow the generic name. A specific name without a generic name is like a bell without a clapper.

QUESTIONS

1. What fact prompted Linnaeus to attempt to lay down a set of rules for the naming of plants?

2. Did Linnaeus think that his rules were the best? What challenge did he hurl out to other botanists regarding them?

3. Which names should be considered the foundation of all classification?

4. What is the language of learned men?

5. Did Linnaeus consider it an honour for a man to have a plant named after him? Would you consider it an honour?

6. How would one go about having a plant named after him? Talk this over with your instructor if in doubt.

7. List at least five of the rules of nomenclature laid down by Linnaeus and explain why you do or do not agree with them.

N. B. Linnaeus was born in 1707 and died in 1778. He promoted the binomial system of nomenclature, now universally used. His Genera Plantarum and Species Plantarum are standard works in the field.

H. A. Gleason

The Reason Behind Scientific Names

Reprinted with the permission of the author and publisher from Journal of the New York Botanical Garden 36:157–162, 1935.

If two people are going to talk together on any sort of subject, they must have names for things. Furthermore, they must have the same names for things, so that they can properly convey their thoughts to each other. If I think of a certain common shade tree, now much under discussion in this vicinity, and say elm, you at once think of the same tree. If I say gasoline, you know exactly what I am talking about. If I say gasoline to an Englishman, he does not know what I mean; he calls it petrol. If I say wallaba to you, you do not know what I mean. Possibly you might think of an Australian kangaroo, which is a wallaby instead of a wallaba, but what I mean is a common tree in northern South America. If you say house or mouse to a German, he will understand you, for the words are just the same, to the ear, in both languages, but if you try to talk about trees to a German tree-expert, he can not understand your English names and you can not understand his German names. You will have to get together in a language that both can appreciate, and the only system of names you can safely use is what we call scientific names. This is just one of the underlying reasons for the use of Latin names for plants. There are others which I will mention later.

"But," my neighbor across the street objects, "I can't pronounce those long scientific names. I like to grow my geraniums and rhododendrons, my iris and chrysanthemums; I like my fine magnolia and catalpa trees, but I can't learn those awful Latin names." Then I reply: "Every one of the names you have just used is a scientific name. If you do not like Latin names, why don't you call your catalpa Indian bean, your rhododendron rose-bay, your chrysanthemum feverfew?"

"Well," he answers, "most of your names are too long and too hard to pronounce. Now let me show you my new rose, Frau Karl Druschki."

"My dear sir," I say, "not one scientific name in a thousand is as hard to spell or as hard to pronounce as Frau Karl Druschki, and all have three advantages which you can never get by using English names. First, they permit you to express your thoughts to students of plants in every country; second, they enable you to specify a particular kind of plant with far greater accuracy than is possible with an English name; and third, the name itself tells you a great deal about the plant, even though you have never seen it yourself."

The inaccuracy of English names is proverbial. The word ivy properly belongs to a European climber, often cultivated in this country, but we have also used the word for other kinds of plants which cling to walls or trail over the ground. Boston ivy is related to the grapes, not to the true ivy; poison ivy is a kind of sumac; Kenilworth ivy is more like a snapdragon than either. Here are four different kinds of plants bearing the name of ivy. To most people the word oak means a good-sized tree which bears acorns. But we also use the word to denote poison ivy and even a little herbaceous plant, while the Australians also use it for two entirely different kinds of trees. And so it goes with any number of other names. The use of the names, their application to plants, varies from one part of the country to another, and even from one person to another.

Now oak and ivy are in a way general terms, not intended to apply to one particular kind of plant, but to a whole group of plants. If we want to be particular about some kind of oak, we can say red oak or white oak or pin oak. But this does not always work, either. There are at least two kinds of post oaks, three kinds of black oaks, three kinds of chestnut oak, probably a dozen kinds of live oak, and even more kinds of scrub oak. Attempts have been made to standardize the English names of our trees, but it can't be done. Names are a part of our language, and a language can not be changed by law or proclamation. Out around Lake Michigan is a rather rare species of oak, *Quercus ellipsoidalis*. The Forest Service says it should be called jack oak, but every farmer who has it growing in his woodlot calls it black oak, and you can't get him to change. Certainly you could never induce him to call it jack oak, because some millions of people in the middle west use jack oak for *Quercus imbricaria*, which the Forest Service says we must call shingle oak. You can invent new terms for new things, and have them generally accepted in a short time, like carburetor, magneto, or kodak, but you can not deliberately change a language. The English are not going to adopt a new word for sycamore, just because the Bible uses it in a different sense, and neither will the Americans. "Through the sycamores the candle lights are gleaming, on the banks of the Wabash, far away," and they will continue to gleam through the sycamores for a century to come, no matter what botanists or foresters may say about it.

Then the use of scientific names tells one a good deal about the plant. If you see or read about an ilex tree in England, it may mean nothing to you. But if someone uses the scientific name, *Quercus Ilex,* you at once get a very definite idea about the plant. You picture to yourself a large tree, slow in growth, with hard wood, bearing its flowers in catkins, and producing acorns for its fruit. Heretofore your idea of *Quercus* has been derived from your experience with the American oaks, now you expand your concept to include this new kind, you store your new knowledge away in a particular corner of your brain with all your previous experience with oaks, and you are a wiser man than you were before.

All scientific names are built in the same way. They invariably consist of two terms and they are always Latin in their form. The advantage of Latin is that it is a dead language. No one speaks it, and these Latin terms can therefore be introduced into scientific use just as we have introduced such new words as magneto and kodak, without interfering in any way with the spoken language of any country.

Individual plants are seldom of suffcent importance to have a distinctive name—with the exception of such noted plants as the Washington Elm or the Grizzly Giant. Names are given instead to the various kinds of plants and designate all the individuals belonging to that kind.

Common names, used in ordinary speech of non-botanical persons, are given to many plants, such as wheat, apple, rose, oak. These names vary from one language to another, and in the same country often from one region to another. Different names are often used for the same kind of plant, and similar names are often applied to different kinds of plants. Common names therefore lack precision and can not be successfully used in science, where precision is necessary.

The reason we use Latin, instead of Greek, or Sanskrit, or Hebrew, is a historical one. Until about a century ago, Latin was the written language used for all branches of learning. Since the plants described in the older books were mostly European kinds, most of them had a Latin name already, which had been the common name used for them by the Romans. The Romans, however, generally did not distinguish the kinds of plants very carefully or very accurately. For example, there are several kinds of oak in southern Europe, but the Romans had only three names, *Quercus, Robur,* and *Ilex.* In scientific writings, the name *Quercus* was gradually adopted for all of them, and a qualifying phrase was added to this term to distinguish the various kinds of oaks from each other. With the spread of interest in plants into other parts of the world, many kinds of plants were discovered which had no Latin names, and new names were coined for them by the botanists. In every case the noun, which is the actual name, was a single word applied equally to one or several kinds of plants, provided these several kinds were sufficiently alike. Thus all kinds of pine had the name *Pinus,* and the one kind of chestnut the name *Castanea.*

The Swedish botanist Linnaeus was

primarily responsible for replacing this system of a single name, followed by a procession of qualifying adjectives to describe and distinguish the plant, by the binomial system. In this system the original noun is still used, but the string of adjectives is replaced by a single word. While this word was often descriptive of a plant, it was seldom definite, that is, it did not enable one to distinguish the particular kind of a plant. It was therefore a name rather than a definition.

To give an example of how this new system saves words, all maples are named *Acer*. To describe the sugar maple sufficiently, we would have to say the maple which furnishes sugar and has leaves smooth beneath. We have taken eight words to describe this common tree. Instead we say *Acer saccharum*, and without description we name it with a single word.

This binomial system is still followed, so that each kind of plant known to science bears a name composed of two words. For example, five kinds of oaks found in the eastern states, differing from each other in the shape of their leaves or the character of their acorns, bear the names *Quercus alba*, *Quercus palustris*, *Quercus marylandica*, *Quercus Michauxii*, and *Quercus prinoides*. They, like all other kinds of oak, have *Quercus* as the first of the two words. To this is added a second word, and the whole may be translated as white oak, swamp oak, oak of Maryland, Michaux's oak, and oak like the chestnut-oak. Not one of these words is definitive; not one gives such information about the plant that a stranger could pick out that oak from the others; they are purely names. Yet they have this advantage: all of them begin with *Quercus*, and a foreign botanist reading about American trees can at once form some idea about these plants because of his knowledge of the kinds of *Quercus* in his own land.

The first of the two terms comprising a name is the generic name, the second is the specific name; that is, the first is the name of the genus (plural, genera) or general group to which the plant belongs, as oaks in general, while the second is the name of the species or particular kind of oak.

Generic names are always nouns, of classical origin or constructed in classical form. Several sources of such names may be recognized:

1. Actual classical names, taken directly from the Latin or Greek languages, as *Quercus*, *Rosa*, *Lilium*, *Populus*, and *Betula*.

2. Commemorative names, coined in memory of some person, usually one who has been of service to botanical science, as *Linnaea* (Linnaeus), *Torreya* (Torrey), *Bartonia* (Barton), *Magnolia* (Magnol), and *Robinia* (Robin).

3. Descriptive names, coined from one or more roots of classical origin and referring to some feature of the plant. Most of these are from the Greek, as *Polygonum*, many joints; *Dryopteris*, wood-fern; *Ammophila*, sand-loving; *Rhododendron*, rose tree.

4. Aboriginal names of plants, provided with a classical ending, as *Catalpa*, *Sassafras*, and *Asimina*.

5. Fanciful or mythological names, as *Calypso*, *Arethusa*, and *Phoenix*.

Specific names are adjectives, or nouns in the genitive case, or nouns in apposition.

1. Adjectival specific names must agree in gender with the generic noun, as *Amaranthus hybridus*, *Rosa lucida*, and *Acer rubrum*.

2. Nouns in the genitive are mostly in commemoration of the discoverer or

some person directly concerned with the plant, as *Quercus Michauxii* and *Amaranthus Palmeri*. Commemorative names may also be constructed as adjectives, in which case they follow the gender of the generic name, as *Spartina Michauxiana*.

3. Nouns in apposition are of various origins, but frequently represent old names for the plant, or for similar plants, as *Verbascum Thapsus* and *Quercus Phellos*. Sometimes aboriginal names are used as specific names of this class.

QUESTIONS

1. Mention five commonly used plant names which, though Latin, are known to almost everyone.
2. List three good reasons for using scientific names.
3. What botanist is given credit for popularizing the binomial system of nomenclature and of what country was he a native?
4. Of what two parts is a binomial composed?

W. H. Camp

The Herbarium in Scientific Research

Reprinted with the permission of the publisher from Journal of the New York Botanical Garden **42**:101–102, 1941.

Emerging from a primitive condition and constantly becoming more aware of his environment, man early acquired the habit of classification—the separation of all objects which entered his consciousness into three main categories: the useful, the harmful, and those which were neither useful nor harmful. As man's consciousness enlarged with the passing of the millennia these rude classifications were broken into more discrete units until, out of this cerebral activity—and prompted both by his curiosity and his needs—there came that body of organized knowledge called Science. Science, therefore, can be no static thing, but must expand in direct proportion as man becomes increasingly aware of his environment through the medium of new instruments and techniques which enlarge the field and scope of his perceptions.

In the beginnings of herbarium practice it was thought that a single specimen was sufficient to represent a species or kind of plant. This, I think, can be linked directly with the Doctrine of Special Creation, a philosophy then current which held that, being specially created, all plants of a given kind must look alike. Therefore, in those early days, it was thought no more necessary to clutter up an herbarium with "duplicate" specimens of a kind of plant than to burden a private library with duplicate copies of the same book. But if man's philosophy in conjunction with his passion for classification, led him to set up a series of definitions bounding these classificatory units, these kinds or species of plants, it was his insatiable curiosity which drove him to determine the modulus of variation permissible within them. But botanists soon discovered that words were not a completely satisfactory medium for the recording of these variations, that a concrete object was in all ways better, for words, no matter how they are used, are often inadequate to express those differences which human perception indicates are present. And thus began the current herbarium practice of having more than one representative specimen of each kind of plant.

But there soon came a time when this curiosity led the botanist into a series of difficulties, for he began to find his former units of classification unwieldy and was faced with the problem of setting up new units bounded by more finely drawn distinctions. It was then that he fully realized the necessity of having easily available at all times a wide assortment of specimens—records of the plants as they are found in nature—for only thus can he arrive at any reasonable conclusion as to where to draw the lines indicative of the limits of variation between his several entities.

I have spoken of new instruments and techniques which enlarge the field and scope of man's perception. Among these we need to mention only one, the microscope. Here is a machine which permits the user to see clearly that which his unaided eye alone could not discern. But the microscope is not solely an instrument of visual perception. It is a tool and, in the hands of the trained worker, ceases merely to be a machine whereby the invisible is made visible but, probing deeply into the recesses of our ignorance, becomes a tester of conclusions derived from the observation of objects in the gross, a dissector of biological hypotheses and thus, out of the fragments of our preconceived notions, an instrument for the building of new and better taxonomic concepts.

In the past the taxonomist, the namer of plants, was not immediately concerned with the mechanics of evolution. Lately he has come to realize that these apparently minor variations with which he has been dealing are of more than casual significance, being the loose ends of threads in the tangled and often knotted skein of evolution, and to understand them is to understand evolution itself. Hence the needs of the taxonomist for as many examples of these variations as possible—herbarium specimens representative of the sum total of the differentiations of plants—for only by a study of these can he hope to reach any conclusion as to the directions which evolution has taken within the group under consideration. Knowing this, he then can draw the lines between his units of classification—his genera and species—in a reasonably satisfactory manner.

As this is read, there are in this herbarium * 1,999,999 specimens of plants. Looked at as they are, each specimen arranged according to its species, each species to its genus, and each genus to its family, this mass of specimens would be only a dry and sterile monument to man's passion for clasisfication were it not put to some use. But it is. Obviously, not each specimen, and every day, but no day passes in the life of any member of this staff without having to make recourse to this repository of botanical variations, this storehouse of information, much of which has not and, by its very nature, cannot be recorded in books.

In this place no outline will be made of the published work by the members of the staff based wholly or in part on specimens in this herbarium, or for that matter, no attempt will be made to list the results of the work done on the more than sixteen thousand specimens on loan last year from this herbarium to workers in other institutions.

Neither can one more than briefly mention a few of the other uses to which the herbarium is put. A physician has a patient allergic to the pollen of a certain plant and inquires: What are its blooming dates so that his patient can arrange his vacation; and where can he go, preferably not too far away, to a place where the air is free of this pollen? A chemist has discovered that the extract of a certain plant —otherwise unknown to him—is a potent insecticide: Where does it grow; and can it be obtained in commercial quantities? A clinician finds that a little-known plant poison is effective in alleviating certain forms of nervous disorders resulting in paralysis: Just what is this plant; and where can it be found? Because of world conditions, a manufacturer of materials based on certain vegetable products suddenly finds himself cut off from his source of supply: Where else in the world does it grow and, if not, is there somewhere a related plant which might be substituted? The horticulturist or agriculturist finding one of his crops seriously threatened by some uncontrollable blight, seeks some immune form with which it may be hybridized and thus partake of its hardiness. Long experience has taught him that nature, with her innumerable variations, has already produced such a form and, being wise, he will consult an herbarium before starting his search, in order to first learn where he is most likely to find such a form, and with a minimum of effort.

To the layman, these queries which come to an herbarium may seem romantic but to the taxonomist they are a daily routine, a part of the job. If he succeeds in answering the question it is because his reply is backed by sufficient information. If he fails, it is because he does not have enough record specimens at his command.

But, as intimated previously, the use of an herbarium is not confined solely to answering these immediately practical and necessary questions. There is back of it a more fundamental thing: the dim but growing realization in the mind of man that, if he is to succeed, if he is to continue his existence, he must first master his environment; but before he can master his environment he must understand it and, his mind being what it is, to understand it, he must classify it.

Now plants are things fundamental to man and he will exist only as he understands them and communicates this knowledge to his fellows. And to communicate this information he must use words and call each plant by name. Therefore, in the final analysis, it is to a place where specimens are kept, aliquot samples of the plants of all the

* New York Botanic Garden—Ed.

world, to an herbarium, where man must turn. Only here will he find the sometimes divergent viewpoints of the cytologist, the morphologist, the ecologist, and the physiologist brought together, integrated, rationalized and organized around the concept of discrete nomenclatural units—things with names. Thus, having a name for things, through words, man is better able to communicate this information, this knowledge, to others of his kind so that, through the use of medicinal plants the sick may be healed; through agriculture the hungry may be fed and the naked clothed; through forestry, man's lot may be made easier in a multitude of ways; through floriculture, beauty may be brought into his life; and, if for no other reason, that mankind himself—through the knowledge of so important a part of his environment—may continue to exist.

QUESTIONS

1. Which practice is more desirable in a herbarium, (a) cluttering up the files with duplicate specimens or (b) having one good representative specimen on hand?
2. What relationship exists between the careful examination of a large group of specimens of the same species and evolution?
3. What types of inquiry are likely to be made of a taxonomist? Mention a few.

R. J. Seibert

Arboreta and Botanical Gardens in the Field of Plant Science and Human Welfare

Reprinted with the permission of the author and publisher from American Journal of Botany **43**(9):736–738, 1956.

The botanic gardens and arboretums are a natural meeting ground for science, history, art and culture in general; yet their basic importance to the broad field of plant sciences seems to have been over-shadowed by a host of circumstances in recent years. Plant science research in certain specific fields has been of a nature which demands that the scientist know more and more about fewer and fewer plants. More than ever before our plant scientist is delving into research on new plants. Through rumor, search of old literature, mass chemical analysis of plants, and ideas inspired by world-wide travel the botanic garden is increasingly more called upon to supply basic information about plants for the general public, the hobbyist, the professional, the industrialist, the technical laboratory, the plant scientist, the home gardener, and the newspaper. Upon this point I would wish to say that the service of a botanical garden called on to give professional opinion, advice, information and service as well as to answer the old questions "what is the name of that plant," "where does it come from" and "how do you grow it," is usually given free of charge. At most, this service frequently goes along with the benefits of taking out a 5- or 10-dollar annual membership, a contribution which scarcely pays for the member's servicing alone, much less for the time of some academically trained person to give a professional answer which may be the result of several hours' or days' research through the literature. May I merely pose the thought that if these services of the botanic garden and its recognized professional staff were paid for on the basis that comparable professional advice, opinion, information and service is given by the medical doctor, the lawyer, the engineering consulting company, the professional art appraiser or the landscape architect, then perhaps the botanic garden, the botanist and the plant taxonomist would be looked upon as a highly respected addition to the community.

The economic plant which was formerly grown and studied at the botanical garden has now been turned over to the experiment station and the chemist, where again the hand of the highly specialized is in demand. The economic plant, as usually referred to, is one which produces food or medicine, or other industrially usable product. We are all familiar with the fact that most of the economic plants were originally introduced and distributed to the other parts of the world through arboreta and botanic gardens. That is still going on today and no doubt will always continue to be an important function of theirs all over the world. I think, however, that we should revise our thoughts about economic plants. Statistics prove beyond doubt that the status of ornamental plants needs to be elevated to a position equal with that of "Economic Plants"—for that is what they are! Therefore, every arboretum and botanic garden is the potential source of new economic plants which eventually work their way into the trade and become that much more "bread and butter" to the nursery and cut-flower industry.

The floriculturist and the horticulturist have become concerned with bigger and better-grown, relatively few flowers and plants which can be mass produced most economically for mass public consumption through high-pressure advertising. Far be it from me to say that the arboretum and botanic garden cannot find or produce and publicize new and highly desirable plants for the trade. It is being done every day and no doubt will always continue. I do think that with a few exceptions far too little credit has been given to the responsible gardens for the hundreds of plants which they have introduced into the trade and which today help to pay the income taxes of thousands of nurserymen and florists, horticulturists and floriculturists.

The nurseryman has learned that it is easier and far more economical to mass produce a relatively few plants than to deal in great quantities of species. The more progressive nurserymen of this country are working closely with the arboreta and botanical gardens and, I might say, do fully realize the value of these institutions. That value, I believe, centers around several theories about the future of ornamental horticulture: A—Fads in flowers (and plants) are and can be as changeably exciting as fads in the clothing industry. B—Although mass-produced plants of relatively monotonous variety will continue to form the bulk of the initial landscaping of newly constructed homes, the demands of the novice home gardener, as he becomes acquainted with the fascination of home gardening, become more that of the connoisseur and he wants something different from that in his neighbor's garden. C—Home gardening is America's No. 1 hobby. Hobbies mean collections and collections lead to the unusual and different. Therefore, the nurseryman who can qualify with these plant materials will increasingly more be sought out by the gardening public. The nurseryman's best source of the unusual is the botanic garden.

The landscape architect, formerly a good gardener, has become involved with drawing board design and mass-produced gardens to keep up with the building boom. Somewhere along the line he has settled on somewhat stereotyped planting materials. The landscape architect, if he is to hold up his end, must not only work on improved design and art appreciation but must keep up with his knowledge of plant materials and their every requirement and characteristic. I know of no better means for him to gain his knowledge first hand than to spend a good deal of time in the botanical gardens exercising a combination of critical observation and creative imagination.

The botanist, taxonomist and plant breeder have all been more or less forced to go into specialities, all too often of little significance to the botanical garden connected with the botanical institution to which they are attached. The botanist and/or taxonomist in some instances either has been placed on a shelf or has placed himself on a shelf in the herbarium to occupy his time solely on the plant or plants of his personal interest, giving too little thought to the wealth of plantings growing in the botanic garden and used in the landscaping of his community. I think it is the obligation of every botanical garden to retain on its staff a man of taxonomic inclination who will devote time to the ornamentals or cultivated plants with which he is surrounded. He is just as essential to the botanical garden as is the propagator and the gardener. Certainly, the plant breeder-geneticist is an integral part of this team, for through his efforts and frequently long-term breeding programs come the improved plants of the future by which the botanical gardens can build a world-wide recognition.

The true naturalist far too often has no advanced degree and is relegated to some field of outlet other than the botanic garden. The naturalist, as I like to see it, is that person who is well versed with the technical but has the patience and aptitude to translate the technical into lay language. He is the bridge between the "technical" and "popular."

Many gardens suffer the constant pressure of encroaching "civilization" and the march of the bulldozer preceding highways, subdivisions, and what not. The encroachment of civilization on the privacy and serenity of the botanical garden is one of our most serious problems. We all realize that we cannot prevent the advance of civilization—but by the same token there is no excuse for the planner to point his finger at the botanic garden with an "it's got to go" attitude. Public opinion is the best tool by which this attitude might give way to fair consideration. There is no way in which the valued specimens of many a threatened garden can be replaced, except by bodily moving many of the time-honored specimens to a new location. I'm sure that were the public authorities forced to dig up the funds for such operations they, too, would look upon the value of a botanic garden or arboretum in a much different light. Arboreta and botanical gardens, in summary, are contributing their share to human welfare:

1. They are the basic source of plants and information about plants for that vast army of Americans who have made home gardening their number one hobby.

2. They are the basic source of new information concerning plants which seeps into every level of education concerning the hundreds of thousands of plants known to science.

3. They serve as training grounds for our future plant scientists and gardeners.

4. More than a serene site of relaxation for "tired" businessmen, they can always add to the facilities available for passive, educational, cultural and meditative recreation.

5. It is to be observed that the trend of most of our park departments in this country is to make playgrounds out of more of our parks. The average person who formerly took a walk in a park because of the beautiful trees and other plants must now fear being hit by a baseball, run down by a charging herd of humanity, or finding some man-made structure where formerly stood a majestic tree. Our botanical gardens and arboreta must, in addition, serve a purpose for which much of the city park was originally designed—beauty.

QUESTIONS

1. What are the three most common questions asked by people of botanic garden personnel?
2. Enumerate some of the benefits that accrue to nurserymen, florists, horticulturists and farmers through the work of the botanic gardens and arboreta.
3. What is America's number one hobby? Can you think of any reason why it should be? Explain.

PART SIX

ANATOMY AND MORPHOLOGY

Anatomy treats of the cells, tissues, and organs of a plant or animal, whereas morphology deals with the external form and features. The latter discipline is older than the former and the reason for this is that the study of anatomy had to await the invention of the microscope in the seventeenth century.

The systematist, in one sense of the word, is a morphologist since he studies the external features of an organism. Some systematists are anatomists part time when they examine a plant's chromosomes (if cytology is considered to be a facet of anatomy). Sometimes species can be distinguished one from the other on the basis of wood structure. Furthermore, the type of wood cell, whether vessel, tracheid, fiber, or parenchyma cell, will determine to what use the wood can be put. Pine boards do not warp or split as much as oak boards do because the pine has only one kind of water conducting cell, the tracheid, instead of both tracheids and vessels. All in all, the anatomist and morphologist, like the physiologist and the systematist, are indispensable to modern research.

Nehemiah Grew was one of the earliest anatomists and Dr. Sinnott is a modern one. Please compare their preciseness and styles.

Nehemiah Grew

Of the Root

Reprinted from The anatomy of plants begun with a general account of vegetation grounded thereupon, 2nd ed. London, W. Rawlins, 1682.

Having examin'd and purfu'd the degrees of vegetation in the seed, we find its two lobes have here their utmost period: and that having conveyed their seminalities into the radicle and plume; these therefore, as the root and trunk of the plant, still survive. Of these, in their order, we next proceed to speak, and first, of the root: whereof, as well as of the seed, we must by dissection inform ourselves.

In dissection of a root then, we shall find it with the radicle, as the parts of an old man with those of a foetus, substantially, one. The first part occurring is its skin, the original whereof is from the seed: for that extreme thin cuticle which is spread over the lobes of the seed, and from thence over the radicle, upon the shooting of the radicle into a root, is co-extended, and becomes its skin.

The next part is the cortical body, which, when it is thin, is commonly called the barque. The original hereof, likewise is from the seed; of the parenchyma, which is there common both to the lobes and radicle, being by vegetation augmented and prolonged into the root, the same becomes the parenchyma of the barque.

The contexture of this parenchyma may be well illustrated by that of a sponge, being a body porous, dilative and pliable. Its pores, as they are innumerable, so, extreme small. These pores are not only susceptive of so much moisture as to fill, but also to enlarge themselves, and so to dilate the cortical body wherein they are: which by the shriv'ling in thereof, upon its being exposed to the air, is also seen. In which dilatation, many of its parts becoming more lax and distant, and none of them suffering a solution of their continuity; 'tis a body also sufficiently pliable; that is to say, a most exquisitely fine-wrought sponge.

The extension of these pores is much alike by the length and breadth of the root; which from the shrinking up of the cortical body, in a piece of a cut root, by the same dimensions, is argu'd.

The proportions of this cortical body are various: if thin, 'tis, as is said, called a barque; and thought to serve to no other end, than what is vulgarly ascribed to a barque; which is a narrow conceit.

Next within this part stands the lignous body: this lignous body, lyeth with all its parts, so far as they are visible, in a circle or ring. Yet are there divers extreme small fibres thereto parallel, usually mixed with the cortical body, and by the somewhat different colour of the said cortical body where they stand, may be noted. These fibres the cortical body, and skin, altogether, properly make the barque. The original of this lignous body, as of the two former, is from the seed; or, the seminal roots of both the lobes, being united in the radicle, and with its parenchyma co-extended, is here in the root of the plant, the lignous body.

The contexture hereof, in many of its parts, is much more close than that of the cortical; and their pores very different. For whereas those of the cortical are infinitely numerous, these of the lignous are in comparison nothing so. But these, although fewer, yet are they, many of them, more open, fair and visible: as in a very thin slice cut athwart the young root of a tree, and held up against the light, is apparent. And as they are different in number and size, so also (whereon the numerousness of the pores of the cortical body depends) in their shape. For whereas those of the cortical body are extended much alike both by the length and breadth of the root, these of the lignous, are only by the length; which especially in vines, and some other roots, is evident. Of these pores, 'tis also observable, that although in all places of the root they are visible, yet most fair and open about the filamentous extremities of some roots, where about, the roots have no pith, as in fenil, and in many roots, higher.

The next part observable in the root is the insertment. The existence hereof, so far as we can yet observe, is sometimes in the radicle of the seed itself; I cannot say always. It is the same with that of the parenchyma of the radicle; being always at least augmented, and so, in part, originated from the cortical body, and so, at second hand, from the said parenchyma.

The pores of the insertment are sometimes, at least, extended somewhat by the breadth of the root, as about the top of the root of borage may be seen; and are thus different from those of the cortical body, which are extended by the length and breadth much alike; and from those of the lignous, being only by its length.

The number and size of these insertions are various. In the roots of most herbs they are more easily discoverable; which may lead to the observation of them in all.

These insertions, although they are continuous through both the length and breadth of the root, yet not so in all parts, but by the several shootings of the lignous body they are frequently intercepted. For of the lignous body it is (here best) observable; that its several shootings, betwixt which the cortical body is inserted, are not, throughout the root, wholly distinct, strait and parallel: but that all along being enarch'd, the lignous body both in length and breadth, is thus disposed into braces or osculations betwixt these several shootings of the lignous body thus osculated, the cortical shooting, and being osculated answerably brace for brace, that which I call the insertment is framed thereof.

The next and last distinct part of the root is the pith. The substantial nature thereof is the same likewise with that of the parenchyma of the seed. And according to the best observation I have yet made, 'tis sometimes existent in its radicle, in which, the two main branches of the lobes both meeting, and being osculated together, are thus disposed into one round and tubular trunk, and so environing part of the parenchyma, make thereof a pith, as in either the radicle, or the young root of the great bean or lupine, may I think, be well seen.

The pores of the pith, as those of the cortical body, are extended both by the breadth and length of the root, much alike; yet are they more or less of a greater size than those of the cortical body.

The proportions of the pith, are various: in trees small, in herbs, generally, very fair, in some making by far the greatest part of the root, as in a turnip.

In the roots of very many plants, as turnips, carrots etc. the lignous body, besides its utmost main ring, hath divers of its osculated fibres dispersed throughout the body of the pith; sometimes all alike, and sometimes more especially in, or near, its center; which fibres, as they run toward the top of the root, still declining the center, at last collaterally strike into its circumference; either all of them, or some few, keeping the center still. Of these principally, the succulent part of the lignous body of the trunk is often originated.

Some of these pith fibres, although they are so exceedingly slender, yet in some roots, they are visibly concave, each of them, in their several cavities also embosoming a very small pith, the sight whereof, the root being cut traverse, and laid in a window for a day or two to dry, may be without glasses obtained. And this is the general account of the root. (If only Grew had a good microscope!)

That the radicle being impregnate, and shot into the moulds, the contiguous moisture, by the cortical body, being a body laxe and spongy, is easily admitted: yet not all indiscriminately, but that which is more adapted to pass through the surrounding cuticle. Which transient sap, though it thus becomes fine, yet is not simple; but a mixture of particles, both in respect of those originally in the root, and amongst themselves, somewhat heterogeneous. And being lodg'd in the corticle body moderately laxe, and of a circular form; the effect will be an earlier fermentation. The sap fermenting, a separation of parts will follow; some whereof will be impacted to the circumference of the cortical body, whence the cuticle becomes a skin. Whereupon the sap passing into the cortical body, through this, is still more finely filtered. With which sap, the cortical body being dilated as far as its tone, without a solution of continuity, will bear, and the supply of the sap still renewed: the purest part as most apt and ready, recedes, with its due tinctures, from the said cortical body, to all parts of the lignous, both those mixed with the barque, and those lying within it. Which lignous body likewise super-inducing its own proper tinctures into the said sap, 'tis now to its highest preparation wrought up, and becomes the vegetative ros or cambium.

That the sap hath a double, and so a circular motion, in the root, is probable, from the proper motion of the root, and from its office. From its motion, which is descent, from its office, which is to feed the trunk for which, the sap must also, in some part or other, have a more especial motion of ascent.

QUESTIONS

1. How does your definition of the bark differ from that of Grew?
2. Do you think it wise to talk about the structure of the root without mentioning what species one is discussing? Explain.
3. If Grew were living today do you think he would be a foremost anatomist or not? Explain.

N. B. Grew was born in 1641 and died in 1712. He was a contemporary of Malpighi and Hooke and could be considered the father of plant anatomy.

Edmund W. Sinnott

Morphology as a Dynamic Science

Reprinted with the permission of the author and publisher from Science 85(2194):61–65, 1937.

When a science has developed to the level where it can recognize the fundamental problems which confront it, it may be said to have passed from youth to maturity. Long ago the physical sciences were able thus to formulate their objectives, and they have made enviable progress in attaining them. Biology, on the other hand, throughout its history has moved from one major interest to another and has never seemed able to distinguish its fundamental problems from a host of minor ones, or indeed to determine whether or not there exist any strictly biological problems at all. Not many generations ago the naming and classification of the host of plant and animal species was regarded as the chief task of the biologist. This naive attitude was altered by an acceptance of the tremendous fact of evolution, which seemed to make obvious that the central problem of both botany and zoology was to write the entire phylogenetic history of the organic world, a task which commanded the allegiance of the majority of biologists for half a century.

As time went on, however, it came to be realized that the ultimate secret of a living organism will never emerge from the records of its ancestry, no matter how completely these may be deciphered. Physiology is evidently nearer than phylogeny to the ultimate problem. Stimulated by the great advances which the physical sciences had made, the attack through physiology began about a generation ago to attract many new workers and gave every promise of substantial progress. The years have found this promise amply fulfilled in our success in plotting the flow of physical and chemical change of which an organism is the seat, but the results of physiological research have tended to emphasize the complexity rather than the simplicity of protoplasm and have entirely failed as yet to solve the elusive problem of what an organism really is. A similar frustration has attended still another line of attack, through the science of genetics. Ever since the rediscovery of the Mendelian principles of heredity, this discipline has been enthusiastically pursued by many students who felt that here, at last, something fundamental in biology had made its appearance. The truly sensational development of the chromosome theory, with its demonstration that the genes are definite physical entities occupying constant positions in the chromosomes, has justified this early enthusiasm; but with their first major objective attained, geneticists are coming to realize that their really basic problem is not the location and transmission of genes but the mechanism by which these control the development of an organism.

To formulate with anything like assurance a problem which is central and fundamental for all biology, the Mount Everest of our scientific exploration, may still seem to many an act of faith rather than of sight; but within the last few decades, and recently in increasing numbers, many biologists, as well as thinkers who have approached biological problems through the physical sciences and through philosophy, are agreed in emphasizing one particular problem, one general phenomenon of life, as of primary and dominant significance. This may be stated in a word as the problem of *organization*. Living things are well termed *organisms*. The activities of their manifold structures are so integrated and coordinated that a successfully functioning whole individual develops. As to how this is accomplished very little is known. The advances of biological science have been chiefly in quite the other direction, in breaking down the organism into its constituent organs, tissues and cells, into chromosomes and genes, into protein molecules and cellulose chains, into potential differences, axial gradients and morphogenetic fields. But analysis alone, however detailed it may ultimately be made, can never lead to a complete understanding of an organism. Synthesis also is required. What it is that coordinates these various parts and processes so that an organism rather than a chaos results, what synthetic factors there may be which knit the organism together into a functioning unit, are extraordinarily difficult problems. It is probably safe to say that the majority of botanists and zoologists today would admit that this problem of organization is indeed their ultimate and central concern; and that if the biological sciences have any problem peculiar to themselves and differentiating them from the physical sciences, this is the one.

My purpose in making such an excursion as this into biological fundamentals is to defend the thesis that the solution of our basic problem can be approached more simply and directly through the study of form than by any other means; and that morphology, far from being the hopelessly static discipline which some would have us believe, therefore touches so intimately the central problem of biology that it may still be described by Darwin's words, in a famous passage of the "Origin," as the "very soul" of natural history. Let us examine the evidence for this contention.

The correlative mechanisms by which an integrated living individual is maintained are, of course, physiological in character and are doubtless ultimately resolvable into physical and chemical processes; but their investigation from the point of view of physiology alone is usually beset by such difficulties that substantial progress on this front must wait until the necessary experimental technique is much more highly perfected than it is today. The coordinating and integrating capacity of protoplasm, however, is displayed not only in those correlations of function which so excite our amazement but also in the more familiar and no less remarkable correlations of growth, operative during the process of development and resulting in the production of those specific and constant shapes of organ and body which are so characteristic of living things. A fertilized egg divides this way and that in such a precise manner that an embryo with two cotyledons, a plumule and a hypocotyl, definite and specific in form, are produced. From a tiny mass of undifferentiated cells at a growing point are developed the primordia of organ after organ in a perfectly regular fashion, and each follows in its enlargement a definite pattern of growth. In all such cases there is manifest in the clearest fashion that coordinating control of which I have spoken. Form is merely the outward and visible expression, fixed in material shape, of that inner organized equilibrium which we are seeking to understand.

If it be admitted that our basic problem can thus be approached most simply and directly through the door of morphology, then an investigation of the factors which determine organic form assumes a major place in biological science. That this importance is coming to be generally recognized is evident in the diversity of directions from which developmental problems in plants and animals are now being attacked. Physiology has always regarded correlative development as an integral part of its domain, but in recent years this subject has assumed a steadily growing importance, as witness the intensive researches on hormones, organizers, metabolic gradients and morphogenetic fields. Genetics is now increasingly concerned with an attempt to discover how genes control development and thus produce the traits by which they are recognized. Ecological attack upon the problem of changes in form through environmental factors has been intensified by discoveries in various fields. Even physicists and chemists have been intrigued by developmental problems and have made important contributions toward their solution.

In this diversified attack upon the problem of the causes of the coordinated developmental processes which result in the production of organic form, only a relatively minor part, strangely enough, has been played by those biologists who might have been expected to be more interested in it than any one else—the morphologists themselves. With important exceptions, those botanists and zoologists whose primary concern has been with the form and structure of living things have contented themselves with the static and descriptive aspects of their science rather than with its dynamic and developmental side. The reason for this one-sided emphasis in morphology is evidently a historical one. The form of organisms has always fascinated biologists. Its constancy in each species, its almost infinite diversity and the existence of underlying similarities in form between groups of organisms have persistently demanded an explanation. Long delayed though this was, it seemed at last to have been completely and triumphantly provided by the theory of evolution. What could be more obvious than that all this diversity of form was the result of evolutionary divergence? What more certain than that structural homology was due to common ancestry? Under the tremendous impact of this new idea it was inevitable that students of organic form should regard as their primary task a careful description of the external and internal structure of plants and animals so that by diligent comparison of a wide range of types the evolutionary history of the organic world could be reconstructed. In the period of its greatest expansion morphology thus became preoccupied with phylogeny to the exclusion of almost everything else, and this primary interest has largely persisted to the present time.

With all these influences at work it is therefore not surprising that the purely descriptive and historical phases of their work have attracted the chief attention of most of those whose major interest is with the study of organic form. The results of this study have been of very great significance in the development of biology, and the writer has no wish to disparage them in any way or to belittle the contribution which they have made and will continue to make toward our understanding of living things. Nevertheless, if the argument developed in the present paper is sound, the dynamic aspect of the problem of form is of far greater ultimate significance than its descriptive side alone. Morphology should concern itself with causes as well as with results, and should not abandon this most promising, though most difficult, part of its territory to be explored by physiology, genetics, biochemistry and other sister sciences whose main interests lie elsewhere.

To all this it may be objected that names are unimportant; that whether those who attack the dynamic aspect of form call themselves morphologists or cytologists or biophysicists is quite immaterial, for no morphological caste or guild can claim precedence for itself here. Of course this is true, but as a practical matter it should not be forgotten that the material which presents itself to the student of morphogenesis is complex and requires a rather special knowledge on the part of the investigator if he is to be safe from error and waste of effort. An outsider is notoriously prone to make absurd mistakes if he works in a field which is not his own by experience and training, and nowhere is this more true than in problems involving the data of morphology. One who is well trained in this field has a very real advantage in morphogenetic studies.

But the morphologist may object again that by temperament and training he is unfit to undertake problems involving the dynamic side of his subject, since these require an approach through experiment and the methods of the physical sciences, with which he is often unfamiliar and unsympathetic. As he cannot thus be of real service here, he may ask, why not leave him in the ivory tower of his phylogenies and his life histories and turn over to the physiologists and their allies, fortified by a little better morphological training, the whole troublesome task of determining the causes of form?

Such a defeatist attitude, it seems to me, is based on the erroneous assumption, often made by both morphologists and non-morphologists, that the only way to attack the problems of morphogenesis is by experiment, involving almost immediately the techniques of the physical sciences. No one, of course, questions the great importance of the experimental method or the desirability of resolving as promptly as possible the problems of development into the simpler ones of physics and chemistry; but as a matter of sober fact, most of these problems are not yet in a position where they can profitably be attacked in this manner at all. Before we can intelligently set up experiments to determine the integrating and coordinating growth processes which control development and produce specific forms, we must first obtain precise descriptive information as to exactly how development proceeds. Furthermore, in most cases where as the result of experiment a difference of form or structure has been produced, it is of the utmost importance to analyze in morphological terms the exact changes involved. Long before normal development, or experimentally produced changes in it, can be expressed in physical or chemical terms, they must be expressed in morphological terms. The first step backward from the visibile end result of a developmental process toward the ultimate inducing cause—be this gene, hormone or radiation—must be a more refined description of this result and of the visible steps which lead up to it. This is obviously a job for the morphologist.

But it is not only a descriptive knowledge of development as expressed in words that the student of morphogenesis requires. In one important particular the morphologist must change his usual technique if he is to make it serve the dynamic aspect of his science: He must present his results in quantitative terms. Only thus can they yield themselves to precise analysis and to interpretation in terms of the physical sciences, and only thus can they serve as a means for the discovery of new facts and relationships. To the scalpel and forceps, the microtome and the microscope, the morphologist must add the ruler and the scale as part of his equipment if he is to make his data serviceable to morphogenetic science.

In my own laboratory we have been studying the genetic basis of shape differences in the fruits of the *Cucurbitaceae*. These characters can be described by the patterns and shape indices of the mature fruits, but such tell only part of the story. It is essential to learn the developmental history of each type if we are to find what the genes actually control here. When length and width are measured at successive stages from ovary primordium to ripe fruit it is found that they grow at different rates, so that the fruit changes in shape somewhat during its development. The relative growth rate is consistently different in different races. In the Hercules Club, length grows faster than width, so that the fruit becomes progressively more elongate. In the bottle gourd, on the other hand, width grows faster than length. Within a given race, however, this relationship is so unvarying that it may be expressed by a simple value or constant and thus used to describe very precisely the most important aspect of a fruit-shape difference. This constant relative growth rate segregates in inheritance and seems to be what the genes governing shape primarily control. It thus constitutes an important step into that unknown territory between the gene and the visible shape which this determines.

Such examples could be multiplied almost indefinitely, and from work with animals as well as with plants. The whole domain of developmental morphology, illuminated by the ideas and viewpoint of morphogenetic research and attacked by quantitative as well as qualitative methods thus offers a wide field for fruitful investigation.

For the welfare of biology as a whole, therefore, it is my plea that those who have been trained in the rigorous discipline of morphology may turn in increasing numbers to the more dynamic aspects of their subject. Especially let us hope that those younger botanists and zoologists who choose to devote themselves to the problems of organic form may realize that these cannot be set apart as a static compartment of biological thought but must touch and illuminate the whole. May they help to resolve for us this fundamental paradox: that protoplasm, itself liquid, formless and flowing, inevitably builds those formed and coordinated structures of cell, organ and body in which it is housed. If dynamic morphology can come to the center of this problem, it will have brought us close to the ultimate secret of life itself.

QUESTIONS

1. What phase of botany did Darwin call the "very soul" of natural history?
2. Morphologists have largely contented themselves with the descriptive aspects. What side of morphology should they seek to develop?
3. What relationship exists between the form of plants and evolution?
4. What does Dr. Sinnott have in mind when he says botanists should pursue the dynamic aspects of their subject?

Aristotle

On Plants

Reprinted with the permission of Harvard University Press from Minor Works, translated by W. S. Hett.

Life is found in animals and plants. But in animals it is patent and obvious, whereas in plants it is hidden and not clear. To establish its existence requires considerable research. The question at issue is whether plants have or have not a soul, and a capacity for desire, pain, pleasure, and discrimination. Anaxagoras and Empedocles maintain that plants are moved by desire, and they assert emphatically that they feel and experience both pain and pleasure, concluding this from the fall of their leaves and from their growth.

Empedocles supposes that the two classes (plants and animals) were mixed in plants. Similarly Plato averred that plants must know desire, because of the extreme demands of their nutritive capacity. If this were established, it would be in accord with it that they should really know pleasure and pain, and that they should feel. And once this is established, it will be in accord with it that plants should know desire, if they ever have sleep and are aroused by wakening. Similarly again, if we inquire whether they breathe, and whether they are born by a union of the sexes or otherwise we shall have considerable doubt on the question, and shall have to prosecute a long search.

We have quoted the belief (of Plato) that if anything receives food, it also desires and has pleasure in satiety, and suffers pain when it is hungry. Plato's theory is marvelous, though its errors are not slight, I mean the theory in which he supposed that plants could feel and desire. We maintain that plants know neither desire nor sensation. Now in plants we find no sensation, nor any organ which can feel, nor anything in the least like it, nor any differentiated form, nor any method of approach to sense apprehension, nor any sign by which we could judge that plants have sensation, corresponding to the signs by which we know that they are nourished and grow. Even this is not established among us except because we are aware that the nutritive and growing faculties are parts of the soul. Whenever, then, we find that a plant of this kind has within it some part of the soul, we necessarily know that it also has a soul, but when it is lacking in sensation, then we have no right to maintain that it is a thing of sense, for sensation is responsible for the illumination of life.

These differences of opinion are produced at this point because it is difficult to find a condition intermediate between the presence of life and the absence of it. One might argue that since the plant is a living thing, we are at once entitled to call it a living creature. But this is not so. For it is difficult to assign the constitution of a plant to the constitution of the soul of an animal. Men's reason for denying life to plants is that they do not feel. For there are some animals that lack cognition. Now we know that shellfish are living creatures, but lack cognition [sic], because they are both plants and animals at the same time. Again there are animals which possess no female sex, others again which do not beget, and others which have no power of movement, others, again, which differ in colour, and others still which have an offspring unlike themselves, and others still are born from earth or trees. What then is the principle of the soul in the living creature? What else but what makes the noble animal, which goes through the heavens, the sun, the stars and the planets, which are raised above the perplexities involved and are not liable to be affected? For sensation is an affectation of those who can feel. But one must recognize that plants have no movement of themselves, for they are fixed in the earth and the earth does not move. But life itself is really an intermediate state; for the soulless has no soul, nor any parts of the soul. But the plant does not belong to the class which has no soul, because there is some part of the soul in it, but the plant is not a living creature, because there is no feeling in it. But even if it has a soul, we do not admit that it has any feeling. Anything that is nourished cannot be without a soul. Every living creature has a soul. But the plant is an incomplete thing. The absorption of food is part of the principle of the plant's nature, and thus is a characteristic common to animal and plant. But there will be no implication of sensation in the absorption of food.

Let us now inquire into a question which has occurred before in our argument, about desire, movement and individual soul in plants, and whether anything is given off from plants, for instance in breathing. Anaxagoras maintained that plants do breathe, but how can this be, seeing that we find many animals that have no breath, and again we find plants that neither sleep nor wake? For awakening means nothing apart from the condition of sensation, and sleeping means nothing but the weakening of this; and neither of these conditions is found in a thing which receives its food at all times remaining in one condition, but which in its own proper nature has no sensation.

But what particularly and specially requires investigation in this branch of inquiry is Empedocles' question, I mean whether two sexes, male and female, are found in plants, or whether the plant shows some kind of mixture of the two types. Now we lay it down that when the male begets, it begets in another, and that the two sexes are differentiated from each other. So when it is found that plants have a male and female sex, and that invariably the male is rougher, harder and more stiff, while the female is weaker and more inclined to bear fruit, we must investigate again further whether these two sexes are found mixed together in plants. Personally I do not believe that the facts are so. For things mixed must first of all have a simple existence in themselves, and the male and female must first have an independent existence and then be mixed. But such a mixture will not occur except by their own proper generation. But on Empedocles' supposition a mixture would be found in plants before the mixing took place, which ought to be both cause and effect at the same time in the process of generation; but male and female are not found combined in any plant. If this were the case the plant would be a more perfect creature than the animal. The seed of the plant corresponds to the impregnation of the animal, which is due to a mingling of male and female. And just as in the egg, when a young bird is born, there is food enough within it to last until the season of its fulfilment, and its natural exit from the egg, and then in a short space of time the female produces the young bird, so also with the seed of the young plant. From it arises a food which nourishes the root at its beginning. We must conclude in the mixing of the male and female in plants, as in the case of animals, that the mixing of the plants is in accordance with their own constitution. But if nature has produced a union of male and female, she has produced on sound lines, because we do not find any activity exhibited in plants beyond the creation of fruits.

There are some who regard plants as perfect types because of their life, and owing to the two capacities which they possess; because they contain the nutrient necessary to feed them; and because of the length of their duration and of the time in which their life grows up and bears fruit; their youth returns to them and there is no waste product in plants. The plant does not require sleep for many reasons; because it lives in the earth, is bound by it, has no movement within itself, has no division between its parts, has neither sensation nor voluntary movement, nor a complete soul. In fact the plant was only created for the sake of the animal, but the animal was not created for the sake of the plant.

QUESTIONS

1. Discuss Plato's and Aristotle's differing views on desire and sensation in plants.
2. What was Aristotle's view on the rotation and revolution of the earth?
3. What was Aristotle's criterion of life? Do you agree with it?
4. Correlate Aristotle's idea on respiration in plants with the modern view.
5. How does our view of sex correspond to Aristotle's view that a plant cannot be both male and female at one time? Think of both the lower plants and the seed plants.
6. What statement shows that Aristotle was aware of stored food in the seed?

N. B. Aristotle was born in 384 B.C. and died in 322 B.C. He was the greatest investigator of antiquity and a genius at the art of observation.

PART SEVEN

PHYSIOLOGY

Physiology deals with the functions of plants such as respiration, digestion, photosynthesis, and protein synthesis. Although starting after anatomy, it has proceeded at a more rapid pace. It was because of its tie-up with chemistry, itself a rapidly growing subject, that physiology moved so fast. As you will note from reading the articles, there is quite a difference in the language used by Aristotle and Ingen-Housz on the one hand and Went and Gray on the other. The comparison is not as striking as it might be because the latter two articles were especially selected and abridged for ease of reading. Modern physiological papers are very complicated.

The study of respiration in yeast cells has had important applications in our knowledge of human muscle fatigue. Since plants are the most important sources of vitamins, much attention has been paid to vitamin synthesis. Protein synthesis in peas and beans is being studied and this will help us in understanding the situation in human beings. The day is almost certainly coming when food chains will have to be shortened as a matter of efficiency, and man may get his proteins from plants entirely. A Kansas City steak may consist of peas and soybeans in the future, truly a gruesome thought.

However, the project upon which full speed is underway is the solution of the photosynthesis puzzle. How can a miserable dandelion make all of the sugar needed from a common gas, carbon dioxide and a common liquid, water? All of man's food, directly or indirectly, must come as a result of photosynthesis. If the plant physiologists can produce sugar in commercial quantities as does the dandelion, one of our most pressing problems will have been solved.

For more papers on physiology, see the book Great Experiments in Biology *by M. L. Gabriel and S. Fogel and in* The Life of the Green Plant *by A. W. Galston.*

John Ingen-Housz

Excerpts from Experiments upon vegetables

Reprinted from Experiments upon vegetables, London, 1779.

I was not long engaged in this inquiry (the relationship of air and sun to plants—Ed.) before I saw a most important scene opened to my view: I observed, that plants not only have a faculty to correct bad air in six or ten days, by growing in it, as the experiments of Dr. Priestley indicate, but that they perform this important office in a complete manner in a few hours; that this wonderful operation is by no means owing to the vegetation of the plant, but to the influence of the light of the sun upon the plant. I found that plants have, moreover, a most surprising faculty of elaborating the air which they contain, and undoubtedly absorb continually from the common atmosphere, into real and fine dephlogisticated * air; that they pour down continually, if I may so express myself, a shower of this depurated air, which diffusing itself through the common mass of the atmosphere, contributes to render it more fit for animal life; that this operation is far from being carried on constantly, but begins only after the sun has for sometime made his appearance above the horizon, and has, by his influence, prepared the plants to begin anew their beneficial operation upon the air, and thus upon the animal creation which was stopped during the darkness of the night; that this operation of the plants is more or less brisk in proportion to the clearness of the day, and the exposition of the plants more or less adapted to receive the direct influence of that great luminary; that plants shaded by high buildings, or growing under a dark shade of other plants, do not perform this office, but, on the contrary, throw out an air hurtful to animals, and even contaminate the air which surrounds them; that this operation of plants diminishes toward

* Air deprived of its principle of inflammability. Oxygen was not known then as it is now. Dephlogisticated air is good air and, as we now know, contains enough oxygen for respiration.—Ed.

the close of the day, and ceases entirely at sun-set, except in a few plants, which continue this duty somewhat longer than others; that this office is not performed by the whole plant, but only by the leaves and the green stalks that support them; that acrid, ill-scented and even the most poisonous plants perform this office in common with the mildest and the most salutary; that the most part of leaves pour out the greatest quantity of this dephlogisticated air from their under surface, principally those of lofty trees; that young leaves, not yet come to their full perfection, yield dephlogisticated air less in quantity, and of an inferior quality, than what is produced by full-grown and old leaves; that some plants elaborate dephlogisticated air better than others; that some of the aquatic plants seem to excel in this operation; that all plants contaminate the surrounding air by night, and even in the day-time in shaded places; that, however, some of those which are inferior to none in yielding beneficial air in the sun-shine, surpass others in the power of infecting the circumambient air in the dark, even to such a degree, that in a few hours they render a great body of good air so noxious, that an animal placed in it loses its life in a few seconds; that all flowers render the surrounding air highly noxious, equally by night and by day; that the roots removed from the ground do the same, some few, however excepted; but that in general fruits have the same deleterious quality at all times, though principally in the dark, and many to such an astonishing degree, that even some of those fruits which are the most delicious, as, for instance, peaches, contaminate so much the common air as would endanger us to lose our lives, if we were shut up in a room in which a great deal of such fruits are stored up; that the sun by itself has no power to mend air without the concurrence of plants, but on the contrary is apt to contaminate it.

All plants possess a power of correcting, in a few hours, foul air unfit for respiration; but only in clear light, or in the sun-shine. This remarkable property of plants is indeed very great; for in a few hours, nay even sometimes in an hour and a half, they purify so much a body of air quite unfit for respiration, as to be equal in goodness to atmospheric air. They will even do it when enclosed in a glass vessel, without any water. One leaf of a vine, shut up in an ounce phial, full of air fouled by breathing so that a candle could not burn in it, restored this air to the goodness of common air in the space of an hour and a half. But plants enjoy this priviledge only in the day-time, and when they grow in unshaded places.

This power of plants extends itself even to the worst of all airs, in which an animal finds his destruction in a moment, such as is pure inflammable and highly phlogisticated air, which is little or scarcely at all diminishable by nitrous air. I observe some difference in various kinds of plants in this respect, and found that water plants seem to possess this quality in a greater degree than others.

Experiments: A sprig of peppermint put in a jar full of air fouled by breathing (so as to extinguish a candle), and exposed to the sun, had corrected this air in three hours so far that a candle could burn in it.

A sprig of nettle was put in a jar full of air fouled by breathing so as to extinguish a candle, it was placed in a room during the whole night, next morning the air was found as bad as before. The jar was put at nine in the morning in the sun-shine; in the space of two hours the air was so much corrected, that it was found to be nearly as good as common air.

A sprig of *Persicaria urens* was put in a vial full of air fouled by breathing, so as not to allow a candle to burn in it;

it was exposed to the sun during an hour and a half, in which time the air was so much corrected that a candle could burn in it. The same effect was obtained from a sprig of a vine, and that of a camomile plant, and from some rushes.

A mustard plant was put in a jar; the stem was cut off on a level with the orifice of the jar; the jar was then inverted in an earthen pan containing some water to keep the plant alive, and placed over-night in a room; next morning the air of the jar was found much fouled, so as to extinguish the flame of a wax-taper; its test by Abbé Fontana's method, was 1.98, 2.87, 3.83.

It was then exposed to the sun, and examined again after a quarter of an hour, and found already somewhat corrected, for its test was then 1.97, 2.84, 3.79.

The jar was again put in the open air, when, after standing one and one-half hours in the sun, the air was found to be remarkably corrected, for now its test was 2.01, 2.25, 3.24.

The jar was again replaced in the sun; when it had been exposed during three complete hours, the air was so much improved as to be better than the common air at the time, for its test was 1.95, 2.21½, 2.20.

The test of the common air was at that time, by Abbé Fontana's method, 1.96; 2.25; 3.26½.

QUESTIONS

1. What is the modern name of the process upon which Ingen-Housz seemed to be engaged in this article?
2. Reproduce here the equation representing the process.
3. With what end product of this process is the author most concerned? With what raw material?
4. When considering plants and animals together, would you say that oxygen was a waste product of the process? Explain.
5. Evaluate this statement. Animals respire all the time. Plants respire only at night. During the daytime, they carry on photosynthesis.
6. Did Ingen-Housz think that the air given off by plants at night was harmful? What is the modern view?
7. From your knowledge of scientific method, point out one major fallacy of Ingen-Housz' experiments.

N.B. Ingen-Housz was born in 1730 and died in 1799. He was the physician to Emporer Joseph II. His work on light and photosynthesis is his greatest contribution.

F. W. Went

The Role of the Environment in Plant Growth

Reprinted with the permission of the author and publisher from American Scientist **44**(4): 378–398, 1956.

Among the many problems facing the biologist perhaps none looms as large or seems as elusive as the how and why of organic form and function. There are many possible approaches toward a solution of these problems. In the following article I want to show to what extent an analysis of the effects of environment can contribute to an understanding of the living plant. But in addition to being a tool in solving problems of growth and development, the investigation of environment in connection with plants is an end in itself, and gives us an insight into plant distribution and may become an important factor in agricultural production.

A fertilized egg-cell or zygote contains in its hereditary make-up the full potentialities to develop into a mature plant. Yet the exact size and shape of this plant are not predetermined; they are conditioned and modified by the environment in which the zygote develops. This is usually expressed by saying that the mature plant is the product of the interaction between its genes and the environment: a modification of either will influence the end-product.

The environment can be considered very broadly, and can be subdivided into internal and external environment. The internal environment for gene action is the cell and its physical and chemical make-up. The cell itself is definitely also a gene product, filtered already through the modifying influence of the external environment, as far as temperature, radiation, and surrounding cells are concerned. The external environment for the developing plant consists of the soil, the surrounding air, radiation in all its forms and manifestations, numerous pests, diseases and viruses, the physical and chemical effects of neighboring plants, and many other factors. Among the latter, man looms large, both through his direct and indirect influences.

Most of the factors of the external environment of the plant have been under intensive investigation for scores of years, largely because they are of paramount importance to man in his efforts to make the plant cover of the earth subservient to his needs. This has led to the development of Plant Pathology, Parasitology, Soil Science, Agriculture, Horticulture, Forestry, Plant Nutrition, Irrigation, and many other branches of the Plant Sciences. In Agricultural Colleges, in Experiment Stations, in special Research Institutions there are hundreds or thousands of Plant Pathologists, Entomologists, Agronomists, Plant Physiologists, Geneticists and other scientists who are investigating all factors of the internal and external environment of the plant with the ultimate aim of better production of plants. There is however one group of scientists which is hardly represented. These are the Plant Climatologists, dealing with the aerial environment of the plant. Yet, the aerial environment or climate is at least as important in connection with plant production, as the soil, pests, diseases, growing methods or genetical background are.

There are many good reasons why the field of Plant Climatology has been so neglected by investigators. In the first place it is difficult to define climate clearly and accurately, partly because of the variability of the weather from day to day and from year to year, and partly because weather is an integration of non-comparable values. In the second place we have not had methods for growing plants under strictly controlled environments or synthetic climates.

Mainly through the efforts of Dr. H. O. Eversole and Dr. L. C. Marshall control over the plant environment has become possible, after they had elucidated the principles upon which greenhouses can be air-conditioned. Also in growing plants we need high light intensities, which are most conveniently available in the form of sunlight. But in greenhouses, using the sun as a light source, the problem of temperature control is critical. On a sunny day at noon one calorie is absorbed per square centimeter of greenhouse per minute. The heat thus generated has to be removed by air renewal, which requires large volumes of air. Even when 20–30 times as much air is circulated through a greenhouse as is ordinarily passed through an air-conditioned auditorium, the outgoing air is still 4–5° C. warmer than the incoming air. But as soon as the sun disappears behind clouds the heat-load on the greenhouse may become negative and the incoming air may require heating. Therefore the air-conditioning equipment of a greenhouse must be highly flexible and must be instantaneously adjustable to changing conditions of radiation.

Completion in 1939 of the Clark Greenhouses and in 1949 of the Earhart Plant Research Laboratory, both at the California Institute of Technology, provided for the first time large-scale growing facilities for plants under controlled conditions. The following article deals with the results obtained in experiments carried out in these laboratories. . . .

One of the most important results obtained in these air-conditioned greenhouses and growing rooms is the extent to which biological variability can be reduced. This variability usually is the greatest handicap in biological experimentation and it reduces the reliability of conclusions based on quantitative responses. The uncertainty in conclusions reached in biological experimentation has led physicists and chemists to distinguish themselves as working in the "exact" sciences.

There are several sources of variability in biological material. The first is the hereditary background. The greater the genetical differences between individuals, the greater their phenotypic variability will be. On the other hand, well-selected seed material, or cuttings made from the same plant, has a potential uniformity which far surpasses the homogeneity of reagent-pure chemicals.

The second source of variability in biological material is the inhomogeneity of the environment during growth. The extent to which this factor contributes to variability had not been properly realized, but experiments make it clear that most biological variability in genetically uniform material was due to uncontrolled environment during growth. Whereas in an ordinary greenhouse the coefficient of variability of, e.g., tomato plants may be 20%, under complete temperature and light control this is reduced to below 5%. Therefore at least 80% of phenotypic variability may be due to uncontrolled environment. . . .

When, instead of growing plants under exactly similar environmental conditions, we subject them to different temperatures, light treatments, wind, or other climatic variables, then an amazing degree of variability in growth rate, yield, form, flowering and fruiting behavior, and chemical composition can be produced. This is a completely different aspect of the Earhart Plant Research Laboratory, and this is the basis on which it can be used to study the effects of climate on plants. Each of the important climatic factors can be investigated separately or in conjunction with one or more of the others in relation to growth and development of the different plant. In this way it can be established which factors are most important in the life of a plant, and it can be judged how climate as a whole may affect a plant.

Almost any character can be modified by one or more of the individual climatic factors, and often various characters are changed in the same direction. In the tomato, for instance, both growth in length, increase in weight, and fruit production are optimal when the night temperature is 17° C. But heaviest stems and largest leaves are produced at slightly lower night temperatures. At high night temperatures flower size and fruit development are more inhibited than vegetative growth. In potatoes it also is night temperature which mainly controls tuber formation. This is optimal at 12° C. and is relatively little affected by the temperature during day. In peas and strawberries the day temperature is more important for growth and fruit set than the night temperature. In peaches and in *Veratrum* normal development is possible only when there is a seasonal fluctuation in temperature. Thus for each species and variety of plant there is a particular climatic factor or set of factors which primarily controls development and growth. Once these factors have been established in the laboratory it becomes possible to interpret field observations intelligently. As an example it can be mentioned that once the significance of the night temperature for fruit set in tomatoes had been recognized through experiments in air-conditioned greenhouses, it became possible to explain poor tomato production in localities with too high or too low night temperatures, or in years with exceptional weather.

Since each climatic factor—day temperature, night temperature, light intensity, light duration, spectral composition of the light, relative humidity, wind, rain, seasonal fluctuation in temperature, gas content of the air, frost, etc.—is an independent variable, and since there can be any conceivable interaction in plant response between these factors, the effect of climate on a plant cannot possibly be expressed in a simple formula, like a "heat sum." We are dealing here with multi-dimensional interrelationships, which can only be expressed in multi-dimensional diagrams. Actually the optima of some plants are so different that they cannot be grown at all. The optimal temperatures for the African violet are so high that the English Daisy dies in them, whereas the African Violet dies under the optimal growing conditions for the English Daisy. Unfortunately so little is known about this subject as yet. . . .

In conclusion it can be said that the investigation of the environment in relation to plant growth and development, as carried out in a phytotron, yields results of such practical and theoretical significance, that its costs are offset many times by the results obtained in it. In a phytotron we just apply the principles which have guided physical and chemical research for so many decades—namely, carrying out work under rigidly controlled and reproducible conditions—to research with plants. Actually, from the standpoint of research efficiency, there is no good reason any more for carrying out experiments with plants in ordinary unconditioned greenhouses. For the results have a low degree of significance due to great variability of the experimental plants and poor reproducibility. Fortunately this is becoming generally recognized and a number of plant growth chambers with proper control over the environment have been constructed or are being planned.

QUESTIONS

1. List five external environmental factors which affect plant growth.
2. What environmental study is not as active as some others, according to Dr. Went? Why is this so?
3. What effect does a controlled environment have on plant variability?
4. Mention some of the results obtained in the Earhart Plant Research Laboratory.

George W. Gray

Our Bridge from the Sun

Reprinted with the permission of Mrs. A. Gray from Harpers Magazine **211**(1264):64–71, 1955.

Man lives in two worlds. There is first the older, larger, less complicated realm of inorganic matter—stars, interstellar gas and dust, planets, and the rocks, metals, and other minerals of the planetary structure; the waters of rivers, lakes, and seas; and the oxygen, nitrogen, and rarer gases of the atmosphere. This is the physical world, and matter in such forms apparently constitutes more than 99.999 per cent of the Universe.

Embedded in the stupendous setting of physical Nature is an entirely different order of creation which scientists call the organic world—the film of life which covers much of the land surface of our planet and populates the waters with a rich and varied flora and fauna. This realm of living things is entirely distinct from the physical in organization and in the ways in which it expresses its existence; and yet the organic world is completely dependent on the inorganic for the chemical elements with which to maintain its life processes. It needs carbon and hydrogen in forms which will serve as fuel to burn with oxygen and release energy. It also needs nitrogen, calcium, and dozens of other elements to combine with carbon, hydrogen, and oxygen in the myriad molecular forms which go into the construction of cells, their extension into tissues, and the constitution of the fluids which bathe the cells and serve as their transports for food and wastes.

These chemical elements exist in profusion in the physical world around us: the great storehouse of all the atoms that we, the animals, the plants, and the micro-organisms require to build and sustain our living systems. The difficulty is that the atoms are locked up in a quite literal sense—for the bonds which hold hydrogen to oxygen in H_2O are among the most powerful known to chemistry, and the same can be said of the attachment of carbon to oxygen in CO_2. Such tightly locked structures can be broken into only by force.

There is no dearth of force. Calculation shows that the solar rays falling in a day on each 1½ square miles of the Earth's surface carry as much energy as an atomic bomb of the Hiroshima type. These rays continually stream through the water vapor and carbon dioxide of the atmosphere, and if only a tiny fraction of their energy were effectively utilized, it would be sufficient to break the molecular bonds and release the atoms of hydrogen, carbon, and oxygen for use by man and the other creatures of the organic world. But the gases of the atmosphere are nearly transparent, and light provides chemical energy only when it is absorbed.

It is here that the green plant assumes a key role in the drama of life, for its chlorophyll serves both as an absorber of sunlight and as a mechanism to convert the absorbed light into chemical energy. Operating on the water molecules from its surroundings and on the carbon-dioxide molecules from the air, the plant reshuffles the atoms of these compounds to make that most basic of all foods, the carbohydrates. (Sugar is the familiar example.) As a by-product of this photosynthesis, the plant releases the surplus oxygen not used in fabricating sugar, and thus continually replenishes the air with fresh breathing material.

Sugar is found in most living creatures, from man to microbe. It is one of life's early inventions, a molecule made up of carbon, hydrogen, and oxygen with the atoms so proportioned among the three and so loosely linked together that in the presence of free oxygen they dissociate and reunite in more stable combinations, with the release of energy. In other words, sugar will burn. In our bodies it is the primary fuel. Its burning supplies the energy to activate our muscles, to power the pulsations of the heart and lungs, and to generate the currents which course through our nerves. As the British chemist F. C. Donnan has expressed it in his oft-quoted phrase, "Without that sugar and oxygen there could be no thought, no sweet sonnets of Shakespeare, no joy and no sorrow."

Photosynthesis thus occupies a primary place in the economy of life. It is the process by which the energy of the Sun is captured and converted to the uses of the living cell. It is, in addition, the beginning process in the transfer of atoms from the inorganic world to the organic. It serves as the very bridge of life—the bridge by which star stuff passes over and becomes life stuff.

In this alchemy through which the nonliving is converted into the living, the green plant stands almost alone. Neither the human body nor that of any animal is able to synthesize sugar or other organic compounds from inorganic materials. The animal kingdom thus is parasitic on the vegetable. There are certain micro-organisms, such as purple and green bacteria, which trap sunlight and use its energy to make carbohydrates, but their production is small in comparison with the vast output of green plants. To live, an animal must either eat vegetation or else eat other animals which have fed on vegetation. There is no other bridge to the free energy and rich material stores of the physical world.

A TRAIN OF DISCOVERIES

The discovery of photosynthesis and the exploration of its hidden processes has been the cumulative work of investigators in many countries, spanning a period of nearly two centuries. The first contributor was Joseph Priestley, the eighteenth-century British clergyman whose hobby was chemistry. Here is how he reported his pioneering experiment of 1771:

> I have been so happy as by accident to hit upon a method of restoring air which has been injured by the burning of candles and to have discovered at least one of the restoratives which nature employs for this purpose. It is vegetation. One might have imagined that since common air is necessary to vegetable as well as to animal life, both plants and animals affected it in the same manner; and I own that I had that expectation when I first put a sprig of mint into a glass jar standing inverted in a vessel of water. But when it had continued growing there some months, I found that the air would neither extinguish a candle nor was it at all inconvenient to a mouse which I put into it.

In this way Priestley stumbled upon the green plant's faculty of producing free oxygen. His observation is one of the landmarks in the history of chemistry. It started a train of experimentation, and other discoveries followed.

In 1779 a Dutch physician, Jan Ingen-Housz, working in England, reported that plants indeed "have the ability to correct bad air" but perform this office only in sunlight. He also noticed that "this service is not performed by the whole plant, but only by the leaves and green stalks."

Three years later came the next step. This was the observation by another clergyman, Pastor Jean Senebier of Geneva, that the plant performs its office of purification only if some "fixed air" is present in the atmosphere. Fixed air was the name for carbon dioxide.

It was not long before oxygen and carbon were isolated and recognized as elements, and the process which Priestley had observed in his sprig of mint became interpreted as one in which green plants, on exposure to light, absorbed carbon dioxide and released oxygen. Chemists guessed that the oxygen was produced by the breakdown of the carbon dioxide; but if so, what became of the carbon? Ingen-Housz came up with the answer in 1796. The carbon, he said, was utilized in the plant's nutrition. Photosynthesis was not just a benevolent scheme to purify the air for the benefit of man and the animals, but was also a process for obtaining carbon and building it into organic material for the nourishment of the plants themselves.

No one had suspected that water might play an essential part. But in 1804 the importance of this ingredient was recognized by another Genevan experimenter, Nicholas Theodore de Saussure, and the picture changed to one in which the light acted on both the carbon dioxide and the water.

Four decades later came a momentous observation from Germany. There the physicist, Robert von Mayer, pointed out that the crux of the whole photosynthetic process was the conversion of light energy into chemical energy. The green plant, illuminated by sunlight, not only made organic matter but it packed this matter with chemical energy.

With this discovery, the general outline of photosynthesis was complete. All the essentials of the process had been identified, including the supremely important energy factor, and the products of the process—oxygen, organic matter, and "the chemical difference"—had been recognized. But it was only a rough exterior picture.

For more than a century experimenters have been seeking to fill in the details, and some of the giants of biochemistry, including four Nobel laureates, have worked on the problem. There are still gaps in the picture, for life does not easily yield up the secrets acquired in its billion years of evolution. But some of the features of photosynthesis have been unveiled, hidden sequences have been worked out, and the picture of a cycle—or a series of cycles—of chemical interactions is slowly emerging.

WHAT HAPPENS—AND WHERE?

What happens in photosynthesis may be presented as an interchange in which six molecules of carbon dioxide combine with six molecules of water in the presence of light and produce sugar and six molecules of free oxygen:

$$\text{Six } CO_2 + \text{six } H_2O \xrightarrow[\text{Chlorophyll}]{\text{Light}} \text{One } C_6H_{12}O_6 \text{ and six } O_2$$

This is a perfectly balanced chemical equation. There are just as many atoms on one side as on the other; but those on the right are in different molecular arrangements, and the key question is: How did they get that way? Does photosynthesis split the carbon off from the carbon dioxide and combine it with the water? Or does it split hydrogen off from the water and combine it with the atoms of carbon dioxide?

Both of these schemes have been proposed from time to time and each has had its advocates over the years, although until the 1930's the arguments were pure speculation. But early in that decade a microbiologist at Stanford University obtained experimental data on the subject. This was Keis B. van Niel, of Stanford's Marine Station at Pacific Grove. While studying purple and green bacteria, which also have the power to trap sunlight and make sugar, Dr. van Niel turned up evidence that photosynthesis was basically a process of transferring hydrogen atoms to carbon dioxide.

Artificial light can power photosynthesis, and early experimenters found that it was possible to increase the rate of sugar production by increasing the intensity of the illumination. But F. F. Blackman, a British botanist, observed that eventually a saturation point was reached, after which no intensification of the light made any difference in the production of sugar or output of oxygen. From this, Blackman suspected that photosynthesis was not a single process activated by light, but that it included a stage which did not require light.

There have been various speculations as to the nature of this "Blackman reaction," but nobody doubts that part of the photosynthetic process in fact requires no light. Numerous experiments have demonstrated this. In 1905 two other British botanists, H. T. Brown and F. Escombe, rigged up a rotating sector (a slotted disk) and found that three quarters of the light could be shut off in each revolution without decreasing the rate of photosynthesis. In 1919–20 a still more convincing demonstration was given by Otto Warburg, then working at the Kaiser Wilhelm Institute for Biology in Berlin. Instead of using leaves, as Brown and Escombe did, Warburg flashed his light on green algae of the genus *Chlorella,* illuminating these water plants with intermittent rays of very high intensity from a rotating sector that gave periods of light and dark every four-thousandth of a second, and he found that the efficiency of photosynthesis doubled.

Clearly, there is a sequence of reactions involved in the green plant's manufacture of sugar, some requiring light, others not; and apparently it is possible for the reactions promoted by light to produce their parts of the sugar molecule faster than the dark reactions can handle them, thus clogging the assembly line and slowing down the overall process.

The specific structure which performs this office has not yet been identified, but the chemists postulate a catalytic molecule—or team of molecules—which has a special affinity for hydrogen and yet will readily release the hydrogen to the carbon-dioxide reducing system when it reaches that part of the mechanism.

It is clear that if the light phase splits water faster than the dark phase can supply the necessary escort, more hydrogen will be freed than can be used in the synthesis. The result will be an imbalance between the two stages and a lowering of the efficiency of the overall process. This explains why an experimenter, using intermittent flashes, can make a plant produce more sugar for a given amount of light than it can turn out under continuous illumination.

What goes on in the light is photochemistry, i.e., chemical reactions which are energized and promoted by light; whereas in the dark the reactions are purely chemical, energized and promoted by molecular forces. The goings-on in the dark have recently been brought into the open in amazing detail, thanks to the ingenuity, enterprise, and persistence of a group of chemists at the University of California.

CHEMICAL DETECTIVE AT WORK

The leader of this group is Melvin Calvin, professor of chemistry in the university. The problem was to track down the intermediate steps between the plant's receipt of a molecule of carbon dioxide and its incorporation into a molecule of sugar. To catch the first step, identify the most primitive intermediate product, and trace the course of the synthesis piece—that was the goal.

The study was made largely with green algae. In Calvin's project, a suspension of algae in water was placed in a closed glass vessel. The vessel was entered at the top by a tube, and could be emptied quickly through a stopcock at the bottom. Carbon dioxide was bubbled in through the tube, light was directed upon the vessel from the opposite sides, and soon photosynthesis was proceeding at a steady rate.

At a given time, the incoming stream of carbon dioxide was changed. Up to now it had been ordinary CO_2, but at this moment a switch was turned and suddenly the stream contained a labeled CO_2 in which the carbon atom was the radioactive isotope, C^{14}. Since these C^{14} atoms continually discharge electrons, any compound into which the isotopic carbon had been built would be immediately tagged. Calvin's plan was to stop the photosynthesis at different intervals of time, draw off a sample at each interval, and see if he could spot the earliest stage at which the C^{14} betrayed its presence. So, after photosynthesis with the radioactive material had been proceeding for ten minutes, he turned the stopcock at the bottom of the vessel, the suspension of algae dropped through into a bath of alcohol which instantaneously halted all biological action, and the experimenter then analyzed the algae and determined which compounds contained radioactive carbon.

To separate the medley of photosynthetic products, Calvin employed a technique known as chromatography. In this a sheet of specially prepared absorbent paper is used. A drop of the mixture to be analyzed is placed on the paper in one corner of its blotter-like surface, and then the paper is installed in an airtight tank and subjected to certain treatments. As a result, the various compounds that are contained in the drop begin to migrate across the paper; but because of differences in molecular structure and in physical properties they move at different speeds. The effect is to separate the substances, and after a few hours each appears as an isolated spot on the paper. Often each such substance has, or can be made to have, a distinctive color—and thus the compounds may show up as islands of blue, pink, yellow, or other tints.

It was not color that Calvin was looking for, but the content of radioactive carbon. So he laid the paper sheet on top of a sensitive photographic film in the dark, and allowed the radioactive spots to photograph themselves. It was like radium, though millions of times weaker. After several weeks of exposure, he developed the film, and there were the tell-tale images marking the spots that contained the radiant atoms. It was then a simple matter to go back to the paper sheet, cut out the spots which had showed the radioactivity, and by chemical analysis determine what each compound was.

This neat scheme—so simple and yet so imaginative—enabled Calvin to look, as it were, into the algal cell at different intervals of time and see how far along its manufacturing processes had carried the radiant atoms. He first allowed the photosynthesis to proceed for ten minutes, and the photograph that resulted showed more than twenty radioactive spots, meaning that the carbon had been built into that many different compounds. The next experiment dumped the algae into the alcohol bath after five minutes of photosynthesis, and again the photograph showed many compounds. Then intervals of one minute, half a minute, and finally ten seconds were tried—and now an interesting result began to turn up regularly. This was the dominating presence of a substance which the chemists identified as phosphoglyceric acid. In all experiments with less than one minute of photosynthesis, this compound showed itself as the principal holder of the radioactive carbon.

Now phosphoglyceric acid (PGA) is a three-carbon compound—that is, its molecule contains three carbon atoms —and because of certain considerations it seemed doubtful that it could be the first step in the synthesis of sugar. There must be some precursor to which the bubbling CO_2 gas joined itself and by which the tagged atom was passed on to form PGA. The search for this forerunner has led Calvin and his team over a wide field during the last five years, but the chase finally ended in 1954 when the bits of circumstantial evidence were pieced together. All pointed to a five-carbon sugar known as ribulose diphosphate (RuDP) as the precursor.

Curiously, RuDP is a more formidable structure than PGA. It is nearly twice as large, and you may wonder where a primary building block of such size comes from. "From the plant," answers Dr. Calvin. "We start with a functioning green plant, and its cells are already stocked with all the ingredients of living matter." These include first of all the indispensable enzymes, those specialized structures which assist or chaperone the reactions of other molecules. Also present are various proteins, acids, alkalis, salts, and sugars, and among the sugars is this RuDP. Thus, to make sugar, the plant must already have some sugar as well as the necessary enzymes and other essential substances.

As the sequence starts, the five-carbon RuDP joins with the one-carbon CO_2 to form a six-carbon molecule. This initial product comes under the chaperonage of an enzyme and promptly breaks in half to form two similar three-carbon structures—two molecules of PGA. Here, then, is the origin of the PGA. The hydrogen—which chlorophyll split off from water in the light phase—now enters the cycle. Accompanied by an input of chemical energy, the atom of hydrogen joins the three-carbon PGA to form a three-carbon sugar known as triose. Thus the first sugar product is achieved, and from then on the plant proceeds to fabricate glucose, sucrose, and the other forms of carbohydrate by using triose molecules or parts of them as building blocks.

This radioactive tracking down of the path of carbon in photosynthesis is a triumph of chemical detection. Although at first Calvin's results were challenged and in some quarters contradicted, they are now universally accepted, and he has turned his attention to the light phase of photosynthesis.

SECRET OF THE GREEN BODIES

Economists predict that within a decade or two the demand for basic food for man and domestic animals will be at twice the world's present production of agricultural products. The chronically hungry in Asia, Africa, and parts of Europe and the Americas number around a billion people, and how to feed more and more billions is a problem that cannot much longer be left to the chance conjunction of whatever quanta happen to fall on whatever molecules of chlorophyll that may be exposed in farm or orchard.

"All agriculture seems to be a primitive, medieval, if not archaic process, even if we use tractors," declared biochemist Albert Szent-Gyorgyi in a recent preview of the shape of things to come. "To wait until plants grow and develop their chlorophyll and accumulate the energy seems ridiculously primitive and slow at our present rate of scientific potential. Why cannot we rather construct a 'chlorophyll bomb' to blow up need and poverty?"

What Dr. Szent-Gyorgyi is proposing, I take it, is the transfer of the photosynthetic process from the green plant's living cell to the chemist's nonliving test tube. This is a dream that harks back through seventy-five years of experimentation; and failure after failure of these efforts confirmed the conclusion that photosynthesis is a business of living matter that cannot be separated from the intact cell. It was so written in the textbooks. Nevertheless, chemists continued to break up plant tissue, to recover the green stuff, and to test the behavior of these fragments in light.

When a leaf cell is examined microscopically, the eye sees at once that its green color is not diffused throughout the protoplasm but is concentrated in small floating bodies. These are called chloroplasts. Further dissection reveals that the chloroplasts are made up of still smaller bodies called grana, and it is these that contain the chlorophyll. A typical square inch of leaf surface has about a billion cells; there are, on the average, from 20 to 100 chloroplasts in each cell, about 100 grana to each chloroplast, and it is estimated that each grana holds about 10,000,000 chlorophyll molecules. One can extract the chlorophyll as a pure chemical, and chemists have found it possible to promote various photochemical reactions by exposing solutions of pure chlorophyll to light—but none has ever been able either to split water or to reduce carbon dioxide by this means.

Early experimenters broke up cells to obtain chloroplasts, even carried the separation down to the grana, and from time to time they obtained small bursts of oxygen when these fragments were illuminated. Such bursts were attributed to the decomposition of residual oxygen compounds left on the leaves. But in 1937 it occurred to an English biochemist that if photosynthesis were possible outside the cell, it might be assisted by providing a substance that had a special affinity for hydrogen. This was Robin Hill, of Cambridge University. Such a substance, he reasoned, by attracting hydrogen would promote the decomposition of water and thus speed up release of the oxygen. There are certain iron compounds which have this affinity. So, after crushing a batch of leaves, separating out the chloroplasts, and suspending these green bodies in a vessel of water, Professor Hill added a feric salt. When the mixture was illuminated, oxygen came off at a steady rate.

The Hill experiment is a milestone in the laboratory attack on the secret of the green bodies, because there, for the first time, a photosynthetic process was achieved outside the living cell. It was only half a loaf that Hill got, however. His experiment split water and released oxygen, and therefore demonstrated the light phase of photosynthesis; but it did not carry the hydrogen atoms over to the carbon dioxide and there was no production of sugar. It blazed a trail, however, which other investigators followed, and one group of them was able to announce to the American Association for the Advancement of Science in December 1954 that chloroplasts in a test tube had carried out complete photosynthesis, and had produced sugar with no assistance from outside except the energy brought by the rays of light.

The leader of this group is Daniel I. Arnon, professor of plant physiology at the University of California. For a number of years Dr. Arnon and associates have been experimenting with isolated chloroplasts under light. Their first results were to repeat the Hill reaction and obtain the release of oxygen. Later they were able to demonstrate that as the chloroplasts split the water they converted the light energy into chemical energy and stored it in the form of high-energy phosphorus compounds (the very same compounds which function as energy-holders in human muscle). Finally, only a few years ago, they obtained unmistakable evidence of sugar and starch which the chloroplasts had fashioned and tagged with radioactive carbon that had been fed to them in the test tube.

The amounts of sugar produced were admittedly small, almost microscopic, but, says Arnon, "The quantity is not the significant thing. The fact that the process has been transferred from the living cell, with it multiplicity of metabolic reactions and other vital phenomena, to the simpler and less complicated environment of the laboratory vessel, is the important gain. To the physiologist and biochemist such a transfer is prerequisite to the unraveling of the detailed mechanism of a complex process."

TEST-TUBE ENERGY

Another development comes from an enzymologist, Efraim Racker, of the Public Health Research Institute of the City of New York. Dr. Racker, in a communication to *Nature* (February 5, 1955) reports the production of sugar by purely chemical interactions. What he did was to crush spinach leaves, separate and discard the cellular fragments, and extract an aqueous solution containing a concentrate of the natural synthesizing enzymes of the plant cells. To this solution he added carbon dioxide, put in certain energy-rich phosphate compounds to supply the energy, bubbled hydrogen gas through the mixture to supply the necessary hydrogen, and added a special enzyme which facilitates the use of molecular hydrogen. There was no need of light, since the phosphate compounds supplied the energy; and for the same reason there was no need of chlorophyll.

Thus, by a cycle of reactions that were strictly chemical, promoted at each step by the appropriate catalyzing enzyme, Racker produced glucose sugar in a test tube. The value of this work is its demonstration of the exclusively chemical nature of the carbon-dioxide reducing system—the dark phase of photosynthesis which takes the hydrogen and the elements of the carbon dioxide and builds them into the energy-packed structure which is sugar.

So the first steps seem to have been taken, their direction is forward, and Szent-Gyorgyi's dream of a benevolent "chlorophyll bomb" may not be so utopian after all. Transferred to the chemist's vats and tanks, isolated from the distracting milieu of the living cell, the processes of photosynthesis should become more manageable, the gaps in our knowledge of its ways be more surely bridged—hastening the day when the world's production of food will catch up with the needs of the world's hungry.

QUESTIONS

1. What is meant by the phrase "Our Bridge from the Sun"?
2. Why is sugar so important to the organic world?
3. Mention briefly the contributions of Priestley, Ingen-Housz, Senebier, de Saussure, von Mayer, van Niel, Blackman, Calvin, Hill, Arnon, and Racker to the solving of the riddle of photosynthesis.
4. The following compounds are involved in photosynthesis. Place them in the correct order of formation, as far as is known: PGA, Triose, RuDP, Glucose.
5. What connection might there be between the world population crisis and photosynthesis?

PART EIGHT

RADIOBIOLOGY

Radioactive carbon, with which Dr. Hutchinson treats, was one of the more recent methods for dating objects. Historians have been aided greatly by data obtained from radioactive carbon. Here the scientist could provide definite data where written records were unavailable. Carbon 14 (radioactive carbon) is a form or isotope of regular carbon 12. In addition to its use as a dater, carbon 14 was used in connection with oxygen as $C^{14}O_2$ to determine some of the intermediate steps in photosynthesis. Other isotopes such as P^{32}, S^{35}, Ca^{45}, and Fe^{59} have been used as tracers in plants to study the speed of movement of an absorbed substance and in what parts of the plant they most frequently lodge. It cannot be too strongly emphasized that radiobiology is one of science's most promising tools. In conclusion, it should be mentioned that medicine has been greatly advanced by the use of tracers.

G. Evelyn Hutchinson

Radioactive Carbon

Reprinted with the permission of publishers from the American Scientist 39:473–476, 1951.

Twenty years ago, the suggestion that pieces of charcoal could bear their own date lines and belemnites their temperature charts, would have appeared preposterous, yet most of the present notes are to be devoted to sober investigations showing indeed that this is the case. Very simply and obviously, the answer is that if a past event has left some trace over a very wide area or volume, we may hope ultimately to find that trace, however small, simply by improving our technique. This is what Libby and Urey have done in the work to be discussed below. If the event, however important its consequences might be in later times, was of a strictly local character, unless it belonged to history recorded at the time, the odds are against us, whether we are searching for the first bird or the Holy Grail. Such a distinction obviously involves considerations not unlike the capacity factors and intensity factors of the physicist and engineer. Where the phenomenon was widespread, the result of our search will be reasonably well-founded scientific knowledge; where it was localized, however intense the local impact, the search will almost always remain historical speculation. But, to distinguish is not to condemn. As long as the human mind is free, it will speculate, and there is always a chance, even if remote, that something will turn up and that the speculative result will be confirmed and emerge as firmly established history.

CARBON

The perfection of the radiocarbon method of dating carbonaceous materials, elaborated by W. F. Libby, has been widely and justifiably regarded as one of the most remarkable scientific achievements of the past decade.

The full series of dates available up to September 1950 has been printed in a pamphlet distributed to interested investigators by the Institute of Nuclear Studies of Chicago University, and has been published with a few additions in a paper by Arnold and Libby. The geological implications of these dates have been considered at length by Flint and Deevey, and some of the European results have also been discussed by Godwin. It is these contributions which will primarily be considered here.

So far, much the most important contribution made by Libby and his co-workers to the chronology of the late Pleistocene has been the dating of the Two Creeks Forest Bed of Manitowoc County, Wisconsin. This bed consists of peaty material containing spruce logs, mostly pointing southwest, and with splintered ends. The bed is overlain by a thin lacustrine deposit and above this by till representing the Mankato substage, the last glacial readvance recorded within the United States. Evidently, the site was occupied, during the somewhat warmer Cary-Mankato interval, by a spruce forest. This became flooded while the trees were still standing and later the advancing ice toppled the trees over and finally covered them with ground moraine. The Mankato ice sheet advanced about twenty-five miles further south and then began its final retreat. Until recently most, though not all, students of Pleistocene glaciation in North America believed that the Mankato ice achieved its maximum southward extension about 25,000 years ago.

Various pieces of wood, collected in the Two Creeks Bed by L. R. Wilson, J. H. Bretz, and L. Horberg, have provided a most encouragingly concordant set of radiocarbon dates indicating that the spruce trees of the Cary-Mankato forest actually were growing between 10,877 and 12,168 years ago. The mean age is 11,404 ± 350 years. Since the Two Creeks forest grew very close to the edge of the Mankato ice sheet, one can safely assume that the time of the maximum development of that ice sheet was about 11,000 years ago or about 9000 B.C.

A warmer episode, comparable to the Cary-Mankato interval, followed by renewed refrigeration, has been recognised in Europe as the Allerod horizon, identified in a number of localities from Ireland eastward into Russia. The Allerod was apparently followed by a glacial readvance, termed the Fennoscandian in Northern Europe. Four out of five samples of supposedly Allerod material, from Ireland, England, and western Germany, collected by G. F. Mitchell, H. Godwin, K. B. Blackburn, and Franz Firbas, give concordant dates, ranging from 9861 to 11,310 years old, this overlapping the narrow range of possible dates for the Two Creeks Bed. It is thus reasonably certain that these two oscillations in climate are contemporaneous and equivalent. This is a result of extraordinary interest. It permits for the first time accurate correlation of the closing events of the Pleistocene glacial on either side of the Atlantic. It shows that the disappearance of the very large ice sheet from continental North America took little if any longer than the time of the waning of the Scandinavian ice, rather than a period more than twice as long, as had often been supposed in the past. It also shows that the Allerod oscillation and the subsequent Fennoscandian readvance were not purely local matters but, having their counterparts in the New World, were presumably due to the variation of whatever planetary and cosmic factors may be involved in producing glacial maxima. This is a matter of considerable interest because local causes have been postulated to explain away the fact that there is no minimum corresponding to the Fennoscandian substage in the "radiation curve" constructed by Milankovitch from precessional and other astronomical changes.

This radiation curve has been widely used in Europe not only to explain the Pleistocene glaciations but also to date them. Since it appears not to apply to the final and now chronometrically accessible closing phases of the glaciation one may be forgiven a certain skepticism as to the validity of Milankovitch's theory as applied to the earlier and more grandiose climatic events of the Pleistocene. It may moreover be pointed out that charcoal from the occupation level of the famous painted cave of Lascaux gives radiocarbon dates of about 13,500 B.C.; a much older date would be assigned to this site on the basis of the Milankovitch theory.

After the ice retreated from eastern North America, a tundra flora developed and then gave place to a spruce-fir forest. This forest has left traces in the form of recognizable pollen grains of *Picea* and *Abies* in the postglacial sediments formed in peat bogs and on lake bottoms. Later, over most of the humid United States, the coniferous forest gave place to a hardwood forest in which the proportions of different species of trees seem to have oscillated in response to minor climatic changes. Wherever the full sequence is developed, a layer of sediment (zone B) bearing little pollen other than that of pine is intercalated between the layers (zone A) bearing spruce and fir and those (zone C) bearing mainly oak, hemlock, and other members of the hardwood community. Most workers have suspected that the pine period implies a cool dry climate, but there is a growing tendency to question earlier interpretations. Whatever ecological and climatic meaning the pine-pollen zone B may ultimately prove to have, it is one of the most conspicuous features of the micropaleobotany of North American bog and lake sediments. It is therefore of considerable interest to find that whatever conditions did produce the pine maximum, they moved northward behind the retreating ice, though at a considerable distance, being established at Cranberry Glades, West Virginia, about 7500 B.C.; at North Branford, Connecticut, about 7000 B.C.; Anoka County, southern Minnesota, about 6000 B.C.; St. Louis County, northern Minnesota, about 5000 B.C.; Aroostook County, Maine, about 4000 B.C. Comparable dates are given by material from the ecologically equivalent Boreal of Europe. Whatever the causes of the characteristic vegetation of zone B and of the Boreal, it is evident that they are related to the process of deglaciation and not to some world-wide climatic oscillation produced by planetary or cosmic variables.

Though the full archaeological discussion of the radiocarbon dates has not yet appeared, it is evident from the papers already published that man entered the New World shortly after the Mankato maximum, if not earlier. Charcoal from occupation sites in a supposedly Mankato alluvium in Frontier County, Nebraska, proves to be from 9000 to 10,500 years old. Other artifact-bearing layers of like age are known in certain North American caves; groundsloth dung, from Gypsum Cave, Nevada, proved to be 8500 to 10,500 years old, while bark sandals from Fort Rock Cave, Oregon, were made 9000 years ago. Burnt bone from a cave in Patagonia, 125 miles east of Ultima Esperanza, proved to be 8600 years old, while sloth dung, not however associated with man, from the more famous cave at the last-named place was 10,800 years old. It is evident, therefore, that human occupation of the New World had begun by the nineth millenium B.C. and that the whole length of the continent had been traversed by about 6700 B.C. A final footnote to American history may be added. The explosion which produced Crater Lake, Oregon, and killed some trees in the process, can be dated, from the wood of these trees, as having occurred about 4500 B.C. The radiocarbon dates also throw some light on the chronology of the various stages in the evolution of the Great Lakes, for which the curious reader is referred to Flint and Deevey's paper.

Summarizing the first geological results of Libby's method, it appears that:

(1) The last glacial substage in the United States, the Mankato, reached its maximum about 9000 B.C., very much later than had formerly been supposed.

(2) The very large ice sheet over northern continental North America must have receded faster than had formerly been thought possible, almost as fast as did the much smaller Scandinavian icecap.

(3) The warm episodes, the Cary-Mankato interval in North America, and the Allerod oscillation in Europe, were essentially contemporaneous.

(4) Such information as is available from radiocarbon dating is not consistent with Milankovitch's astronomical theory of glaciation.

(5) The pine zone (B), evidently the equivalent of the European Boreal, intercalated in many North American pollen profiles between the zone (A) of the spruce-fir forest and that (zone C) of the hardwood or deciduous forest, represents an episode dependent on the retreat of the ice and occurs at a progressively later date in more northerly latitudes.

(6) Man entered the New World by the ninth millenium B.C. and penetrated to the extreme south of South America within one or two thousand years.

If these conclusions were all that could be obtained by radiocarbon dating, the elaboration of the method would have been a most remarkable achievement of lasting importance. Actually such results are only fragmentary beginnings.

QUESTIONS

1. What use can be made of radioactive carbon in dating individual objects and in correlating events in widely separated areas?
2. When was the last glacial period in the United States?
3. What is meant by "the ninth millenium B.C." and what significance does this figure have for people of North America?
4. Explain fully what is meant by radioactive carbon.

PART NINE

SPACE BIOLOGY

What will the first human being find on the Moon, or on Venus, or on Mars? Will there be food plants there to sustain him and if so, how will they differ from earth's plants and how will he know which ones are edible and which ones are deadly poisonous? Is there a book available on "Edible Plants of the Moon"? If space men have to carry their food with them, how much will they need and how can it be kept in an edible condition? Some success has been had with growing an alga called Chlorella in liquid media, but can this be transported to the planets and can it be made to grow there? Lacking the solution at present, man may have to carry a ton of dried food and sandwiches with him on his first few trips.

Another danger in space travel is the possible contamination of the planet or satellite to be visited by earth's microbes. At present, as much sterilization of the equipment as is possible is being done.

Despite all these problems that must be overcome, no one doubts that space travel will become both common and safe in time. Indeed, the Moon may become the greatest tourist attraction of all time.

Wallace O. Fenn

The Challenge of Space Biology

Reprinted with the permission of the author and publisher from the A.I.B.S. Bulletin 8(2): 15, 1958.

In a sense it is regrettable that the American Institute of Biological Sciences had to raise its voice recently in protest against the ruling of the Civil Service Commission which specifically excluded biological scientists from participation in a general salary increase provided for physicists and engineers. In general AIBS aims to campaign not for special favors for biologists but for better opportunities for biology to serve the present needs of man. The new space era will offer many such opportunities, some of which will be mentioned here; but every biologist knows that the real challenge to biology is to gain a better understanding of the nature of the life process itself. Biology is basic to both medicine and agriculture, and progress in both sciences is dependent upon advances in basic biological research. Support of this simple but little appreciated thesis is always the most vital objective of AIBS and its chief excuse for existence. Meanwhile, however, biology must be ready to respond to more immediate and practical demands including those connected with the satellite program.

The immediate problem for biologists of course is to think of ways in which satellites in orbit could be used significantly for biological research. One such experiment has already been suggested by an AIBS-ONR committee. This would involve the measurement of the CO_2 output of a yeast culture which could be telemetered in terms of the electrical conductivity of a solution of barium hydrate in which the CO_2 would be trapped. Such an experiment would tell us at least as much as the Russians can learn from their little dog. Even this simple experiment with yeast is no mean achievement for a weightless environment.

Both the yeast and the dog experiments have their limitations however. In both cases life and survival possibilities should be predictable within certain limits of temperature, oxygen, and carbon dioxide pressures, nutrient supply, radiation intensity, etc. If these are adequately monitored and kept within acceptable limits any failure of growth or survival can only mean the presence of some unpredicted environmental factor. However unlikely this may appear to be, the demonstration that life is actually possible in a satellite for long periods of time would be very reassuring. For a biologist also it would provide a real thrill to be in continual communication, of a sort, with any living cell circumnavigating the earth above the atmosphere. The effects of radiation could be tested in this way if yeast could remain exposed in a nongrowing state in the satellite for varying periods of time before the initiation of growth by the automatic influx of nutrients. While there are many variations of this plan which would be of interest, most of the results could probably be predicted from terrestrial experiments if physical measurements were available of the radiation intensity in the environment of the satellite.

Another point to explore is the possibility of the existence of variable spores or virus particles in space. While this is highly unlikely because of the intense ultraviolet light to which such cells would be exposed, direct proof of the complete sterility of space would still be useful. It would help to dispose of the old panspermia theory of Arrhenius which supposed that living spores could be widely disseminated throughout the universe by the pressure of light rays. Possibly spores could be found in space on their radiation wings even though they might not be any longer viable.

A related problem is the possibility of testing the surface of the moon for the presence of living cells. However, if the moon is once hit by a missile fired from the earth the interpretation of such data might be ambiguous. In any event, a primeval surface would offer more points of scientific interest than one more or less disturbed by previous human intervention.

Surely landings on the moon are far in the future but not too far for scientific interest. Among the many difficult biological problems involved is the effect of gravity. On the take-off fortunately the acceleration is within tolerable limits provided the occupant can orient the long axis of his body transverse to the line of thrust. The complete absence of gravity when the satellite is in orbit will pose a still more serious and in some respects perhaps a more amusing problem.

For the maintenance of man over long periods in a satellite the nitrogen of the inspired air will presumably be completely eliminated and pure oxygen at a pressure of perhaps 15–21% of an atmosphere will be substituted. This will minimize the pressure differential on the walls of the satellite and will provide an adequate oxygen tension for survival. The effect of removing all the nitrogen from the ambient atmosphere has not yet been adequately determined although some have claimed that it tends to inhibit oxidations to some extent. Some decrease in basal metabolic rate may also result from decreased tone of the anti-gravity muscles. The diet should be designed for minimum weight and possibly also for minimum indigestible residue. At best it will have to be a survival menu of spartan simplicity. A new diurnal rhythm will be imposed upon the occupants, with night occurring perhaps every hour or half hour as in the present orbiting satellites. It will be interesting to discover how long the 24-hour rhythm will persist under these conditions and indeed in which direction it may become modified. For interplanetary flights the problem is still different with perpetual daylight—or at least a bright sun in a black sky.

For the biologist the most fascinating and challenging of all problems is the possibility of making a sealed cabin into a "balanced aquarium" or an autotrophic unit dependent only upon the input of radiant energy from the sun. A man is approximately equivalent in rate of energy turnover to a 100 watt light and this is in turn about equal to the radiation falling on each square foot of surface exposed to the sun. If, therefore, this energy could be used with sufficient efficiency the problem is not theoretically insoluble.

For this purpose one must either complete the solution of the chemical mechanism of photosynthesis or invoke as usual, the aid of plants. Neither of these methods seems impossible. Great progress has been made by chemists and plant physiologists in their study of photosynthesis and some day it is probable that a useful test tube process for the removal of oxygen from carbon dioxide or its equivalent of water might become realized. It would certainly be as revolutionary for human life as the attainment of a method for using fusion energy.

On the other hand much attention is also being paid to the possibility of using cultures of chlorella to augment the food supply of the world. If optimum conditions for growth could be supplied, calculations indicate that it is not impossible to make effective use of chlorella for this purpose. This, however, involves recovery of all waste products in the excreta including nitrogen, minerals and water and their addition to the chlorella culture in useful form. Such a system if successful would at least substantially supplement the oxygen supply and nutrient supply of the satellite occupants and it is a problem well worthy of the serious consideration of biologists.

By effective participation in these and other problems there are many ways in which biologists will be able to qualify as "first class citizens" in the age which is before us.

QUESTIONS

1. If a yeast culture was supplied with a three months supply of food, sent aloft for three months in a satellite and returned to the earth in a living condition, what would this prove?
2. What are some of the problems of man in space?
3. What is meant by an autotrophic unit designed for a space capsule?

PART TEN

LOWER PLANTS, DISEASES, AND MEDICINE

Dangers from lions, automobiles, and icebergs are easier to avoid than the perils of bacteria, molds, and viruses because of the larger size of the former. Not only have the lower plants been a scourge to man for centuries but they have taken a heavy toll of his livestock and of his food plants.

Some of the well-known diseases caused by the inhabitants of the microscopic world are tuberculosis, leprosy, typhoid, Rocky Mountain spotted and yellow fever, bubonic plague, venereal diseases, and sleeping sickness. Strangely enough, although many people have died from these diseases, other uncounted thousands have been saved from death by the antibiotics prepared from molds, for example, penicillin.

Who has not heard of wheat rust, corn smut, potato blight, and cucumber wilt? These diseases affect our food supply. The work of the Doctors of Medicine, the Veterinarians, and the Doctors of Philosophy (Plant Pathologists) cannot be lauded too highly in the constant struggle against disease and death.

For more papers in this interesting area, read Milestones in Microbiology *by Thomas Brock.*

Johann Christian Fabricius

Attempt at a Dissertation on the Diseases of Plants

Reprinted by permission of the American Phytopathological Society from Phytopathological Classic, No. 1, 1926.

Knowledge of the diseases both of animals and plants forms an important part of our rural economy, but it is still too much neglected. We see our cattle fall and our plants wither away without being able to render them assistance, lacking as we do understanding of their condition. Doctors have disdained to condescend to dumb brutes and have delegated them to the mercies of horse-doctors and quacksalvers who are accustomed to use certain mixtures for all diseases without insight and without method. They are acquainted neither with the construction of the body nor the effects of cures, and are therefore unable to adapt or modify the treatment to the conditions or to the observations of the causes of disease. That is why our knowledge of the diseases of cattle is still very incomplete and limited. It is true that of late this science has been studied with great eagerness.

At present, however, we remain in expectation of the many improvements to result therefrom, and which we at least hope for and desire.

With plants the condition is far worse; rural economy contains no complete description of their diseases. To be sure from time to time agricultural publications note the best known, though totally without system, and practically no two writers agree as to the causes of these diseases.

Many have attributed the damaged growth of their plants to the earth, the sky, and the unsound air; this common refuge for the ignorance of doctors has not been forgotten in the case of plants. However the diseases of plants like those of animals seem to be due to internal causes, though indeed I recognize that the conditions of the air can sometimes aggravate the same.

I will therefore essay in this attempt to treat the diseases of plants and their causes, briefly but systematically.

It is only an attempt, and far from

complete, but I will be glad indeed, if I can encourage others to make closer observations on this so important part of agriculture.

The classification of these various diseases is arbitrary; several could be made and for each could be found arguments for and against. Hitherto attention has been directed only to that part of the plant on which the disease is observed, yet the same disease can attack various parts of the plant; other diseases appear sometimes on one part sometimes on another, while the injury or cause of the disease lies hidden in quite other parts. I will therefore attempt a new method and deduce the classes and genera according to the apparent cases, but the species according to the causes of the disease.

Class 1. Rendering unproductive are those cases in which the plants are prevented from setting fruit or are rendered distinctly less fruitful. This is frequently not observed until after blossoming.

Class 2. Wasting are those diseases in which the plants are slowly killed, their growth and strength gradually decreasing.

Class 3. Decaying are those cases in which the main parts of the plants are decomposed and become a rotting mass, which by degrees is transformed to mouldy soil.

Class 4. Discharging are those cases showing an abnormal flow.

Class 5. Rendering misshapen, recognized by the abnormal development of the external parts.

Class 6. Extraneous are those cases due to the apparent injury to the parts.

(Examples From Some of the Classes)

Class 1—Smut. *Ustilago*

Smut on cereals is one of the most common and best known diseases; it often nullifies all hope of a good harvest. It attacks by preference wheat, barley and oats, while rye and millet seldom or never suffer. Eradicating this disease has become the more difficult after recent careful investigations have proved it contagious. When it has once gained the upper hand in a field, it increases in strength year by year. Smut only attacks the floral structures which it gradually transforms to a loose black powder easily blown about by the wind.

Tillet claims that smut is spread by contagion alone. In this he only upholds our own opinions in regard to its contagious qualities without showing the real causes.

Professor Gleditsch, on the other hand, attempts to prove that those kernels which have not attained full maturity at harvest time, undergo, in their place of storage, a kind of fermentation, from which later, when the seed is sown, smut is derived. How can it be that only a few species of plants are attacked by smut even though undeveloped seed are to be found in all.

Two remedies are used to prevent smut on our fields: sowing pure seed, and soaking the seed in a solution of salt or lime. Both remedies are highly praised and indicate, moreover, that the cause of smut is not to be sought in the soil but in the seed. . . .

Class 4—Rust

Rust appears both on the stem and on the leaves of plants; it rends the tender covering and hides the surface under a brownish and light powder. Often it only occasions small spots on the leaves and affects the development of the plant but slightly. However, when it gains the upper hand and attacks the stem, the plant suffers greatly, sometimes dries out entirely.

Rust seems to me to bear much resemblance to smut. Smut transforms the organs of fructification to a black powder; rust transforms the parts below the epidermis or outer covering to a brown powder. At all events I believe that the cause of both these diseases is one and the same. As remedies for rust the farmers suggest the same as used for smut.

Class 5—Galls

Galls is the name applied to knobs and excresences due to the stings of various insects. The so-called ergot (Clavus) is no other than a form of this disease. It comes about in a similar way: *Thrips Physapus* Linn. attacking the tender rye kernels and laying its eggs in them, the kernels develop over the husk, become blackish, lumpy, internally fungous and containing a rotten, brownish powder.

QUESTIONS

1. When was Fabricius born?
2. What kind of a plant scientist does he best resemble?
3. Would you say that during the 200 years intervening between his birth and the present day, most of the problems of plant disease have been solved? Discuss this with your instructor.
4. Try to find out what are some of the unsolved problems of plant pathology.
5. Did Fabricius consider this field well developed in his day?
6. Which seemed more important to Fabricius as causes of disease, the internal or the external ones?
7. Compare in a paragraph or two the modern theory of the cause of smut with that held by Fabricius. Use corn smut as an example.
8. Do the same with rust, using wheat rust as an example.
9. What is ergot of rye?

N.B. Fabricius was born in 1745 and died in 1808. His observations were a valuable contribution to knowledge concerning plant diseases.

James G. Horsfall

The Fight with the Fungi

Reprinted with the permission of the author and the publisher from American Journal of Botany **43**:532–536, 1956.

The title of this paper sounds as if the roof were about to fall in on us—that we have lost or are about to lose the fight with the fungi. Say not so! We have only begun to fight, but fight we must.

We may easily forget that fungi feed at the same table with us. This is so because they have a ticket to the first sitting. They consume our food in the farmer's field, on the trains and trucks that bring it to us, and in the grocer's store. If this fight go not forward to success, we may one day not be able to smile at the "naïvete" of Mr. Malthus who thought that we would soon eat ourselves out of our own food supply.

Fungi have been on this planet longer than we. They have developed some fantastically efficient devices that serve them in their fight with us. They are well able to search out our food plants so that they also may eat, drink and be merry.

It has been fun to help a little in the research to develop the countermeasures that we use in our fight with them. Before we come to the countermeasures, however, I should like to discuss some of the famous plant diseases of antiquity and how some of them have altered the course of history.

Three plant diseases of modern times are known to almost everyone. Perhaps the best known is the chestnut blight that swept every chestnut tree from the hills from Maine to Georgia. The second is the Dutch elm disease that is marching down the streets of cities and killing the elms from Montreal to Denver. And the third is oak wilt. It is scaring the wits out of the people who produce the oak flooring for our houses and kegs for our beer.

These diseases latch onto our consciousness because they are new and they strike down handsome big trees. These are some of the blasts and blights that beset us, but what really robs us are such diseases as wheat rust and potato rot.

Wheat rust is perhaps the most famous disease of antiquity and it is still with us. Wheat rust robs us of our bread, the very staff of life. Those of us who went through both World Wars remember the "wheatless days" of World War I. We had wheatless days in that war because 1917 was one of those years when wheat rust swept the plains and consumed the grains like a prairie fire. The wheat rust fungus ate most of our bread at the first sitting. We had to settle for rice and corn bread.

We were lucky during World War II. Wheat rust did not stage another such ruinous raid and we did not have wheatless days. Of course, scientific research had also been at work in the meantime and had won part of the fight with that fungus.

Wheat rust was known to the Israelites who talked about it in Genesis. It was known to the Romans. And it was known in Colonial America. On this last point, there hangs a tale of the impact of a plant disease on civilization. This is the tale of how wheat rust altered the eating habits of a group of people.

When the English colonists came to America, some settled in New England, and others in tidewater Virginia, Plymouth and Jamestown being settled within a few years of each other. Undoubtedly, both groups of immigrants brought wheat with them, and they both found the Indians growing corn. The wheat rust disease, however, acted differently on the wheats in the two colonies, just as it does today.

WHEAT RUST ALTERS EATING HABITS

Wheat rust is a much more serious disease in a warm than in a cool climate. It was to be expected, therefore, that wheat rust proved much more damaging to the Colonial crops of wheat in warm Virginia than in cool New England. It is probable that the settlers of Virginia found wheat a difficult crop on account of rust whereas the settlers of New England found wheat a good crop as it had been in England itself.

It seems to me quite likely that wheat rust explains today's difference between the carbohydrate diets of the southern and the northern United States. Bread, we say, is the "staff of life." In the South bread means corn bread. In the North bread means wheat bread.

I submit that wheat rust was so destructive in the South that the colonists, perforce, had to eat corn bread, grits, and hominy. Difficult as food habits are to change, the southern colonists had to change from wheat to corn. Wheat bread was so rarely obtainable in the South that it came to have its own name, light or white bread.

Wheat grew well enough in the North so that wheat bread remained the "staff of life."

Now you may be thinking that wheat can be and is grown in some of the warm parts of the United States—in Texas and Oklahoma. The explanation for this is that wheat rust is severe only when warmth is accompanied by moisture. In Oklahoma and Texas there is much less moisture during the wheat-growing season than in the more humid areas of the eastern part of the South. Hence, wheat rust does not make the crop unprofitable in the dry Southwest as it does in the humid Southeast.

The relation of moisture and warmth to wheat rust has also resulted in some interesting dietary habits in Europe, and in turn in the development of a scourge known as St. Anthony's Fire.

A MEDIEVAL SCOURGE

The same pattern of food habits applies in Europe as in America. Wheat grows well in England, which like New England, is moist enough for wheat rust but a little too cool. Therefore, in England, bread is wheat bread. Wheat also grows well in Italy, which like Oklahoma, is warm enough for wheat rust, but a little too dry. Therefore, in Italy also bread is wheat bread —and spaghetti and macaroni are wheat also.

Wheat grows relatively poorly, however, in Central Europe, which like Virginia is warm and moist in the wheat season. This makes wheat rust bad there. In turn this makes bread in Central Europe rye bread. Central Europe is a rye-eating area.

Let us see how St. Anthony's fire was related to this interesting distribution of staple food plants brought on by the action of wheat rust. St. Anthony's fire was a strong malady that afflicted the people in the Middle Ages. The characteristic of the disease was the raging fever that gave the disease its name—St. Anthony's fire. In the Middle Ages it was supposed that the disease could be cured by the intercession of St. Anthony.

The fever led to mental failure and often to death. The victims suffered initially with nerve tingling in the feet and hands. They might lose the sense of touch. Then gangrene would set in and the extremities might have to be amputated.

Like the plague, it struck down large numbers of people but, it was not "catching."

This peculiar disease occurred mainly in central Europe, seldom in Italy or England. In other words the disease was coexistent with the occurrence of rye. It occurred where wheat could not be grown on account of rust.

It is not surprising, then, that as early as 1630 the French physician, Thullier, recognized that St. Anthony's fire was caused from eating rye kernels infected with another plant disease called ergot. Ergot, like wheat rust, liked the warm humid climate of central Europe. It did not attack rye seriously enough to curtail the yield disastrously but it did produce enough diseased kernels to contaminate the flour for bread.

Of course the disease was most serious in those years when the rye crop was the shortest. In those years it was sometimes difficult to get rye that did not contain ergot and the people, especially the poor, had to eat it. These were the years when St. Anthony's fire scourged the population. If wheat rust had not been so serious in the warm, humid areas of central and southern Europe, St. Anthony's fire might never have reached such gigantic proportions and caused so much suffering and sorrow as it did during the Middle Ages.

St. Anthony's fire began to decline in the 18th century and was only occasionally serious in the 19th century. This decline in severity of St. Anthony's fire was due to the rise of the potato as a source of carbohydrate in Europe. People began to eat potatoes and reduce their use of rye. This had a salubrious effect on St. Anthony's fire but it led inevitably to one of the most devastating famines of modern times, for which a plant disease was again the cause.

THE IRISH FAMINE

Sir Walter Raleigh, visiting in Virginia in the early part of the 16th century, discovered the Indians cultivating a plant, the name of which he transliterated as *potato*. He took it to Europe where it remained a botanical curiosity for a while. Eventually, the people began to eat it in some volume and the crop spread rapidly across Europe. The peasant farmer of Europe soon discovered that the potato would produce more carbohydrate per acre than either rye or wheat. Slowly in some areas, rapidly in others, the potato replaced the cereals which had been the staple diet of the white men since the dawn of history. Lush fields of green potatoes began to appear all over Europe, instead of the nodding waves of wheat and rye. The potato was adapted to as wide an area as any cereal, in fact, far wider than wheat. This shift from cereals to potatoes was particularly prominent in Ireland; that's the reason why we often refer to a potato as the Irish potato. Ireland was so densely populated in the early part of the 19th century that the potato was a godsend to them. The first thing anybody knew, Ireland had almost ceased to grow cereal of any kind and was depending almost exclusively on the potato.

Just about 100 years ago a new disease of potato appeared in central Europe. It had never been seen before. It was a nasty disease; it made the leaves suddenly turn water-soaked, slimy, rotten, and black. That wasn't such a bad symptom except that the fungus that caused the disease spread from the leaves into the tubers and caused them to decay with a very curious and unusual sort of hard rot. The disease, which we now know as late blight, spread with lightning rapidity over Europe and appeared in Ireland in 1844. We might describe its catastrophic attack on Ireland in the words of an eye witness, Father Matthew, who says, "On July 27th I passed from Cork to Dublin, and the doomed plant bloomed in all the luxuriance of an abundant harvest. Returning on August 3rd, I beheld with sorrow mere wastes of putrefying vegetation."

In the 7 days mentioned by Father Matthew, the stage was set for a famine in which a quarter of a million people actually starved to death from slow malnutrition and a million and a half emigrated, many of whom became Irish policemen in the United States. Essentially the entire potato crop of Ireland was wiped out. The people who had been dependent upon potatoes to pay the rent and to carry them through the winter suddenly found themselves without any potatoes, and they knew that they faced a dreadful winter. A few feeble efforts at public relief were undertaken, partly by the Church and partly by the State, but they were inadequate and probably could never have been adequate to feed the whole population of Ireland. The best they could do was to stave off the evil day for a few people. The starvation showed first as dull headaches and bloated bellies; finally, the sufferer came under the spell of hallucinations and finally died from weakness. Terror and panic were common throughout the land and the ships sailing westward to the United States were packed to the gunwales with people rushing away from the famine that had encompassed their homeland.

So much for a couple of plant diseases that altered history.

WHAT CAUSES DISEASE

In the fight with the fungi, we had to find out first that it was fungi that we were fighting. We had somehow to discover what it was that caused plant disease. This was not so easy. The ancient man knew some of the causes of food destruction. He could see the locusts that ate his wheat in the field and the rats that ate his wheat in the granary. But he could not see the fungus that was stealing the starch from the grains and causing them to shrivel and shrink.

We very glibly say these modern days that plant diseases are caused chiefly by fungi, and we all pretty well understand that a fungus is a small, chlorophyll-free thread that we can see quite easily under the microscope. How did we arrive at this simple-sounding conclusion?

First of all, what is a disease? Is disease a condition? Some people would say that it is. In that case, would you say that fever is a disease? Well, most of us would say that fever is not a disease. Fever is a condition. When our temperature goes up, we have the condition called fever. Is a leaf spot on a plant a disease? No, that is like fever, that is a condition—a *symptom* of disease. We see that it is not the disease but it is a symptom of a diseased plant, the same as fever is a symptom of a diseased human.

A characteristic of disease is that it is continuous. If we cut our finger, we don't say that it is a disease—it's abnormal but it's not diseased, because we know that it is a transient and temporary thing and so we distinguish an injury like that from a disease. Similarly a lawn mower does not produce disease in the grass; it cuts the grass off, producing some injury, but we don't say the grass is diseased. We can, therefore, help to distinguish disease from injury by saying that disease is a continuously acting process, not a transient, temporary one such as the bite of a dog or the cut of a lawnmower in the grass. So in simple language we can say that disease is an abnormal and deleterious process caused by something which acts more or less continuously.

The crux of this matter of plant disease lies in that term *caused by*. Cause is not a very difficult concept. We have seen that reckless driving causes accidents, and we say that eating a green apple causes a stomach ache. But what causes plant diseases? The cause of plant disease remained enigmatic for a long time because for many centuries we could not see the fungus involved.

We could not see it or feel it or otherwise experience it with one or more of our five senses.

The Israelites were told (*Deuteronomy* 28:22) that God was responsible for wheat rust, that the Lord would smite them with blasting and mildew if they didn't obey the commandments of Jehovah. There must have been some doubters about this point, however, because four or five hundred years later the prophet, Haggai, says "I smote you with blasting and mildew and with hail and yet ye turned not to me, saith the Lord." It is not recorded in the Bible what the people thought caused wheat rust, but they must have doubted that the Lord did or Haggai would never have said that in spite of the blast and mildew, they still did not obey the Lord. . . .

SEEING IS BELIEVING

It so happens that a Dutch lens grinder named Leeuwenhoek had invented the microscope the latter part of the 17th century and now we could see. Leeuwenhoek was a few years ahead of Jethro Tull, but not far enough ahead so that Tull knew much of anything about a microscope. Some hundred years after Leeuwenhoek described his microscope, an Italian, Fontana, in 1766 looked through it at diseased wheat leaves and found the microscopic fungus which we today call *Puccinia graminis*. Fontana, however, did not conceive that these microscopic bodies that he saw were the cause of wheat rust. He got himself embroiled in another mixup in causation. He decided that the fungus bodies he saw were excrescences growing out of the diseased tissue. Fontana thought that the rust disease was the cause of the fungus rather than that fungus was the cause of the rust disease. This is a curious inversion of reasoning as we look back on it from here, but it was not so strange to Fontana.

Ten years later, Tillet, the master of the French mint, who as an amateur plant pathologist on the side, was working with another ancient disease of wheat called smut. Tillet looked through Leeuwenhoek's microscope and discovered the fungus of the wheat smut, but he also tended to overlook the cause thereof. Later, however, he changed his mind because he was actually able to take the small spores of the fungus and mix them up with healthy wheat seed. Wheat so inoculated came down with the disease. This is probably the earliest experimental production of any disease, plant or animal, on record. We might pause for just a second to note that this was almost an even 100 years ahead of Pasteur and his famous demonstration of anthrax in sheep, normally recorded as the first demonstration of the germ causation of disease. Tillet's work, however, did not convince very many people; more people were inclined to consider the fungus as an excrescence from diseased tissue rather than the cause of disease.

In 1844 when the potato blight was devastating the potato crops of Ireland, Dr. Lindley, the well-known editor of the *Gardener's Chronicle* in London, was writing that the fungus that he could find with his microscope on the leaves of the diseased plants was an excrescence from diseased tissue and not the cause thereof. Thereby, Dr. Lindley did a great disservice to the Irish. If he had truly sensed the nature of the fungus that he found on the diseased tissue, he might very well have solved the potato blight problem right then and there. But enough of that for now.

EXPERIMENTAL DISEASE

The critical consideration in deciding about the cause of a plant disease is whether or not one can produce the disease experimentally. This is the hard core of the science of plant pathology. Can we, in any given disease, dig out the cause, bring the suspected cause to bear on healthy plants, produce the disease and isolate the cause again? In the case of the potato blight that devastated the potatoes in Ireland, it is technically possible, although not easy, to find the fungus that is suspected to cause the disease. One can grow it free and clear of all other fungi in test tubes in the laboratory, examine its characteristics, its nature, inoculate it into living healthy plants that are separated from other plants and produce the typical disease. One can then re-isolate the fungus clear and free back in the test tube again. If the disease agrees with the disease normally found in the field, and the fungus that is taken out of the artificially infected plants looks like the fungus that was put in, then we say that we have fulfilled the basic postulates to prove causation of any given plant disease.

The interesting point to note here is that we didn't discover the true cause of plant disease until the invention of the microscope. We would probably still be speculating as to what causes plant diseases and still not have any very good methods of controlling them, if it were not for Mr. Leeuwenhoek's invention, which made it possible to see fungi and demonstrate their association with plant diseases.

With a brief digression, one might say, however, that several plant diseases are now known which are caused, not by fungi, but by bacteria which are too small to be seen with Mr. Leeuwenhoek's miscroscope. The discovery of bacteria had to await the arrival of an improvement in the microscope, called the oil immersion lens. As soon as the oil immersion lens was invented, we could find bacteria in the diseased tissues. Once observed, the bacteria could be isolated like the fungi, grown in pure culture, inoculated into plants, reisolated and compared with the original, thereby proving that bacteria produce plant disease.

Once the importance of bacteria was settled there was still a residue of diseases which were "catching" like other diseases but which were not caused by either bacteria or fungi. Techniques had been devised by then for inoculation and experimental production of disease, and it could be shown that the disease could be transferred from plant to plant but no "causal organism" could be found. It was suspected then that the "causal organism" was ultra-microscopic and it was labeled by the old term, virus, which originally meant poison. But virus has now come to mean a cause for disease that cannot be seen with a microscope. In the middle of the 1930's, the Radio Corporation of America invented a new kind of microscope depending upon a beam of electrons, not light. With this machine, viruses can now be seen; we know about how big they are, and can make out something of their characteristics and structure.

CHEMICAL WARFARE

Once the role of fungi in causing disease was established, control measures became feasible. Much of the modern control of plant disease is accomplished with fungicides that search out the fungus and kill it.

In the last 10 years, more has been learned about chemical control of fungi than in the whole course of history before. Chemical killers of fungi are called fungicides. These are the substances that will help to keep the roof from falling in. They are the substances that will help in the fight with the fungi. They comprise nowadays a vast armamentarium to assure farmers of the means to protect food from fungi so that people may have it to eat.

These compounds also were the end of a long and toilsome road.

We have mentioned Dr. Lindley and his misconception of the role of the fungus in producing the rot of the Irish potato in the famine year, 1844. In the very same year, an amateur plant pathologist, Judge Cheever of the Court in New York City, came mighty close to providing the Irish with an answer to their blight problem. Judge Cheever had read some of the agricultural literature and remembered that a Frenchman, Prevost, had killed the fungus of wheat smut with copper sulfate and thus had been able to control the disease. Prevost worked in 1807, almost 40 years ahead of the Irish famine. The control of wheat smut by treating the seed with copper sulfate to kill the fungus had become almost standard practice by the time of the famine in 1844.

Judge Cheever, knowing this control of the wheat smut, had suggested that copper sulfate be applied to the potato plant for the control of blight. As far as I can find, there is no record that Judge Cheever ever tried this experimentally, but I suspect that he did try it and it failed, because the copper sulfate burned up his plants just as badly as the blight and was, therefore, not practical. Copper sulfate does not burn wheat seed for numerous technical reasons, but it does burn foliage and therefore could have been of no use in the control of potato blight.

The same year a Belgian amateur named Morren actually did put together a safe mixture of copper sulfate. He mixed copper sulfate with lime and table salt and applied it for the control of potato blight. The only trouble with Morren's method was that he poured the mixture on the ground where the fungus was not and he did not pour it on the foliage where it was. Morren missed the significance of the fungus on the leaf. He thought that the disease came from a miasma arising from wet soil. Hence, he poured his mixture on the ground where it was worthless, rather than on the foilage where it would have solved the Irish famine.

In 1882, almost 40 years after the Irish famine, Morren's mixture, minus the salt, was rediscovered in the province of Bordeaux in France by Professor Millardet. Thus was born Bordeaux mixture, the most famous fungicide of all time. If Judge Cheever, who recognized the fungus, had used the lime with his copper, or if Morren who used the lime, had recognized the fungus, we would probably have fewer Irish policemen in Boston today than we do.

QUESTIONS

1. Discuss the nature and importance of wheat rust to man.
2. Explain the nature and effects of St. Anthony's Fire. Is it known today?
3. Trace the history and consequences of late blight of potatoes.
4. Who produced experimentally the first plant disease and what time relationship did this work have to that of L. Pasteur?

E. C. Stakman

The Role of Plant Pathology in the Scientific and Social Development of the World

Reprinted with the permission of the author and publisher from The A.I.B.S. Bulletin 8(5):15–18, 1958.

"The history of man is the record of a hungry creature in search of food." Thus wrote van Loon in *The Story of Mankind*. The statement may shock some people but it will not even surprise biologists, who are concerned with problems of life and what sustains it and of death and what causes it. They are more likely to be shocked by the general lack of comprehension of the basic truth in the statement. Primitive man must have led a precarious existence, both because of the uncertainty of food supplies and the uncertainty of continued existence in the face of violence and disease. The fundamentally biological nature of many of man's problems is too often overlooked; much history is indeed a record of man's attempt to assure his food supplies.

Man had to become at least a practical biologist in order to develop a civilization; and he has had to become a continually better biologist in order to preserve it. His most basic problems still are biological; human subsistence, human health, and human relations.

One of man's greatest mysteries is man himself. Being alive, he is concerned with life; knowing he must die, he is concerned with death. Even primitive men wanted to live; they wanted so much to continue to live that they believed in life after death. Nearly all men want to live long and they want to live comfortably; and some have faith that biology may enable them to realize their hope, even though they may not realize exactly what biology is.

Biology could be defined as the most important science in the world. Even the more ardent biologists, however, probably would insist that this is not a definition but mere statement of fact. And they would be right. In a world that is still populated largely by human beings, who are anthropocentric enough to be interested in themselves, in their persistence, and in their civilization, biology is a most important science.

In an age of mechanization there is a tendency to forget that machines do not make the food contained in cartons, cans, kegs and bottles—unless they make it more expensive. Only a catastrophic food shortage can shock many people into the realization that food production is a biological process carried on by plants and animals under the supervision of practical biologists, commonly known as farmers.

In countries which, like the United States, produce market surpluses of food-stuffs, it may be difficult to realize that about three-fourths of the people in the world are now hungry and that the population threatens to double within the next 40 years. Dare we be smugly unconcerned about the problems of feeding more than 5 billion people in 1998, when we cannot adequately feed half that number now? Surely we are not obtuse enough to think that we will be immune from the dangerous consequences of world over-population, even if we ourselves are not over-populated.

Biology is the hope of the world. It is the science that shows how better to sustain life and how to save it, how to produce food and how to protect against disease. But are lives to be saved from disease only to perish from hunger? It would be inhuman not to control diseases; we preach the doctrine of the sanctity of human life, and must live it. Society begged, and still is begging, medical science to make life long and painless. But is society really conscious of the enormous hunger pain in the world and of the scientific effort required to alleviate it? Must we ignore population explosions while preoccupied with other types of explosions?

Like Bacon, many biologists ask "Is truth barren? Shall we not thereby be able to produce worthy effects, and to endow the life of man with infinite commodities?" Bacon pitted knowledge and invention against ignorance, hunger and poverty. In his *New Atlantis* he not only recognized scientists and technologists as special social assets, but he put them in charge of social affairs; he had them run the government so well that there was little need for government. There were no politicians, and the scientist governors were engaged in studying and controlling nature rather than in ruling men. Biologists were improving plants and animals that man might be better fed; they were improving medical science that men might longer enjoy their better food. Psychologists and sociologists were studying man that men might be better behaved.

The *New Atlantis*, thanks to biologists and other scientists, subsisted its own people, did not war for foreign markets, but sent "Merchants of Light" to the far corners of the earth to garner wisdom and bring it back to

Solomon's House, the parliamentary body in which intelligence, not politics, reigned supreme. This was indeed Utopia, conceived three and a half centuries ago. Have we inched toward it or have we strayed afar? Do we need philosophers from Solomon's House to tell us that we cannot embellish life if we cannot sustain it? Was the idea of the *New Atlantis* so good that it was good for nothing? Or did some scientists read, "Men ought to know that in the theatre of human life it is only for gods and angels to be spectators," and profit thereby?

Conspicuous among the biologists who realized that they were neither gods nor angels were the plant pathologists. As they were not even angelic, they went to work on earthly problems; they went into the fields and the market places and tried to earn their keep by killing noxious plants in order that useful plants might live. And so it is time to tell plant pathologists what wonderful people they are.

Plant pathology has a rich and varied history and a potentially brilliant future. The principal reason for going backward into history is to see more clearly what is ahead. But how far back do we need to go; when did plant pathology become a science? To adduce documentary evidence that plant diseases were destructive throughout the ages of recorded history is easy. It is harder, however, to evaluate their rôle in scientific and social development, because much of the evidence is purely circumstantial.

Among Jehovah's terrible curses for disobedience were blasting and mildew; locusts and caterpillars; the botch of Egypt, scab, and itch; and blindness and madness. Solomon prayed for deliverance from "blasting, or mildew, locusts, or caterpillars." Amos and Haggai both stated that God actually had punished with blasting and mildew. Although the exact nature of blasting and mildew is not known, whether due to bad weather or bad pathogens, they obviously imply serious deviation from the normal, and can therefore be considered diseases. When plant diseases were among the severe penalties for wrongdoing, they must have been widely known and feared. They, therefore, made at least some contributions to the development of the moral code of ancient Israel.

"Stern Robigo, spare the herbage of the cereals; withhold, we pray, thy roughening hand . . ." is the beginning of a well-known prayer to Robigus, the special rust god of the Romans. The annual festival of the Robigalia is reputed to have been initiated by King Numa Pompilius, possibly about 700 B.C., and was continued with modifications into the Christian era. In his *Rerum Rusticarum,* probably the best Roman treatise on agriculture, Varro includes Robigus among the twelve councillor-gods who are the special patrons of the husbandman, distinct from "those urban gods, whose images stand around the forum, bedecked with gold, six male and a like number of females. . . ."

In a polytheistic system there is likely to be specialization of function and form among the gods. That the twelve councillor-gods were assigned to agriculture is a tribute to the importance of Roman agriculture; that one of them was assigned full time to a single kind of plant disease is a tribute to the discernment of the Romans. At least they recognized the great importance of diseases and put both the gods and science to work in controlling them.

To Varro and many other Romans science had to be practical; they were a practical people. Even their gods were practical, and they were practical about their gods. Three centuries after Varro, Constantine the Great, in 313 A.D., granted to Christians and all others freedom of worship "in order that whatsoever divinity and celestial power may exist may be propitious to us and to all who live under our government." Thus were all gods nationalized and put into the service of the state together.

That plant diseases continued to vex and puzzle peoples after the fall of Rome is certain, although records are fragmentary and much is left to be conjectured. The so-called Dark Ages were not very articulate about the effect of plant diseases on social development. It seems improbable, however, that diseases declined with the decline of Rome, or that they had a private renaissance when the minds of men again awakened. The foul fiend Flibbertigibbit probably was not a sudden invention, but rather an evolutionary product in the minds of men to whom the cause of misfortunes was so obscure as to force resort to mystical explanation. Shakespeare probably was merely an accurate social reporter when he wrote in King Lear, about 1600,

> This is the foul fiend Flibbertigibbet; he begins at curfew and walks till the first cock; he gives the web and the pin, squints the eye, and makes the hare-lip; mildews the white wheat, and hurts the poor creature of earth.

In many ancient societies the enforcement of public health measures was entrusted to the priestly class; accordingly many peoples were accustomed to this type of regulation. But when positive secular laws were first enacted about plant diseases, they represented a change in mode of thought and considerable social development. Some good thoughts about plant diseases were incorporated into laws long before the nature of disease was really understood.

The first known attempt to control a plant disease by legal measures was made about 300 years ago, when Rouen, France, required the destruction of barberry bushes in order to control stem rust of wheat. Connecticut, Massachusetts, and Rhode Island enacted barberry eradication laws, some very strict, between 1726 and 1766; and shortly after 1800 several German states took similar action.

The pioneer barberry-eradication laws represent a triumph of common sense over intellectual orthodoxy and authoritarianism. Practical agriculturists were concerned about rust because it menaced their daily bread, and it was their common experience that the menace was greatest near barberry bushes. Many scientists, however, maintained that it was not true, because they could not understand how it could be true. The farmers who lived with wheat did not know why barberry was baneful but they did know how baneful the barberry was. And so, unencumbered by preconceptions, they passed laws to eradicate the bane. How simple, and how significant!

Thus was born the concept of public health for plants. But not without pain. For the first law was enacted a hundred years before Fontana and Targioni announced their conviction that rust was a minute parasitic plant, disseminated by invisible seeds, and two hundred years before the Tulasnes showed that fungi could be pleomorphic and DeBary proved that stem rust was heteroecious. During two centuries, then, mandatory laws were passed about something that was known but not understood.

Wheat rust was a pioneer in impelling society to organize measures to help safeguard its food supplies by laws. The laws stimulated experimentation and research, which finally justified the pragmatic actions of society and helped revolutionize man's outlook. But rust was not the only social reformer. It must share honors, and dishonors with the potato murrain.

"Famine forces Peel's hand" is a chapter heading in McCarthy's *History of our Own Times*. Sir Robert Peel was Prime Minister of England when the terrible murrain devastated the potato fields of Ireland and destroyed the country's food. The epidemic itself is important in the history of plant pathology, for it intensified efforts to find out what caused the blight. But its social consequences loom large in the recent history of Britain and far beyond. Wheat rust had impelled legislation against an accessory to the disease, but the potato blight was a decisive accessory to legislation for social reform. It helped put an end to the protective tariff on imported grain, the so-called cruel Corn Laws.

News came from Ireland in the autumn of 1845, that potato blight threatened to destroy "the food of a people." The Relief Committee of Dublin demanded that the ports be opened to free entry of grain and denounced the Ministry for its inaction. The Anti-Corn-Law League also was clamoring for the removal of restrictions on the importation of grain. And still the Conservative Cabinet did nothing, except appoint an anti-famine commission. But Lord John Russell, leader of the opposition Whigs, wrote to some of his constituents that "Indecision and procrastination may produce a state of suffering which it is frightful to contemplate. . . ." Potato blight had converted him to the principles of the League. This forced Peel's ministry to introduce a bill for the virtual abolition of the laws, and, after various vicissitudes, it was enacted into law in the summer of 1846. Britain was on the way to free trade.

Thus did a plant disease force reforms which may otherwise have been long delayed; the potato famine was too tragic for politicians to ignore. Whatever the true number of deaths, it is certain that Ireland quickly lost two million of her eight million people, from starvation, consequent disease, and emigration.

Plant diseases have indeed played an important role in the social development of the world. Their greatest single contribution, of course, was the science of plant pathology itself. Society sired the science because it wanted help, and the science is doing its filial duty by helping with the chores and with the education of its sire. Exactly when plant pathology was born is a moot question; why it was born is no question at all. It was born of necessity.

For better or for worse, plant pathology had its genesis in fields and granaries more than in halls of ivy. Society needed agriculture and agriculture needed plant pathology. Of course plant disease excited curiosity, but the curiosity was more excited because the diseases struck in vital spots, the breadbaskets and the fields that filled them. It was essential to social progress that the baskets be filled, and men of scientific bent tried to fill them.

Not until the microscope was invented could there be a science of plant pathology based on understanding. Micro-organisms had been postulated long before but they could not be proved. Even the practical Varro stated as simple fact that minute invisible creatures were bred in swamps, were carried by the wind, and, when inhaled, caused serious diseases of humans. One can only speculate about what Varro might have discovered with the microscope.

The microscope, from about 1590 onward, was ready to reveal an entirely new world to those who would look for it. Not until a century and a half had passed, however, was it used systematically to elucidate the nature of plant diseases, for most botanists were preoccupied with other problems. The basis for a real revolution in concepts about disease was laid by three brilliant men in the second half of the 18th century: M. Tillet, Felice Fontana, and Giovanni Targioni Tozzetti.

Brilliant pioneers though they were, these men were not the fathers of plant pathology, but they deserve almost more credit for having been its grandfathers. It was they who started the revolution that eventually modernized plant pathology. They substituted systematic observations and experimentation on diseases for scholastic argumentation about them. One small but important fact, however, eluded them.

By epoch-making experimentation Tillet proved conclusively that bunt of wheat was contagious, and he demonstrated that the smut dust, the spores, carried the contagion, but the nature of the contagion which they carried defied his understanding. Both Fontana and Targioni said categorically that wheat rust was caused by a microscopic parasitic plant, but they did not demonstrate it; they inferred it. They could not quite get the idea, sharply perceptive though they were, that the spores which they observed so carefully and described so accurately were the reproductive bodies of the rust plant instead of the rust plant itself.

There was just one more little hill to climb, and they did not quite get over the top. But they did succeed in changing man's way of looking at things, and that is one of man's greatest accomplishments, if the new look is better than the old. In this case it was. Targioni's comprehension was truly remarkable; and it would have been completely amazing if only he could have comprehended the true nature of spores instead of postulating that they produced myriads of invisible infectious particles.

What is the contagion in smut and how is rust contagious? These were the questions provoked by the work of the great triumvirate. Prévost answered the first part of the question in 1807, after years of experimentation and study. The component particles of the smut dust were the contagion, not merely the carriers of it; Prévost proved that they were the propagative bodies of the microscopic plant that causes the disease.

Prévost undertook to find a remedy for bunt or stinking smut of wheat, a vulgar subject and an unworthy object in the eyes of many of the purer scientists of that time. The methods used for controlling bunt were not effective, so Prévost set out to find a better one. He succeeded, and there is a tablet to his memory in Montauban, France, honoring him for it. But that is not honor enough. For his experimentation with preventatives drove him to more basic research on the nature of what he was trying to prevent. He found the preventive in copper sulphate and demonstrated that it prevented the development of a microscopic parasitic fungus. In commenting on the fact that Tessier regarded fogs as the cause of rust—a widely prevalent view—Prévost asserts that it is now proved that they are no more the cause of rust than of bunt, for "How could fogs be the cause of a plant?" Which was a very pertinent question.

Was not Bénédict Prévost the pioneer in establishing the germ theory of disease? He clearly demonstrated that a microfungus caused a plant disease, thus establishing the principle of pathogenesis.

As a science, plant pathology is scarcely a hundred years old. It now comprises not only a coherent pattern of activities but also a reasonably cohesive group of scientists. The early plant pathologists emerged largely from botany and gradually coalesced into groups with a core of common purpose. A pioneer concrescence, of the massive type, was the American Phytopathological Society.

The American Phytopathological

Society has not only witnessed much scientific history but has helped to make it. Like plant pathology itself, the Society was born of need. Grave problems required solution, and although the dollar sign was on many of them, the dollar was only a symbol of a surer and better life. The pioneers had but few dollars for their work, so they borrowed "e pluribus unum" from the dollar to help their dollars do more work. The demands on plant pathology have become so varied and diverse that manifold intellectual attainments and diverse skills are required to meet them. But there is a unity . . . in the purpose to solve practical problems and to contribute to human enlightenment. The American Phytopathological Society, model of efficiency in democracy, is a powerful synergistic system in furthering that purpose.

Plant pathology has helped reveal profound and useful truths. It was among the pioneers in revealing the vast and variable world of micro-organisms and in identifying man's friends and foes amongst them. It has rendered similar services in the vastly significant field of virology, with its ramifications and applications to plants, animals, and humans. And it has helped elucidate the role of chemical micro-elements in the health and diseases of plants. It has not only helped man solve many of his most basic problems, but it has helped illuminate his intellect and expand his intellectual horizons; it has helped man to comprehend infinity in minuteness as he had begun to comprehend infinite magnitude. Plant pathology has helped to satisfy man's hunger for good and his thirst for knowledge. And is not that reason for pride? May there ever be reason for more and greater pride!

QUESTIONS

1. Why should anyone worry about the fact that plants can become sick?
2. What connection is there between overpopulation of people in the world and the work of the plant pathologists?
3. Are plant diseases of ancient origin or are they the result of soil depletion and the use of chemical fertilizers as some "organic gardeners" claim? Explain.
4. What possible connection could there be between wheat rust and the barberry?
5. What plant disease was so severe that a political upheaval resulted? Explain.

as related by A. F. Blakeslee

Male and Female Bread Moulds

Reprinted with the permission of the author and publisher from Vol. 11, No. 6, News Service Bulletin, Carnegie Institute of Washington, 1930.

Sex is a vital phenomenon, almost universal among organisms. The attempt, through study of higher organisms, to learn what the fundamental difference is between the sexes is complicated by differences in structure. In the moulds, however, the problem can be approached favorably because there are no structural differences apparent between male and female plants to confuse the results. In fact, they cannot be distinguished except by their sexual reactions.

Indeed, not until this investigation was undertaken, did we learn what the conditions are under which sexual spores (zygospores) in moulds develop. It had been observed that such spores appeared in fungus plates at times but at other times, apparently under like conditions, the moulds failed to produce them. It could be demonstrated that the cultures which produced the zygospores are not single fungus plants but consist of two breeds or strains, in which the filaments from each grow together and fuse. For purposes of identification, these can be called plus and minus strains.

NATURE OF FUNGI

The moulds belong to that great group of plants, the fungi, which have no chlorophyll, the green coloring matter, which, in combination with sunshine, enables many plants to manufacture their food.

Having no chlorophyll, the fungi cannot make the carbohydrate food which they need, the sugars, starches, celluloses, as do green plants, from the water of the soil and the carbon dioxide of the air. They must obtain their food from food already made so they are dependent plants and live either on dead organic matter or on living organisms.

It is possible for them to secure their food materials in this manner because they have the power of secreting ferments capable of decomposing the sugars, the starches, the fats, and the other complex substances formed by animals and by chlorophyll-bearing plants. In so doing they play a vital role in the economy of nature for, through the process of decay, for which they are responsible, the chemical elements out of which the green plants make their foods are returned to soil and air for recurrent use in the never ending cycle.

Numbered among the more familiar kinds of fungi are yeasts, moulds, mildews, blights, rusts, and mushrooms.

THE BREAD MOULDS

The investigations conducted by Miss Satina and myself were made upon that group of the fungi commonly called Bread Moulds and known in science as Mucors. The structure of the plants of this group is simple. Each consists of a branching, thread-like growth devoid of separate cells. In many species of mould the threads grow to a length of from two to four inches, in some, however, they attain a length of from fifteen to eighteen inches.

At the free end of the thread-like filaments, spherical swellings form, about the size of a pin head. These contain enormous numbers of minute, non-sexual, reproductive bodies called spores. At room temperature, when the air is sufficiently moist, a spore germinates readily and grows rapidly on any substance which contains proper nutrition. Soon a thread-like mass develops which, in turn, produces a crop of spore cases.

As the cycle from spore to spore requires but from one to five days and as each spore case contains a multitude of spores, the spread of the plant, under favorable conditions, may be extraordinarily rapid. Indeed, calculations have shown that in some species one spore case may contain 70,000 spores and that each culture which develops as it does from a single spore may form hundreds of spore cases.

FORMATION OF SEXUAL SPORES

Although the Mucors are all able to multiply rapidly, perhaps indefinitely, by means of non-sexual spores, the great majority of these moulds also produce sexual spores, an outcome made possible only when plants of the opposite sexes are brought together. The process of the formation of sexual spores (zygospores) can be described as follows: two filaments from plants of the two opposite sexes, provisionally designated as plus and minus sexes, grow toward each other and their ends touch. After contact, food materials flow into these ends producing swellings. Cross-walls are now laid down cutting off the two ends so that the young zygospores, at this stage have at least three walls across them. Then the intervening double wall breaks down thereby bringing the contents of the two sex cells into contact. The fusion cell thus formed develops into a mature, thick-walled zygospore around which forms a brown, protective coat with irregular markings.

IDENTIFYING SEX OF MOULDS

Male and female plants of the Bread Moulds cannot be distinguished by their appearance or structure, neither does the structure nor function of their sexual cells appear to differ so far as the formation of the sexual spore is concerned. It is therefore not possible to tell by inspection which of the mould plants is male and which is female.

A very effective method is employed for identifying the sex of unknown races and species. Two Bread Moulds, originally designated as plus and minus strains forty-one years ago, are used as testers.

For example, if a culture of an unknown race forms zygospores when it is brought into contact with the plus tester, then it is clear that it is a mould of the opposite or minus sex. If, on the other hand, sexual spores develop only in the presence of the minus tester,

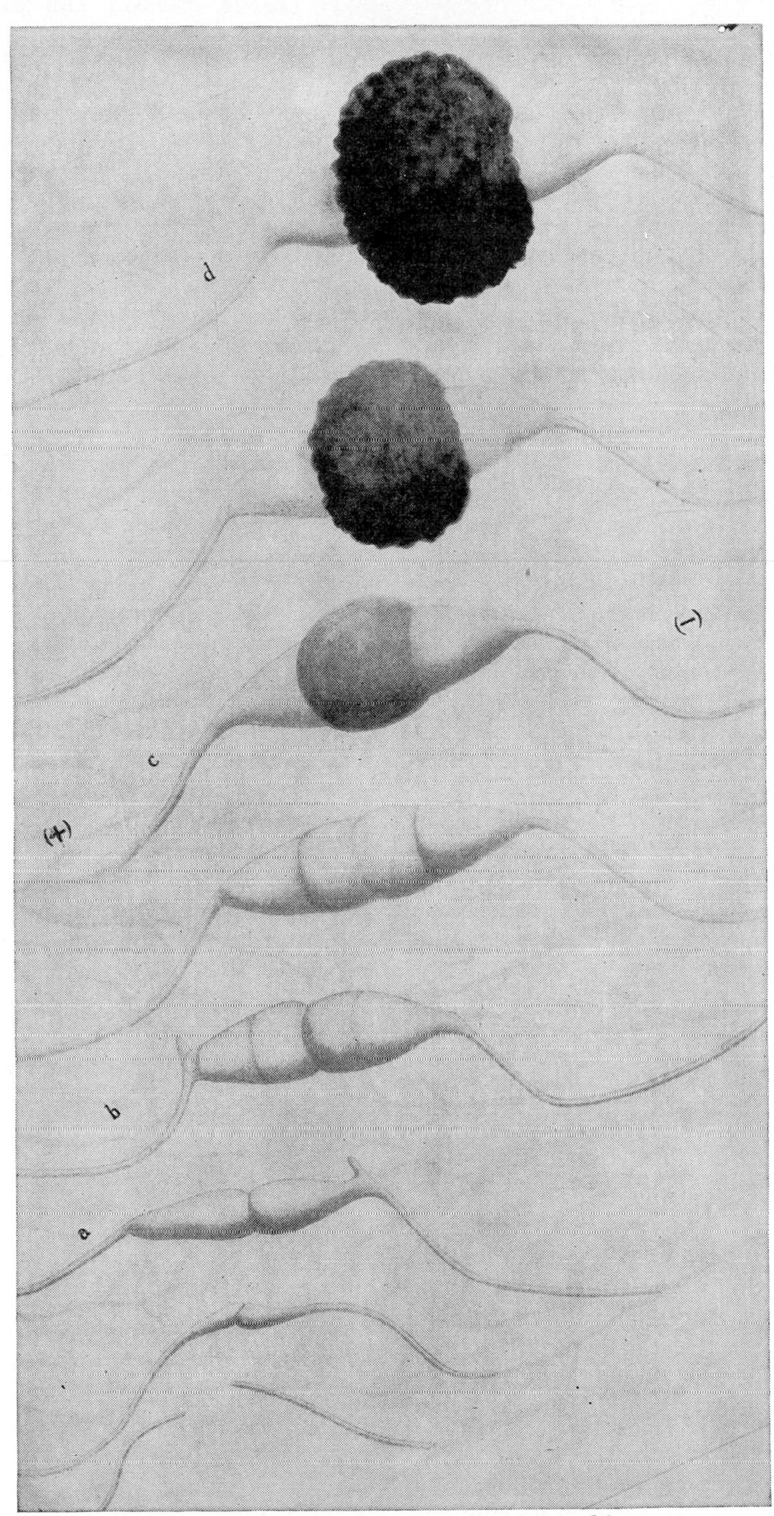

Sexual Reproduction in a Bread Mould.

then the race in question belongs to the other or plus sex.

It is also possible, in a similar way, to identify the sex of species other than that to which the two plus and minus testers belong.

A race, the sex of which is to be determined, is brought into contact with the plus and minus testers, as before. If it belongs to the plus sex the beginnings of sexual reactions will be observed at the point where the undetermined race come into contact with those of the minus tester.

Threads of opposite sex meet and produce swellings which enlarge and sometimes form sexual cells, but the sexual cells never fuse as they do when the opposite sexes belong to the same species and consequently no fully matured sexual spores will be formed. The sexual reaction, although begun, is not carried to completion.

BIOCHEMICAL TESTS FOR SEX

Although it is impossible to distinguish the plus and minus moulds from appearance, a distinct difference between opposite sexes can be shown when they are subjected to certain chemical tests.

If part of the oxygen in a solution of potassium permanganate be removed (reduced), the purple color of the solution changes to pink-yellow or it may become decolorized. Various substances added to the purple solution will bring about these changes in color through their effect as a reducing agent of oxygen. Many tests with extracts prepared from the thread-like masses of plus and minus races of moulds have shown that in the majority of cases the extracts of the plus races produce a greater change in color of the potassium permanganate than the extracts of the minus races. The plus races are also stronger reducers than the minus races.

In the amount of sugar which can be extracted from the plus and minus races, lies another distinct biochemical difference between the two races. Careful tests repeated many times indicate that the plus races contain a higher average sugar content than do the minus races.

This study of sex in moulds is a fundamental study in establishing a chemical basis for sex differences in what appears to be structurally identical strains of Mucors.

QUESTIONS

1. Mention the two main reproductive methods by which bread molds reproduce.
2. Describe sexual reproduction in bread molds.
3. Is there any way by means of which the plus and minus strains can be told apart?

Eugene W. Nelson

Vegetable Jewels at Work

Reprinted with the permission of the publisher from Nature Magazine 40(3):121–124, 1947.

About two hundred and fifty years ago a queer fellow dwelt in the city of Delft, Holland. His name was Antony van Leeuwenhoek. He had absolutely no scientific training. In fact, he seems to have been some sort of small business man, although he had a considerable fortune to fall back on in hard times. Another asset he had was an intense interest in the then little-known instrument, the microscope. He even taught himself how to make fine lenses, and how to assemble his lenses into primitive microscopes. He made nearly two hundred and fifty such instruments during his long life, and, simple as they were, they were better than any others of that period.

Once, van Leeuwenhoek looked at a drop of what he thought was "clear" water. He was astounded to find a number of "wretched beasties"—as he called them—swimming about in the liquid. One of these animals, as we can tell by his further written description of it, was actually a tiny and exquisitely formed plant. Later-day scientists were to call this a "diatom," and discover its vital place in Nature.

Since that time, many facts concerning the nature, life, and uses of the diatom have been established. Great progress has also been made by industrial research workers in putting the dead remains of these microscopic bits of life to work for us. Although the diatom plays a remarkably interesting and important role during its short lifetime, this delicate plant has a record as a hard worker that is scarcely surpassed by any other form of vegetable or animal life in the entire world.

A diatom is a single-celled plant. It is familiar to everyone who has ever been exposed to high school botany. To make out all the minute details of a diatom's structure requires a microscope of fairly high resolving power. In fact, diatoms are so tiny that the number of them necessary to fill the space of only one cubic inch is counted in the billions.

These tiny plants produce a liquid composed of pure silica. The liquid hardens and forms a protective coating all around each of the individual plants. The covering takes the form of a crystalline, glasslike box—for glass itself is composed mainly of sand, and sand, in turn, is silica. The diatom's box is in two separate parts. One part laps snugly over the other half like two sections of a pill box. The two halves of a diatom covering are fastened together with a sort of elastic belt that allows the plant to grow during its lifetime.

The shell covering is so thin and strong that the diatom can float about in water. Since this glassy covering will not permit any water to seep through to the plant growing inside, the box-like shell is pierced by minute pores that enable the diatom to absorb both food and water. The diatom stores up its food—*not* as starch or sugar, as other plants do, but in the form of drops of oil. Numerous scientists have come to the conclusion that we owe many of our petroleum deposits to the industry of the hard-working diatoms.

The shells that encase the diatoms are ridged and molded in an infinite variety of ways, giving strength to the structure. The designs of the transparent structures are so beautiful, when seen under a microscope, that enthusiastic diatom students have called these forms of life "Jewels of the Vegetable Kingdom." Experts have classified more than 10,000 different varieties of diatoms—each individual variety differing from all others in size, shape, and shell design.

When a diatom dies, its shell—which is practically indestructible—drops to the bottom of the body of water wherein the plant has spent its life. It joins the countless billions of diatom shells already there. In time, this process builds up a considerable deposit of the tiny shells. The deposits of diatoms, called diatomaceous silica or earth, as it is mined today, are one of man's heritages from the Miocene age. Nature was occupied for many millions of years in accumulating the deposits.

The numerous lakes formed during the Miocene age, as well as the sea waters of that time, appear to have contained a greater-than-normal amount of silica in solution, probably as a result of volcanic activity. So it was that the diatoms flourished and multiplied as never before, or since. To this condition, then, we owe the vast deposits of diatomaceous earth that we have today. All except minute traces of other substances have disappeared, and the present material is practically pure silica, shapeless in nature rather than crystalline.

Today men take "white gold" from the diatomaceous deposits. In Nevada there is an entire mountain of diatomaceous earth, locally known as "Toothpowder Mountain." Many million pounds of the material have been removed, with little apparent decrease in the bulk of the mountain. Another deposit in California occupies an area of five square miles and extends downwards for more than fourteen hundred feet.

The crude diatomaceous earth is removed from the deposits by quarrying, or, as it is frequently termed, "open pit mining." Varying thicknesses of "overburden," of course, must first be removed in order to reach the pure material.

Much of the diatomaceous earth used today is quarried with power shovels. Since the uses of the material depend a great deal on the preservation of its original structure, however, hand quarrying is also used where extra careful handling and selection of material are required.

Little commercial use was made of this shell-earth until 1870. Then it was that Alfred Nobel, of Nobel Prize fame, made dynamite by soaking sticks of diatomaceous earth in nitro-glycerine. This one invention would have been enough to make diatoms famous, because dynamite has been responsible for much of the large scale mining, railroad construction, and building in our country during the past sixty or seventy years.

The uses of diatoms are not confined to this one field, however, for modern industrial research engineers have probed deep into their possibilities.

As can be seen from a microscopic view of this tiny vegetable, a single diatom has a very intricate design made up of extremely delicate lines. Microscope workers—biologists, chemists, metallurgists, and others—have found that single diatoms are valuable for testing the quality of expensive, high-powered microscope lenses. A good lense will show the lines on a diatom shell sharply and clearly; a poor lens will cause these lines to blur and appear to run together.

Another use that chemists have found for diatomaceous earth is in the handling of the large glass bottles called "carboys," in which strong acids are shipped. These bottles are packed in crates, surrounded with powdered diatom material. If the glass bottle is broken during shipping, the shell-earth, which is very absorbent, will soak and hold all the acid, thereby preventing the spilled liquid from doing any damage.

If you have the opportunity to examine a diatom under a good microscope, you will notice that the shells all have a file-like surface. This fact gave researchers another idea. If you want to remove rust from iron, you can use either a file or sandpaper. But when expensive silverware and silver plate become tarnished, it must be polished so that the tarnish and stains will be removed, but the silver itself will not be marred. So in most kitchens today there is a jar "full of diatoms"—actually, silver polish made from diatomaceous paste.

In modern sugar refineries, a little diatom earth is added to the sugar syrup. When *this* solution is put through the filter, the microscopic diatoms pile up on the cloth, and the fine shells catch and hold the dirt. As more of the sugar syrup is poured in, more shells fall to the bottom, and so on during the entire process. There is no hard cake of dirt forming against the cloth to slow up the filtering.

Diatoms added to paint make it last longer. The ridges of the shells lock together as the paint dries, forming a hard, thin film that will neither crack nor peel. Added to dry cement powder, diatoms have much the same effect, making the finished concrete materially harder and stronger.

When shell-earth is mixed with fine asbestos fibers, the resulting material forms an excellent insulating material for modern homes. Stuffed between the walls of a house, the material keeps the interior cool in summer and warm in winter, cutting down street noises.

Still another important war-time use of diatoms, requiring many hundreds of tons of material, was as a "flatting" agent in camouflage paints, enamels, and lacquers, as well as in flat finishes used on all kinds of military equipment. A flat finish, incidentally, is one that has little or no gloss. A flat finish is desirable because it does not reflect light and so betray positions to the enemy. Camouflage paints were used in tremendous quantities.

The uses to which diatoms are now being put run literally into the hundreds. They pop up in all sorts of unexpected places. They are used in making soaps and cosmetics; in the manufacture of ink; as "filler" materials; to improve the quality of paper, and in many other ways.

Thus has the trained, disciplined imagination of the industrial engineer taken advantage of the peculiar properties and structure of the diatom. Forty years ago, people knew little about this particular form of life. They were useful mainly in biology classes as something interesting to study with a microscope. Today, these tiny, fragile shells form the foundation of many thriving and important industries.

QUESTIONS

1. Name two accomplishments of Leeuwenhoek.
2. What is a diatom? Describe its structure and life history.
3. What name is applied to fossil diatoms?
4. List 9 uses to which diatoms are put.

H. W. Youngken, Jr.

Botany and Medicine

Reprinted with the permission of the author and publishers from the American Journal of Botany **43**:862–869, 1956.

Obviously, man's first interest in plant life dates back to earliest time when, in order to survive, he soon recognized a need to become familiar with the plants of his environment and to engage in food crop development. This was long before botany took form as a science. Concomitantly with the earliest need of plants for food there was a keen awareness of the values of many forms of plant life as sources for medicines. Admittedly, the use of plants in early medicine was often cloaked in mystery and physician-botanists, of which there were many, were frequently better psychologists, philosophers or in many cases tribal witch doctors, than medical scientists. Nevertheless the influence of a botanical interest in medicine, or medicine in botany as one might also look at it, was stimulated early and long before both sciences became formalized as we know them today.

Before dealing with some of the modern concepts of botano-medico relationships it is perhaps pertinent that several of the highlights of early materia medica which played an important part in the development of botany as a science be reviewed. In the pages that follow it will be seen that even today much of the influence of botany on modern medicine comes from an interest in certain plants which yield therapeutically useful constituents. The fact is that many of these plants were described as useful crude drugs in the materia medicas of ancient time.

Undoubtedly the early descriptive materia medica and botany texts of Greek and Roman physician-botanists such as Theophrastus (often called the Father of Botany), Dioscorides, Pliny the Elder and Pliny the Younger, Galen and others had much to do with the beginnings of scientific botany. On the other hand the botany of the first centuries A.D. could hardly be called a science.

Students of medical and pharmacy history are well aware of the great influence played on medical practice since 77 A.D. by the famous "De Materia Medica" of Dioscorides, the Greek physician-botanist. In fact, the descriptions of Dioscorides were often extensively copied in the herbals and medical botanics which followed soon after the event of printing in the early 16th century. As the years of the Renaissance passed, writers of herbals began to show more originality and imagination.

Although at first drawing heavily upon much of the style of Dioscorides during which the medical virtues of various plants were extolled, more descriptive imagination characterized the early German, Italian and British herbals. Folklore and empiricism were, indeed, the only bases upon which these early botano-medico compendia were written. Nevertheless, beginning with the herbals of the German "Fathers of Botany," for example in the works of Otto Brunfels, "Herbarium Vivae Icones" and "Simplicium Pharmacorum" (1542) and Hieronymus Bock, "De Stirpium" (1552), a greater botanical interest was aroused in medicinal plants. Undoubtedly the German herbals had much influence on others which soon followed in the 16th, 17th and 18th centuries. William Turner's "Herbal," corrected and enlarged to include three parts, was published in 1568. John Gerarde published his famous "The Herbal, or General History of Plants" in 1597 and a parade of famous descriptive histories, plantarum, flora and/or catalogues of various kinds of plants became available from then on.

Fortunately plant taxonomy as a science did not remain long bound by the methods of classification so artificially employed in the botanical works of the 16th and 17th centuries. A keener awareness of plant morphology was obviously stimulated to some degree by the use of plants for medical purposes, as it was also stimulated by the knowledge of the plants of the time. The result of a greater interest in plant morphology which was generated to some extent by the early herbals and the direct influence of comparative natural history and phylogeny which soon became dominant, pointed to an urgent need for systematic plant classification according to more scientific relationships. These relationships were at first largely structural ones based upon comparative plant anatomy. Later, in the early 19th century during the Darwinian period, they became intensified to include more phylogenetic relationships. Indeed, the beginning of this new interest in comparative structural and phylogenetic relationships was reflected early in the writings of Nehemiah Grew, "An Idea of a Phytological History" (1673) and "Anatomy of Plants, with an idea of a philosophical History of Plants" (1682). Soon after, in the 18th century, came also the great works of Linnaeus and Jussieu which established many of the fundamentals of plant taxonomy as this phase of botany is known today.

It was probably at this period when botany as a science shook off much of the medical influence which had dominated many of the 16th and 17th century writings. On the other hand, botany continued to be a major subject of medical school teaching until well into the 20th century. Apart from the general biological or natural science value of botany in medical education, the applied aspects of medical botany such as medicinal plant exploration, identification and crude drug studies gradually were taken over by faculties of pharmacy.

Great advances were made during the late 19th and early 20th centuries in standardizing the descriptive nomenclature of botanical drugs. Pharmacognosy, that area of pharmacy which deals with natural products as pharmaceuticals, had been established as a science by a German medical student at Halle in 1815. For more than 100 years this pharmaceutical science in which plant drugs are extensively studied, has been responsible for carrying on medical aspects of botany, particularly those aspects that are important in drug standardization, drug plant exploration, and medicinal plant chemistry. Using the conventional methods of the anatomist, pharmacognosists soon began amassing extensive histological descriptions of almost every medicinal plant used by mankind. Many of these became reference descriptions for standard materia medica and pharmacopeia compendia. So intensive was this type of research in pharmacognosy between 1900 and 1940 that much less effort was devoted by the pharmacognosist to plant chemistry and physiology. The science unfortunately soon became a predominately descriptive science of crude botanical drugs. It has only been during the past decade that this trend has been somewhat changed whereby greater interest has been shown by several experimental pharmacognosists in plant chemistry, biochemistry and physiology. Botanical drugs reached a peak in the numbers that were employed in medicine and pharmacy at the turn of the 20th century. At that time the major contents of pharmacopeias and formularies of many nations, including the "United States Pharmacopeia," the "British Pharmacopeia," "British Codex" and "National Formulary" of the American Pharmaceutical Association were the descriptive standards of crude plant drugs and some of their medicinally valuable constituents.

Beginning with the time of Wohler, the distinguished German chemist, early in the 19th century and with the advance in medical pharmacology, which began almost one hundred years later under the stimulus of John Jacob Abel, much of the empiricism that had been formerly applied to the drug action of plants as medicines had given way to rationalism. Today drugs from plants which are to be used in the treatment of disease must have had tried and trusted chemical, pharmacological and clinical scrutiny. How much more exacting it is for a chemist and pharmacologist to demonstrate the properties of a pure and single crystalline compound, regardless of its source. Therefore the use of a great number of plant drugs per se in medicine has significantly decreased. On the other hand the "pharmacotherapeutics" of several purified plant constituents (digitoxin, cocaine, quinine, caffeine, morphine, codeine, reserpine, ergotamine, etc.) has remained important to medical science.

The age of "pharmacotherapeutics" which means the study of the uses of drugs in the treatment of disease has followed the "pure compound line." It is based, wherever possible, upon a correlation of pharmacological action with pathological physiology or the microbiological aspects of disease. To a great extent it has been based also upon relationships between chemical structure and pharmacological action, the so-called "molecular structure-activity" relationship. Out of this development has come the age of chemotherapy, the latter stimulated in the late 19th century by the contributions of the German biologist Paul Ehrlich, his "magic bullet" and antisyphilitic arsenicals. The chemotherapeutic age in medicine was given great exploitation in 1935 when the Nobel Prize winner, Domagk, discovered the chemotherapy of prontosil, the forerunner of the synthetic sulfa drugs.

RE-INVESTIGATION OF PLANTS FOR MEDICINE

With a modern advance in synthetic medicinal organic chemistry there has developed recently a very keen interest in the re-investigation of the constituents biosynthesized by plants and animals. Again botany has become a tool of medicine through the need to properly select plants for new drugs. Research in this phase has increased more during the last decade, because of success with the antibiotics and plant drugs such as *Rauwolfia,* than at any time during the previous period of the 20th century. It has also brought medical scientists into closer contact with botanical experts in taxonomy, anatomy, and plant biochemistry. Such investigations have been prompted by three general interests: 1. the search for plant constituents responsible for a biological activity; 2. the search for newer therapeutically active chemical derivatives of natural compounds; and 3. the investigation of the biochemical and physiological role played by plant and animal constituents in the organisms producing them. The discussion that follows will deal with the first two of these interests.

1. The search for plant constituents.—*Antibiotics.*—It has been stated that the most recent stimulus leading to the investigation of plants for biologically active compounds began about two decades ago in the early nineteen-thirties. It may be recalled that this was the period when Flemming, Florey and Chain described the antibiotic properties of extracts from the blue-green mold *Penicillium.* From these observations came the antibiotic, crystalline penicillin. But lest we become too smug in our beliefs, it must be noted that molds were employed for similar purposes by the Chinese thousands of years ago. And several hundred years ago North American Indians are known to have employed both soil and rotting wood for the prevention of wound infections and for healing festered cuts. Nevertheless, the penicillin discovery was the forerunner of the modern antibiotic age and it undoubtedly set the stage for a tremendous interest in the *re*-investigation of lower and higher plants for new biologically active constituents. At least two hundred antibiotics have been discovered in living organisms since 1929. Yet, thus far only about a dozen therapeutically useful antibiotic compounds have been successfully isolated from molds, bacteria, and soil actinomycetes, all lower plants. Most of these have been procured since 1939 when Dubos isolated tyrothricin from the filtrates of cultures of *Bacillus brevis;* streptomycin was discovered from cultures of an actinomycete in 1944, bacitracin in 1945, polymycin and chloromycetin in 1947, aureomycin in 1948, terramycin in 1950, and erythromycin in 1952.

Vasodilators and antihypertensive agents.—Since glyceryl trinitrate was discovered by Sobrero in 1847 and amyl nitrate was introduced to medical practice by Guthrie about ten years later for the treatment of angina pectoris, nitrites and organic nitrates have been, with few exceptions, the outstanding agents in the treatment of angina and arterial hypertension. However, an intensive re-investigation of one well known plant drug, *Veratrum viride* or green hellebore and a similar study of two lesser known plant drugs, *Ammi visnaga* (Khella) and *Rauwolfia* species, have resulted in several new and useful pharmaceuticals of the hypotensive class. *Veratrum* and *Rauwolfia* represent botanical crude drugs which have been employed in folklore, domestic and foreign medicine for centuries and for a variety of purposes. The dried roots of *Rauwolfia serpentina*, a small shrub of India, have been used empirically by people of India for a large variety of conditions, such as in the treatment of snake bites, insanity, high blood pressure, and cardiac disease.

The question naturally raised is what differences do *Veratrum*, *Rauwolfia* and Khellin possess with each other and over other well established vasodilators in the treatment of essential hypertension? *Veratrum* and its alkaloids cause widespread reflex vasodilatation including that of cerebral and renal arteries and its effects are more rapid than the other two botanical agents. However, much evidence can be shown that *Veratrum* alkaloids or crude drugs are not significantly effective by the oral route in the majority of ambulatory hypertensive patients and rather high incidences of toxicity have been reported following its use, i.e., vomiting and hiccoughing. Much better results have been reported from the use of the alkaloids via the parenteral route.

Rauwolfia and its alkaloids are much slower in their onset of activity than *Veratrum* and Khellin. On the other hand, as a hypotensive agent *Rauwolfia* reduces arterial blood pressure and slows the heart rate somewhat in the same manner as *Veratrum* by inhibiting centrally mediated cardiovascular reflexes. *Rauwolfia* is efficiently absorbed by the oral route but it possesses a significantly long latent period before activity can be observed. Incidences of toxic effects have been much less than those from *Veratrum* medication but nevertheless some side effects such as nausea, headache, dizziness and diarrhea have been reported following *Rauwolfia* alkaloid medication.

One of the outstanding attributes of *Rauwolfia* and its alkaloids has been its tranquillizing action on the higher centers of the central nervous system. This sedation effect is unlike that of the barbiturates and other hypnotics. It has widespread application in the treatment of schizophrenia and other forms of mental disease, particularly such as cause deep mental depression. In fact, the use of this drug in neural psychopathic conditions has almost superseded its use as an antihypertensive agent. *Rauwolfia* medication has practically replaced frontal lobotomy operations in many mental hospitals in the United States. Its effect in this respect has indeed created significant social problems as far as long term mental patients are concerned.

Khellin, the component of *Ammi visnaga*, has not proven to be the efficient hypotensive agent that was originally attributed to it. It does, however, possess a more direct anti-spasmodic effect on the smooth musculature including the blood vessels than do *Veratrum* or *Rauwolfia*. The action of Khellin as a smooth muscle relaxant has led to its use in bronchial asthma with some success. It is rapidly and efficiently absorbed and found to be widely distributed in the body. Side effects from Khellin medication have been chiefly those of nausea, mental depression, and some insomnia. But its margin of safety has been considered to be rather wide.

Muscle relaxants and anti-spasmod-

ics.—A number of botanicals have in the past been employed for sedative effects in intestinal and stomach cramps and essential or functional dysmenorrhea. Atropine and atropine-like synthetics certainly lead the field of anti-spasmodics today. But the side effects from most of these still limit their applications. Plant drugs such as *Viburnum, Aletris, Helonia,* Blessed thistle, Jamaica dogwood (*Piscidia* spp.), and *Potentilla* (Silverweed) are examples of a few botanicals that have entered into pharmaceutical formulations for anti-spasmodic purposes.

Laboratory investigations which employ tissue tests both in vitro and in living animals do show rather positive muscle sedative effects when highly purified extracts of all of these plants are biologically tested. For example, *Viburnum* and *Potentilla* extracts show about equal activity to that of papaverine in isolated uterine and intestinal muscle strips. Several components of *Potentilla* (Silvery cinquefoil) have been found to have approximately the same results. Petroleum ether extracts of the bark from Jamaica dogwood show even better relaxant activity and give indication of possessing a depressant effect on the nervous system.

Miscellaneous.—A number of other drug plants have recently turned up with rather extraordinary new uses apart from those previously mentioned. For example, the irritating resin of the May apple, *Podophyllum peltatum,* which has long been employed as a cathartic and which years ago was used to destroy venereal warts, has now yielded three very active compounds, called peltatins. These have been found to destroy cancerous tumors in mice and the application of such activity is being investigated in humans.

The juice from the "old" drug *Aloë,* again the source of a well established cathartic, has now been applied in the treatment of atomic radiation burns. Collins and Collins reported similar effects in the treatment of X-ray burns as early as 1935 and Rowe in 1941 showed the curative principles to be present in the rind and pulp of the plant leaves. It is interesting to note that this extractive has now proven to be the only effective agent in the healing of the peculiar burns inflicted on the natives of the South Pacific during the fallout of radiation particles from atomic bomb explosions in that area a few years ago.

Mescaline, a narcotic-like alkaloid from a cactus, *Lophophora williamsii* (Mescal buttons, or peyote), growing in southwestern U.S.A., is being currently investigated in humans for its effects on the cerebral centers, an activity which produces initial stimulation accompanied by hallucinations and later intense cerebral depression. Such activity under carefully controlled conditions can serve as a kind of chemical and biological tool for inducing effects against which to measure the psychiatric activity of the tranquillizing drugs *Rauwolfia* and Chlorpromazine.

2. The re-investigation of well-established plant compounds.—*Steroid sapogenins.*—Two very widely distributed classes of chemical compounds known to exist in plants are the steroids and alkaloids. Among the steroids many have recently been extracted from several species of *Yucca, Agave, Dioscorea* and *Strophanthus,* and these have been employed for chemical and biosynthetic purposes. They are chemically called sapogenins. A great many sapogenins hemolyze red blood cells and therefore are toxic to humans. However, several are now found to possess a useful "precursor" value in the chemical synthesis of medicinal agents as the adrenal hormones, cortisone and hydrocortisone. At the present time progesterone is the principal intermediate in cortisone synthesis but

there are four sapogenins which are used for progesterone synthesis. One of these, diosgenin from the "old" botanical drug *Dioscorea,* Mexican Yam, is most useful in this respect. From this finding one is set to speculating whether the natives of Mexico, Central America, and Africa, where most of these plants grow, weren't correct after all centuries ago in attributing considerable benefits to certain yam roots and *Strophanthus* fruits in the treatment of adrenal hormone and corpus luteum deficiency diseases.

Alkaloids.—In the realm of alkaloids that can be separated from plants there are many examples of new drugs prepared by chemical modification of existing molecules. This has been especially true among certain tropane types, for example the cocaine, atropine and ergot alkaloids.

Ergot alkaloids, for example, ergonovine, have been the chief chemical sources for the synthesis (and probably biosynthesis) of an indole acid known as lysergic acid. This acid is found in the crude drug but it has had only academic interest up until a few years ago. An amide derivative, known as lysergic acid diethylamide has been prepared from lysergic acid and this derivative has been shown to have marked stimulating and, later, depressant effects on the higher brain centers. Visual perception is greatly altered and marked hallucinations occur. More important, however, is the depressant effect of this drug on the mind. Humans are reported to respond as though in a hypnotized state and to reveal events which might otherwise be retained as guarded secrets. Human subjects are reduced mentally to placid followers of the slightest persuasion. The military applications of such a compound are far-reaching. There are strong indications that lysergic acid diethylamide (LSD-25) has already been put to military and political use by some foreign nations.

Conclusion—Plant cells fundamentally are chemical factories and many possess a rich supply of therapeutically useful constituents. As long as man is driven to seek better medicines, particularly those which have selective actions, he will explore the laboratories of nature. With the improved techniques at his command today it is likely that new drugs will continuously emerge from plants. Many of these will be the result of the re-investigations of older botanicals and the clues for pursuing such investigations will frequently come from a more careful attention to the history of botany in medicine and to the customs and folklore remedies of bygone generations. Other new drugs will come from the great efforts of the chemist who seeks by application of the simple and most complex rules of organic chemistry to modify the products of nature in order to suit his objectives in medicinal chemistry.

QUESTIONS

1. What contribution did Dioscorides make to medicine and for how long did his influence extend?
2. What profession serves as the closest link between botany and medicine?
3. Describe the field of pharmacognosy.
4. Who was Paul Ehrlich and what was his connection to chemotherapy?
5. What was the relationship of the ancient Chinese to antibiotics? Discuss modern antibiotics.
6. Discuss the history and uses of *Rauwolfia.*
7. What two interesting uses does the Aloë plant have?

PART ELEVEN

HORTICULTURE

Travelers are immediately struck by the great green carpet that covers the earth. Deserts have a surprising number of plants and even the apparently barren oceans have their quota of large and small algae.

Horticulture deals with cultivated annuals, herbaceous perennials, ornamental shrubs, and fruit trees. The modern horticulturists are quite different from those practising this art in the 1930s. Today frequent use is made of radioactive tracers, of the auxins indole acetic and indole butyric acid, of 2-4-D and many other modern chemicals. Plastic greenhouses are being experimented with. Potted plants on greenhouse benches are being watered automatically. The importance of day length in flowering has been discovered and chrysanthemums and some other plants are covered and uncovered for pre-determined lengths of time to bring the plants into flower at the proper time.

Not only does the horticulturist bring joy to the hearts of the flower gardener but he helps the nurseryman, the greenhouse grower, and the orchardist. He is going more and more into pure research and the fundamental information gathered is being used in solving practical problems in this area.

H. B. Tukey

Horticulture is a Great Green Carpet that Covers the Earth

Reprinted with the permission of the author and publisher from American Journal of Botany **44**(3):279–289, 1957.

From the air the earth looks green—a great green mantle stretched out protectingly and warmly over the good earth. This is a proper concept, because without the chlorophyll that gives this green color, the good earth would not be so good. There would be no life, no coal or wood or oil for fuel, no foodstuffs or fiber, and remarkably little shelter. The green mantle has that wonderful property of being able to capture the energy of the sun and tie it up in what we call the products of photosynthesis—the sugars and the starches and other organic compounds made from the carbon dioxide of the air. No, there would be no plant life and there would be no animal life. The GOOD earth might perhaps more properly be called the GREEN earth. This is the sort of thing with which Horticulture deals—a great green mantle or carpet covering the earth.

On this green carpet of Horticulture are gathered all kinds and conditions of men. There are (1) those interested in the science or biological side of Horticulture—botanists, chemists, physicists, geneticists, plant breeders, soil experts, and the like; (2) those interested in the business or affairs side of Horticulture—seedsmen, nurserymen, florists, fruit growers, vegetable growers, produce merchants, canners, freezers, and the like; and (3) those interested in the home or art side of Horticulture—the amateur gardener, the housewife, and all those who enjoy plants for the satisfaction they derive from them.

Horticulture is not restricted to professional horticulturists. There were stars before there was astronomy and there were plants before there were professional horticulturists.

THE SCIENCE OR BIOLOGICAL SIDE OF HORTICULTURE

Over a period of generations many individuals have developed an understanding of plants and how they grow, which is as though they had become a part of the plant and were able to thread their way in and about it as easily and with as much understanding as they would their own homes. Some people have dubbed this "experience," "common sense," or the "green thumb."

And while all of this is fine, there are not enough craftsmen with the green thumb to satisfy all needs. Further, while the green thumb may have its virtues, it may also have its faults. And so, sooner or later, we invariably turn to some system whereby the art and the folklore of a subject may become tested, rationalized, and catalogued, so that it can be handed to a great number of men for use. This is particularly so in America, where the exactitudes of conquering and subduing a Continent have left little opportunity for some of the qualities which only time provides. The tendency in America has been to work as much as possible, therefore, by rules and handbooks and charts and tables as the engineer would do when he builds a bridge, so as to remove the guess work and the gamble.

From this has come a sort of "biological engineering," or in our case "horticultural engineering." It is all based on research and the research method, which is essentially a careful or critical search for knowledge, participated in and enjoyed by many—trained scientists, professional horticulturists, fruit growers, and amateurs alike.

Scientific plant breeding.—Happily, there is already a good start toward "horticultural engineering." The creation of improved varieties of horticultural plants by scientific breeding methods is an example. In the past left largely to chance, new varieties are now made to order for particular needs. The hardy chrysanthemums from Chicago, the hybrid onions from the U. S. Department of Agriculture, the Great Lakes lettuce from Michigan, the improved Pascal-types of celery from Cornell, the disease-resistant cabbage from Wisconsin, the V-peaches from Canada, the Cortland apple, the Stanley plum, and the Catskill strawberry from New York, the series of Haven peaches from Michigan, the Shasta and Lasher strawberries from California, the Latham red raspberry from Minnesota, the Blakemore strawberry from Louisiana—these are all products of scientific plant breeding.

Chimaeras, polyploidy, and plant breeding.—The scientist has learned that many fruits are truly monstrosities, or chimaeras as they are properly called. Some bud sports, many variegations, and such odd fruits as the Sweet-and-Sour variety of apple, with one portion sweet and an adjacent portion sour, are now explained as chimaeral, and composed of a mixture of tissues of varying genetic make-up—not the uniform, solid, simple creation we have often surmised.

Basically, most plants are diploids, that is, they have two identical sets of chromosomes in each cell. The raspberry, for example, has two sets of seven chromosomes—a total of fourteen. Plants with more than two sets of chromosomes are called polyploids. Specifically, if they have two sets they are diploids; if three sets, triploids; if four sets, tetraploids—and so on.

Many polyploids have arisen in nature during thousands and thousands of years by chance doubling of chromosomes. From these, man has selected many desirable forms for cultivation, which are now the varieties of commerce. The cultivated strawberry is an octoploid, with eight sets of chromosomes; and the blackberry ranges from diploid to twelve-ploid.

The thornless blackberry is found to consist of a layer of thornless tissue covering an interior tissue of thorniness. When a "thornless" blackberry is propagated from stem cuttings, the resulting plants are thornless because the thornless tissue still continues as the other layer. But when propagation is by root cuttings the resulting plants are frequently thorny, for the reason that roots arise from the internal "thorny" tissue.

Further, a plant chimaera may consist of a mixture of diploid and polyploid tissues, in which the typical number of chromosomes (diploid) may be covered or mixed with a higher (polyploid) or lower (haploid) number of chromosomes. Since polyploid tissues are frequently coarser than tissues which contain a smaller number of chromosomes, the result may be apple fruits with uneven polyploid sectors or ribs, flowers with large and small petals in the same flower, and anthers which contain pollen with varying chromosome number. When such anomalous flowers are used as parents in breeding, the resulting progenies are in consequence confusing and unpredictable.

But the plant breeder is no longer ignorant of these situations. By means of a drug (colchicine) derived from a species of *Colchicum*, he is able to induce an artificial change in one season so as to provide him with just the plant material he needs for breeding purposes.

Thus, the southern muscadine grape is a diploid with 40 chromosomes. It does not cross readily with the northern bunch grape which has 38 chromosomes. By treating both species with colchicine, the chromosome number of each has been doubled (tetraploid). These new forms will now combine to blend the characters from both species. Again, a variety of apple may have three sets of chromosomes (triploid), and may not be useful as a parent in breeding because of the abnormalities which arise during reduction division. Happily, the plant breeder can induce a doubling up of the chromosome number to form a fertile hexaploid which can now be successfully used in breeding.

The plant breeder has been given additional new tools by the geneticist, cytologist, chemist and plant physiologists. By performing a Caesarian section on immature fruits, removing the partially developed embryos, and culturing them like incubator babies as with certain species of *Prunus*, he has succeeded in making heretofore impossible crosses.

The contributions of hybrid vigor have been put to valuable use. In the case of those plants which carry the male flowers and the female flowers in separate parts, as in corn, it has been possible to remove the male parts (tassels) easily and so effect the cross-fertilization from selected inbred lines to produce seed stocks with hybrid vigor and other desired characters. But with many other plants which carry both male and female parts in the same flowers, as the onion, snapdragon, tomato, petunia and carrot, the tedious separation of male and female parts has made hybrid seed expensive and difficult. Here again, however, the plant breeder has used his scientific skills effectively. He has located individual plants which are by nature male sterile, as with male-sterile onions. He has found ways of producing lines of male-sterile onions, which when planted with selected male-fertile lines produce an abundant supply of hybrid onion seed. Other vegetable and flower plants are responding to this approach, promising to revolutionize the seed trade.

Pollination and fruit set.—As recently as the 1890's pollination and fruit set were little understood by commercial fruit growers, and their importance was poorly appreciated. Compatabilities and incompatabilities are now better known. No one today would plant a solid block of Delicious apples, Bartlett pears, Windsor sweet cherries, or J. H. Hale peaches. These varieties have been found to be self-unfruitful for one reason or another. The modern orchardist must select varieties to interplant for effective cross-pollination and fertilization. And he would not use as pollenizers such triploid varieties as the Gravenstein and Baldwin apples, nor the J. H. Hale peach, all of which have defective pollen. This has been the product of research.

In commercial practice, the bee may be used as the agent for pollinating with some regard to temperature, bee flight, and number of bees required for a given area. Traps have been devised so that pollen is scraped from the creatures as they enter the hive loaded with pollen. In turn this pollen has been placed in trays at the hive egress, so that bees emerge coated with proper pollen ready for business. Hand pollination has been found practical in some areas, and shot-gun shells loaded with pollen have been fired with some success at trees in the unfortunate modern tempo of treating everybody and everything as an adversary!

Some plants, as the tomato and cucumber will respond to applications of certain chemicals such as parachlorophenoxyacetic acid for fruit setting, and will produce seedless fruits without pollination and fertilization. Further, it has been found that the tomato does not set fruit when night temperatures are below 59° F. Under such conditions, hand spraying with plant regulating chemicals and raising the night temperature by artificial covering, have both proved effective.

Blossom thinning and fruit development.—In recent years, securing a set of fruit has become less a problem generally in orchard circles than thinning off of excess fruits. Here it has been found that early thinning is most effective, beginning with blossom thinning. Thinning of apples by means of blossom-thinning sprays has become standard practice in large areas, and there is some success with peaches from applications several weeks after bloom. Dinitrocresols have been used in some regions, but growth regulators, such as naphthaleneacetic acid and naphthaleneacetamide have been found more effective in others. It has been learned that such sprays tend to "knock off" the weak blossoms and leave the strong, so that the quality of the remaining fruit is improved both by reduction of competition, and by "the survival of the fittest." The concentration of the chemical is adjusted to the variety, the season, and the vigor of fruit buds.

Studies with growth-regulating chemicals have shown some possibilities. For example, the Kadota and Mission varieties of fig commonly set fruit parthenocarpically, whereas the Calimyrna variety requires pollination and fertilization. Yet this last named variety can be caused to set fruit parthenocarpically by the use of certain growth regulators and without the aid of the caprifying wasp. It now appears that the varieties which set fruit without resort to pollination have a higher content of native hormone than does the Calimyrna. Research shows that fruit set and fruit development is related to liberation of specific hormones by pollen, by endosperm, by embryo, and probably by other parts. Extracts of corn pollen and of corn embryo will set tomato fruits. It is not too much to expect that the research worker will in time appear with methods of controlling fruit set more exactly.

Research in the field of plant regulators has made, and is still making, contributions to the horticultural industry equal to, if not greater than, any other field of endeavor at the moment. Not only are blossoms and fruits both set and thinned, but the time of blossoming may be delayed. Maleic hydrazide has proved suited to the raspberry and related brambles. No practicable method of delaying fruit blossoming of tree fruits has yet been devised, but the possibilities are there.

Sprays of certain plant regulators, as indolebutyric acid, applied to developing figs at the proper time cause them to ripen 14 days after treatment as compared with 75 days for typical development of non-treated fruit. The strawberry fruit develops because of the diffusion of plant regulating materials from the achenes which dot its surface. About the sixteenth day after bloom, the supply of regulator is low. Additional amounts of synthetic regulators, as beta phenoxyacetic acid, applied at about this time apparently induce continued growth and increased size. Improved size of blackberries has similarly been secured by similar treatments.

The application of plant regulators to prevent pre-harvest drop of fruit has become standard practice with both apples and pears. The action is apparently to delay the development of the abscission zone in the pedicel of the fruit. Napthaleneacetic acid and naphthaleneacetamide are the materials most frequently employed. Proper timing with relation to temperature, rainfall, and fruit development is critical.

Blossom induction and .photoperiod.—One of the features of Horticulture is that it frequently removes plants from their natural habitat and places them in an environment where one or more climatic variables is markedly altered.

Light, daylength, temperature, nutrition, and various chemicals treatments have been shown to induce blossom formation. Thus in the case of the tomato, a cool temperature early in the life of the plant induces the formation of flower clusters, a fact which explains why northern tomato plants grown in the field directly from seed may in a cool season produce fruit earlier than from southern-grown transplanted plants.

An undesirable effect of early cool temperatures is found with early celery. When exposed to cool temperatures, blossom formation is induced and seedstalks are produced (bolting) which makes such celery unsaleable. Lettuce tends to form blossoms and seedstalks with high summer temperatures and long days. Breeding programs for these crops are aimed at selecting plants with "non-bolting" characters.

Some plants, as the chrysanthemum, respond to short daylength. By extending the daylength with artificial light, plants may be prevented from forming flowers. By reducing daylength, they may be induced to flower. By proper attention, chrysanthemums can be brought into flower at any month of the year.

Other plants, as the cineraria respond to long daylength and may be similarly controlled in flower formation by adjusting the daylength.

More recently, the gibberellins have been shown to affect flowering in several plants. Applications of gibberellic acid to some biennial plants, as the carrot and the collard have resulted in these plants developing as annuals.

Environmental adaptation of horticultural plants.—It is known that certain areas are suited to peaches, others to pears, potatoes, celery, and so on. Yet too much of this has been learned by bitter experience. The new technique is to study adaptation by controlled experiments and to be able to predict. Thus, branches of trees are enclosed in cooled and in heated chambers as desired to simulate different climatic conditions.

Delayed dormancy of fruit trees is another problem in adaptation which has been met by research. Considerable distress has been experienced in southern sections in some seasons with delayed and scattered foliation and blossoming and attendant financial reverses. The answer has been found in varying hours of chilling required by different varieties of peaches, so that varieties which are adapted to the long chilling provided by nothern winters do not break dormancy in southern regions. Varieties of tree fruits for the South are now catalogued as to the amount of chilling required to break dormancy.

The bulbing of onions, the tubering of potatoes, the bolting of celery and lettuce, and the adaptation of certain floricultural crops and woody ornamentals to various geographical locations are now better understood and predictable.

Another recent contribution to orcharding has come from studies involving the growing of fruit tree rootstocks at controlled root temperatures. Until recently, there has been great difficulty in determining the natural adaptation of several of the clonal Malling apple rootstocks. Now it is found that certain of these rootstocks, such as Malling IX produce new roots even at root temperatures of 44° F., whereas they disintegrate in soil temperatures of 77° F. and higher. On the other hand, French Crab seedling rootstocks produce no new roots at 44° F., but grow luxuriously at 77° or higher; and Malling VII seems adapted to a wide range of soil temperature, producing roots at 55° F. as well as at 77° F. The results explain the growing popularity of Malling IX in the North and of Malling VII as a widely adapted apple rootstock in the United States, and the abandonment of Malling IX in southern regions in place of French Crab rootstocks which will tolerate high soil temperatures.

Nutrition and fertilizers.—As regards fertilizers and fruit tree nutrition, the case no longer rests with chemical analysis of the soil alone. Analyses of the tissues of the plant have been found valuable to supply additional information. The use of nitrogen has become fairly well standardized with either fall applications or early spring applications. But, as dependence has been placed largely upon nitrogen, other materials have been found of increasing importance, such as phosphorus and potassium. Various other deficiency troubles also have been identified, and have been corrected by the application of specific materials, as the little-leaf disease of citrus with zinc, and the internal corking of apples with boron.

Perhaps the outstanding contribution to general orchard management practices has been the use of mulches. While first found beneficial in apple orchards, they have since proved of value for pears and to a limited degree for peaches and cherries. Minor element deficiencies have tended to disappear under mulch, potash and phosphorus have become more readily available, and moisture supply has been increased. Associated with mulching are improved soil structure, better aeration, and increased penetration of rain.

As the appraisal of nutrition becomes more refined and more exact, there is considerable interest in foliar sprays. Such deficiencies as manganese, magnesium, zinc, and boron have been corrected by foliage applications. Further, it has been shown that bark applications may be effective under certain conditions.

Propagation and weed control.—The propagation of horticultural plants by vegetative means has been greatly improved by research. Studies have shown the differences which exist in plant parts used as cuttings which are taken from plants of varying age and composition. Plants in the so-called "juvenile condition" root more readily than do so-called "adult plants." In the apple, cuttings taken from plants no older than two years from seed may be rooted easily, but with difficulty thereafter.

A number of plant regulators, such as indolebutyric acid, have been found helpful in the rooting of cuttings. However, the general effect has been more to speed up the process of rooting than to induce new roots to form.

Since many horticultural crops require intensive culture with much hand labor for the control of weeds, research on chemical control of weeds has had success. The most spectacular results have followed the use of plant regulators, such as 2,4-dichlorophenoxyacetic acid and 2,4,5-trichlorophenoxyacetic acid. These materials have proved selective in action. 2,4-dichlorophenoxyacetic acid has proved valuable in controlling broad-leaved weeds in strawberry beds, the strawberry being resistant to the chemical. Isoprophylphenylcarbamate is helpful for control of chickweed, and EH-1 for pre-emergence treatments. Another interesting possibility is the destruction of strawberry runners by chemical means, thus permitting retention of the old bed for longer periods of high productivity.

The nature of horticultural research. —And finally, a word about the pattern of research. Research is the critical search for knowledge. The word is often used to imply only professional or high-level scientific activity. One sometimes hears the expression "pure research" as though there were a form of research which is impure. The terms "fundamental" and "basic" are employed often with the connotation of superiority. Yet, fundamental research is simply research which is fundamental to something else, as trees are fundamental to lumber and lumber is fundamental to carpentry. What is fundamental research of today is the applied research of tomorrow only to be replaced in turn by something else fundamental.

It would seem that the real test of research is its quality. A fruit grower, vegetable grower, seedsman or florist who is diligently and self-critically seeking information is a useful research worker. There is no reason to exclude anyone from the field; in fact, the more inclusive the term can be made, the better. Some of the most worthwhile leads and suggestions have come from the careful study and observations of amateurs. In the final test there are but two kinds of research—good research and bad research—the product of the long hard road requiring much time, or the easier and shorter road of mere superficial and often misleading observation.

Of course the emphasis in the program of research may vary. There may be the emphasis on solving the little problem that arises day by day—what we call "trouble-shooting," and there may be the more carefully considered development type of research. Also there may be the closely directed research and there may be disinterested research, of which patience and free time are the essence.

Generally speaking, the horticultural industry is well aware of the value of research. But it is becoming increasingly aware of the dividends of the long range not closely directed type of research. More and more a publicly supported research laboratory may be asked to spend less of its time and energy on so-called "practical" problems, and be left to spend the larger percentage on the "cast-your-bread-upon-the-waters" type. No reflection is meant upon the abilities of highly trained research workers, but much of the developmental research can be carried on even better by advisers and practical men in industry.

THE AFFAIRS OR BUSINESS SIDE OF HORTICULTURE

The discussion so far has been aimed primarily at problems of production. But the greatest change that has come to research in American Horticulture during the past decade has not been along the lines of production; it has been along the lines of outlets, markets, and consumer aceptance.

This has been brought about by the tremendous competition between foodstuffs on the American market. In 1951 there were 125 different fruits and vegetables offered for sale, 98 of these in larger than carload lots. Some of these products are relatively newcomers in quantity, such as escarole, dasheens, cranshaws, papayas, mangoes, kumquats, avocados, and prickly pears. The housewife is no longer required by necessity to take what is set before her, but may select what she wishes; and she is a very shrewd and efficient buyer.

Studies of the purchasing activities of Mrs. Housewife and the retail store have revealed interesting facts. As an example, it has been found that in the Detroit market between November and February the sale of oranges averaged $32.00, and of apples $29.00, both together constituting two-thirds of the fresh fruit sales. Retailers set aside an average of 97 square feet of floor for display of fruits, of which 25 per cent was for apples. Apple sales averaged $1.19 for each square foot of display space. When the display space was increased 10 per cent, sales increased 4 per cent. A 2-pound unit of sale moved less fruit than larger units up to 6 pounds. Bulk displays placed alongside packaged displays increased sales as much as 35 per cent.

It has been found that the American diet has shifted remarkably in 40 years. The per capita caloric intake has declined from 3,500 to 3,200, expressed largely in reduction in consumption of potatoes by nearly a half, and cereals by nearly a third. On the other hand, there has been an improvement in the use of the so-called protective foods. Yellow, green, and leafy vegetables have increased about one-third. Fruits have increased about 14 per cent. Milk and dairy products have increased nearly as much.

Another change has been the increase in processing of horticultural products. More than half of all the vegetables, and more than half of all the fruits produced in America, are now processed in one way or another. Frozen foods, fruit juices, and prepared baby foods have increased tremendously in amount. In fact, the quantity of so-called "baby foods" is equivalent to 36 pounds per year for all children under 3 years of age! Over 60 per cent of the retail stores in the major cities are now equipped with frozen food cabinets.

Since the shortage of labor is the major problem on American farms, every conceivable gadget has been introduced to effect efficiency. Pneumatic pruners and hydraulic pruning and harvesting platforms have shown their worth. A strawberry planting machine will set 25 acres of strawberries in a day. In the pruning of black raspberries a vertical and a horizontal power mower has been devised which hacks the plants into control most brutally, but most efficiently. It will be interesting to see what progress the fruit grower, the agricultural engineer, and the manufacturer will make in these directions in the next few years.

THE ART AND HOME SIDE OF HORTICULTURE

It is the art and home side of horticulture that at the moment is crying for attention. We become so involved in the biological and the affairs side that we overlook the one that is likely to be the most important in the years immediately ahead. As Dr. Crow of Canada once said: ". . . horticultural science could make no greater mistake than to underestimate the importance of Horticulture at large to the amateur and his special interests."

Abraham Cowley in his essay on "The Garden" explained the esteem in which gardening should be held by reminding us that: "The three first men in the world were a gardener, a ploughman, and a grazier; and if any man object, that the second of these was a Murtherer, I desire he would consider, that as soon as he was so, he quitted our Profession, and turn'd Builder."

L. H. Bailey has written: "Every generation sees some great addition to the depth and meaning of the home. . . . Every perfect home has its library; so in turn it must have its garden—a room, perhaps out-of-doors, in which plants grow. . . . One third of our city and village improvement is horticulture. Another third is achitecture; and the other third is common cleanliness and decency."

Dr. W. H. Camp tells us that gardening began 20,000 years ago when man first used cultivated plants for food. Many of these plants remained as a matter of sentiment or because they had become associated with religious ceremonies. Tulips, hyacinths, narcissus, Star-of-Bethlehem were first used as bulbous crops, like onions and garlic. Others had medicinal properties, as foxglove (*Digitalis purpurea*) from which is derived digitalis; and sweet scabious (*Scabiosa atropurpurea*) which was used as a cure for the itch. Rosemary, sage, lavender, and many mints were valued as herb plants. The root of elecampane was used as a tonic. Its age is indicated by its name, which is a corruption of the Roman *inula campana*. The garden pyrethrum (*Chrysanthemum commineum*) is closely related to the source of the insecticide, pyrethrum, derived from the dried heads of *C. cinerariaefolium*, used to rub on the body against lice and fleas.

Perfume, too, had its value, as a substitute for soap and water in times when baths were less frequent. The sweet-scented, orris root was used as a dusting powder. Rose petals, lilac, lily-of-the-valley—how many of the fragrances we value have come from flowers. The dye, saffron, is from *Crocus sativus*. The drug colchicine is from the autumn crocus (*Colchicum autumnale*).

Someone needs to chronicle more completely the importance of Horticulture to modern society. The fleur-de-lis appears in heraldry. The Chinese willow pattern involving peach tree, willows, and garden, is only one of many familiar horticultural designs on dinnerware and dinner service. Rugs, tapestries, wallpaper, mural paintings, furniture, Corinthian columns, iron work, pottery, jewelry—all have some touch of Horticulture. Bailey says "Rob the race of the art suggestions that it has had from plants and you rob it of its architecture and its decorations."

In music we find the "Last Rose of Summer," MacDowell's "To a wild Rose," Tschaikowsky's "Waltz of the Flowers." Most of such music is soft, warm, tender, or sweet. In poetry there are Wordsworth's daffodils in "I Wandered Lonely as a Cloud," Tennyson's "Flower in the Crannied Wall," the Mother Goose rhymes of childhood, Stevenson's "A Child's Garden of Verses," and the sentiments of James Whitcomb Riley.

In triumph we give the laurel wreath, or in modern usage, "Orchids to you"—a combination of the highest phylogenetic form and the ultimate in modernity! In sorrow, we give the funeral wreath and the floral tribute. In affection we offer flowers—"A rose by any other name, would be as sweet."

It is because of some of these values, asociated with healing, that medicine turns to Horticulture. The nervous tensions of modern living are eased by the creative and muscular outlets of gardening. The cures that have been effected and the maladies that have been prevented are uncounted. "Horticultural therapy" is a branch of occupational therapy that is developing rapidly.

On the social side, gardening is the safety value of society. Better than standing armies and regimented recreation is the outlet of the garden. One may garden as little and as inexpensively as he likes, or as much and as extravagantly as he likes. With the drift to the cities, the country is found in the backyard garden and is carried indoors in house plants and window boxes. When grandmother can no longer tend her garden, she is found seated lovingly and shawl-covered in a rocking chair next to the window in which are growing the plants that she loved best. Plants and gardens anchor society. A geranium growing in the yard signals a home of warmth, permanence, and hospitality.

Gardening means health, stability, and happiness. The 20 million Victory Gardens did more for America than produce food. The support which industry has given to the garden movement indicates the value it has found in gardening. The appointment of committees and commissions to promote better use of leisure time on the part of both rural and village people, is recognition of the trend. There must be more emphasis on living and less on making a living. This is the field in which horticulturists could well afford to spend more of their time, energy, and resources.

QUESTIONS

1. What significance does the "Great Green Carpet" have for man's survival?
2. What has taken the place of "the green thumb"?
3. How is cytological knowledge used in fruit breeding?
4. What is the advantage of blossom thinning?
5. What, in brief, are Dr. Tukey's ideas regarding pure and applied research?
6. What contributions have plants made to (a) art, (b) music, (c) death, (d) medicine, and (e) health?

PART TWELVE

FORESTRY

Like horticulture and bacteriology, forestry is a child of botany and it restricts itself to the study of trees. In later years, forestry has itself become fertile and has given rise to an area known as "Forest Products."

Before the white man came to our shores with his image of wooden houses, great tracts of virgin timber were found wherever growing conditions were suitable. Expansion of the country has wiped out much of this type of timber, although some remains. Today's forestry viewpoint is aimed at preserving these virgin tracts as museum pieces and raising what timber we need from seed. Foresters are not only found in the woods but in the laboratories working on basic problems long neglected by the pioneers. Forest taxonomists are minutely studying the variation exhibited in the population of a species, and in some cases they are finding differences wide enough to justify setting up new species. Forest geneticists are making many crosses of forest trees in an effort to produce more valuable lumber or wood products of various sorts. Large forestry departments have their own anatomists and physiologists to study these aspects of trees.

How can water rise 300 or more feet in a tree? This is an astounding feat, apparently defying some of the laws of physics. We have explanations of this phenomenon but it will be some time before we can write the full answer to this question.

There are hundreds of sizes, shapes, and uses of trees. Tree species have their own characteristics and requirements. There are trees good for bottom lands, trees for hillsides, trees for erosion control, trees for the desert, and trees for city planting. If the forester has his way, there will always be trees for man to use and enjoy.

Theophrastus

Excerpts from "Enquiry into plants"

Reprinted with the permission of Harvard University Press from Enquiry into plants, Loeb Classical Library, Vol. 1, Trans. by A. F. Hort, 1916.

OF THE TIMBER OF VARIOUS TREES AND ITS USES

We must endeavour to speak of timber, saying of what nature is that of each tree, what is the right season for cutting it, which kinds are hard or easy to work, and anything else that belongs to such an enquiry.

OF THE SEASONS FOR CUTTING

Now these are the right seasons for cutting timber: for 'round' timber and that whose bark is to be stripped the time is when the tree is coming into leaf. For then the bark is easily stripped because of the moisture which forms beneath it. At a later time it is hard to strip, and the timber obtained is black and uncomely. However square logs can be cut after the time of peeling, since trimming with the axe removes its uncomeliness. In general any wood is at the best season as to strength when it has not merely ceased coming into leaf, but has even ripened its fruit; however on account of the bark-stripping it comes to pass that 'round' timber is in season when it is cut before it is ripe, so that, as it happens, the seasons are here reversed.

But since they strip the bark of hardly any trees except silver fir and pine, these trees are cut in the spring, for then is the time of coming into leaf. Other trees are cut sometimes after wheat-harvest, sometimes after the vintage, and the rising of Arcturus. The oak is cut latest of all, in early winter at the end of autumn. If it is cut at the time of peeling, it rots almost more quickly than at any other time, whether it has the bark on or not. What is cut after the ripening of the fruit remains untouched by worms, even if it has not peeled: however worms get in under the bark and mark the surface of the stem. Oak-wood if cut in the right season does not rot and is remarkably free of worms, and its texture is hard and close like horn.

Again, if the trees are cut at the time of coming into leaf, the result is the opposite of that which follows when they are cut after fruiting: for in the former case the trunks dry up and the trees do not sprout into leaf, whereas after the time of fruiting they sprout at the sides. At this season however they are harder to cut because the wood is tougher. It is also recommended to do the cutting when the moon has set, since then the wood is harder and less likely to rot. But, since the times when the fruit ripens are different for different trees, it is clear that the right moment for cutting also differs, being later for those trees which fruit later. Wherefore some try to define the time for the cutting of each tree, for instance for fir and silver fir the time is, they say, when they begin to peel: for beech, lime, maple and *zygia* in autumn; for oak, when autumn is past. Some however say that the fir is ripe for cutting in spring, when it has on it the thing called 'catkin,' and the pine when its 'cluster' is in bloom. Thus they distinguish which trees are ripe for cutting at various times; however it is clear that in all cases the wood is better when the tree is in its prime than when it is quite young or has grown old; the wood of quite young trees being too succulent, and that of old ones too full of mineral matter.

OF KNOTS AND 'COILING' IN TIMBER

The strongest wood is that which is without knots and smooth, and it is also the fairest in appearance. Wood becomes knotty when it has been ill-nourished and has suffered severely whether from winter or some such cause; for in general a knotty habit is supposed to indicate a lack of nourishment. When, however, after being ill-nourished, the tree recovers and becomes vigorous, the result is that the knots are absorbed by the growth which now covers them; for the tree, being now well fed and growing vigorously, recovers, and often the wood is smooth outside though when split it is seen to have knots. And this is why they examine the core of wood that has been split; for if this contains knots, the outside parts will also be knotty, and these knots are harder to deal with than the outer ones, and are easily recognized.

'Coiling' of the wood is also due to winter or ill-nourishment. Wood is said to 'coil' when there is in it closer twisting than usual, made up of an unusual number of rings: this is not quite like a knot, nor is it like the ordinary curling of the wood, which runs right through it and is uniform. 'Coiling' is much more troublesome and difficult to deal with than knots; it seems to correspond to the so-called 'centres' which occur in marbles. That vigorous growth covers up the knots is plain from simple observation of the fact and also from other similar instances. For often some part of the tree itself is absorbed by the rest of the tree which has grown into it; and again, if one makes a hole in a tree and puts a stone into it or some other such thing, it becomes buried, being completely enveloped by the wood which grows all around it

OF DIFFERENCES IN THE TEXTURE OF DIFFERENT WOODS

Corresponding to the individual characters of the several trees we have the following kinds of differences in the wood: it differs in closeness, heaviness, hardness or their opposites, and in other similar ways; and these differences are common to cultivated and wild trees. So that we may speak of all trees without distinction.

Box and ebony seem to have the closest and heaviest wood; for their wood does not even float on water. This applies to the box-tree as a whole, and to the core of the ebony, which contains the black pigment. The nettle-tree also is very close and heavy, and so is the core of the oak, and to a still greater degree this is true of the core of the laburnum; for this seems to resemble the ebony.

The wood of the terebinth * is also very black and close-grained; at least in Syria they say that it is blacker than ebony, that in fact they use it for making their dagger handles.

There is also, they say, another tree which, as well as the black colour, has a sort of reddish variegation, so that it looks like variegated ebony, and of it are made beds and couches and other things of superior quality. This tree is very large and has handsome leaves and is like the pear.

These trees then, as well as the black colour, have close wood; as also have maple *zygia* and in general all those that are of compact growth; so also have the olive and the wild-olive, but their wood is brittle. Of wild trees which are used for roof-timbers the wood of the silver fir is the least compact and among others that of the elder, fig, apple and bay. The hardest woods are those of the oak zygia and aria (holm-oak); in fact men wet these to soften them for boring holes. In general, woods which are of open porous texture are soft, and of those of fleshy texture the softest is the lime. The last-named seems also to be the hottest; the proof of which is that it blunts iron tools more than any other, for they lose their edge by reason of its heat.

Ivy and bay are also hot woods. The coldest woods are those which grow in water and are of succulent character. The wood again of willow and vine is tough; wherefore men make their shields of these woods; for they close up again after a blow; but that of the willow is lighter, since it is of less compact texture; wherefore they use this for choice. The wood of the plane is fairly tough, but it is moister in character, as also is that of the elm. The wood of the mulberry is at once of close grain and tough.

The wood of the elm is the least likely to warp; wherefore they make the 'hinges' of doors out of elm wood; for if these hold, the doors also keep in place. They make the 'hinges' by putting wood from the root above and wood from the foliage below, thus reversing the natural position. For, when these are fitted the one into the other each counteracts the other, as they naturally tend in opposite directions: whereas, if the wood were set as it grows, all the parts would give where the strain came.

Palm-wood is easily worked and soft like cork-oak, but is superior to that wood, as it is tough, while the other is brittle. However the fibres do not run throughout the wood, nor do they run to a good length, nor are they all set symmetrically, but run in every direction. The wood dries while it is being planed and sawn.

All wood of wild trees is closer, harder, heavier, and in general stronger than that of the cultivated forms, and there is this same difference between the wood of 'male' and 'female' trees, and in general between trees which bear no fruit and those which have fruit, and between those which bear inferior fruit and those whose fruit is better.

* *Pistacia terebinthus,* a tree yielding turpentine—Ed.

QUESTIONS

1. What reason is given for the ease with which the bark peels off? You might try to find out how this agrees with statements in modern textbooks.
2. The stars and the moon were thought to influence the trees in some way and some farmers today plant by the moon. What do you think of the importance of these heavenly bodies in these respects?
3. What is meant by the 'catkin' of the fir?
4. What is meant by the 'cluster' of the pine?
5. What is given as the cause of knots and how does this theory coincide with the modern idea?
6. Do you think that the softest woods are of an open porous texture? You might compare pine and oak wood.
7. Why were woods called 'hot' woods?
8. What do you think of the method they used for making hinges?

N.B. Theophrastus was born about 370 B.C. and died about 287 B.C. He studied under Plato and Aristotle, had 2000 disciples and wrote 200 treatises.

J. W. Severy

Plant Anatomy and its Relation to Forestry

Reprinted with the permission of the author from Forestry Kaimin, School of Forestry, Montana State University, 1927.

The development of any field of knowledge is usually accompanied by a demand for greater specialization, which requires a higher degree of technical training on the part of its workers. This is especially true in the field of Forestry at the present time. The depletion of the forest resources of the country is causing the "hit and miss" methods of the past to be rapidly done away with and the development of a genuine scientific forestry program. At the present time it may be generally said that the man combining technical knowledge with practical experience is far more valuable than the man having only the practical experience.

The School of Forestry at the University of Montana early recognized the new point of view, and shaped its courses to develop technically trained men. Recognizing the fact that Forestry is really a phase of Applied Botany, a broad foundation in Botany was not only held desirable, but actually necessary. Botany was not so essential in the early days, when the main aim was to get the timber crop harvested and converted into lumber without paying any attention to the sources of future timber supplies, or the conservation of the timber supplies already at hand. Those days are past, for the most part. Our fast disappearing supplies of timber point to the fact that attention must be paid to the seeding and growing of the greatest possible timber crop on a given area, and to the efficient utilization of all materials in the harvesting and preparing of the timber for market. The successful forester then, must know the tree—the plant with which he is dealing. He must know its structure, its physiology, its relation to disease, and the influence of environmental factors upon growth, quality of product, etc.

Plant Anatomy occupies rather a unique position in reference to either Forestry or Botany. It is the foundation upon which the rest of the structure is built. Without a knowledge of anatomy the student can not really know physiology; without a sound foundation in anatomy and physiology, the student is not properly prepared for ecology or silviculture; and without a knowledge of all these, the student can not adequately understand the cause, effect, and control of timber diseases. To the botanist, of course, the study of anatomy serves another purpose. The study of structure is helping us to establish the relationships between plants, and the study of the anatomy of the fossil plants has made it possible to picture more or less accurately, the sequence of evolution among the plants of the past. However, such questions are only of passing interest to the forester.

A rather specialized phase of plant anatomy has to do with the microscopic identification of wood. A systematic study of this kind should serve two principal functions: (1) It should familiarize the student with the structural characteristics of most of the woods of commercial importance, and (2) It should give the student the training and practice necessary to distinguish between woods, which under the naked eye or hand lens, look much alike. In most cases an absolute identification can be made with the microscope.

A knowledge of the structure of woods is already of immense value in helping to solve practically all problems having to do with the utilization of forest products. As methods of ultilization and disposal are refined and improved, this knowledge of structure will doubtless become of increasing importance. We know that there is a definite relation between structure and the ease of penetration of preservatives. Technical men believe that there is a relation between structure, and the durability and strength of woods, although this phase is little understood at the present time. The utilization of certain species for pulp-wood also seems to be closely correlated with structure.

In the early days wood was plentiful, and there was practically no tendency to substitution. With the growing scarcity of some woods in particular, there has developed a tendency to substitute under the guise of trade names. In many instances, only a microscopic identification will serve to protect the buyer. For instance, there are five species of *Swietenia* so closely alike that they can be legitimately sold under the trade name "Mahagony." But in the Tropics and Sub-tropics there are many other woods which appear so similar to mahagony that they are oftentimes successfully substituted for it.

Sometimes a manufacturer buys some wood for a particular purpose under a trade name. He finds that this wood is particularly adapted to his purpose. When it comes to re-ordering, he must know the species in order to make sure of getting the same wood. Such an instance occurred when the writer was a graduate student at the Shaw School of Botany. A certain manufacturer of umbrella handles had made a purchase of some tropical wood which he had found particularly desirable for his purpose. He sent a specimen of the wood in to the graduate school for identification, and he was thus enabled to order the same wood by its specific name.

In the gaining of a professional training no one subject is important to the exclusion of all others. Plant Anatomy is no exception to this statement. The writer has simply tried to point out a few of the ways in which a sound foundation in Plant Anatomy may benefit the student of Forestry.

QUESTIONS

1. Explain the relationships existing between technical knowledge, practical skill and the general, all-around usefulness of a forester.
2. Why must foresters pay a great deal of attention to the seeding and growing of the timber crop?
3. What branch of science is Forestry most closely allied with?
4. Why does a forester have to understand something about Botany?
5. Would you say that anatomy or physiology is more important in determining the use to which lumber is put? Explain.

Charles D. Stewart

The Tree as an Invention

Reprinted with the permission of the author and publisher from the Atlantic Monthly, April 1929.

A man without bones would lie flat as a flounder. He would be as unable as an oyster to raise his head or stand upright. The skeleton, that core of life he leaves behind him to be dug up by the ologist and displayed in all its completeness behind glass, is the thing by which he performed his comings and his goings, and without which he would have lived a life without works. It was bones that raised him up and made him the king of beasts, an animal standing on end with a tool in either hand.

But while the stiffening structure is thus important, it is far from being the vital part of him. This is lime and not life; mere mineral from the quarry. Those hinges did not work themselves, nor did those bones keep their own balance. It is but a trellis—those tubular legs and those latticelike ribs—by which the living creature lifted itself from earth and stood a few feet nearer heaven.

A tree is in much the same case. Its solid body is all skeleton, and the skeleton is essentially dead. In any tree, however live and growing, the substance composing trunk and branch is inert and lifeless matter. The heartwood of a tree, the heaviest and solidest part, extending a considerable distance from the center, is dead in every sense of the word. Its tubes no longer convey the sap upward, because their walls have become thickened and filled with lignin. From the heartwood outward to a point very near the surface we find the water-conveying structure consisting of long tubes; and these tubes are mere conduits, inert and lifeless. They serve a useful purpose in conveying the water upward, but they are not themselves alive. At first, when they were being built, there were live cells working inside of them, little bags of protoplasm, but once they were completed, the live tenants disappeared.

When a tree is cut down, the circling grain on the stump tells something of the age and the story of growth. But if we were to saw the whole tree into small sections or divide it lengthwise with a view to tracing the course of these rings all the way to the top, we should learn something more of a tree's inner nature. A cut across a tree near the ground may show three hundred annual rings, while cuts at higher points will disclose but a hundred, or fifty, or forty. The rings become fewer and fewer.

If we take a particular ring and follow it up we find that it grows smaller and smaller till it diminishes to a point, a ring near the centre of the stump coming to an end at no great distance from the ground, while one a greater distance from the centre reaches to a correspondingly greater height. And each of these rings, according as it is the fortieth or fiftieth or hundredth from the centre, will show the height, as well as the thickness that the tree has attained in that number of years. As anyone can see by its mere outer form, a tree grows smaller upward, tapering from a considerable girth at its base to a fine point at its extremities. And when we examine these inner sheaths of annual growth we find that they do the same.

Thus we see what a tree really is. It is a sheath of life spread over the dead trees of other years. Generation stands within generation, successively wrapped about. The outer life of cambium and leaf and bud uses this as a trellis to go up and reach out sunward and skyward. Instead of throwing its old skeleton aside each year and starting anew, it clings to its dead bones, profits by their stature, and makes tubes in them to provide the supply of water for a larger and more ambitious growth. When we compare this way of growth with other methods, both animal and vegetable, it must strike us as a most interesting invention.

As the inner or lifeless part of a tree is incapable of growth or upward expansion, a nail driven into a young tree at any particular height will remain at that distance from the ground throughout the life of the tree. And a branch coming out at any point will not be carried upward as time goes on.

In the giant sequoia of California we have trees whose long life is a matter of constant marvel. But the part of them that is really alive is of quite recent growth. A sequoia may be three or four thousand years old, and an oak or elm three or four hundred, provided the inner part, which was actually in existence that long ago, is not rotted away and represented by mere space.

II

In the essential matter of life and death, a tree presents two great points of difference from an animal. An animal is alive all the way through, even its bones, tendons, and cartilaginous parts containing live cells which are engaged in the work of upkeep and repair. As we have seen, a large tree is not alive all the way through, the bulk of its body being all skeleton and dead. But when we consider the live tissue that its skeleton supports, we find that the tree offers a different sort of contrast. An animal grows rapidly at first. It has an exultant original cell which contains the whole beginning, measures but .004 of a cubic centimetre. By the time the child is born, it has increased—by one of those biological feats of geometrical progression—to a billion times that size. Here nature steps in with inhibiting hand, and the life processes begin to slow up, so that, from his babyhood to his twentieth year, a man has increased but sixteen times. At this point all growth stops, and the vitality steadily declines until finally the forces of life and death are just about balancing one another and the machine may stop in an instant.

Take note of a tree and consider how different all this can be. A tree never loses the vital power of growing. It starts out as rapidly, retains the power of geometrical progression, and is ever young. There seems to be no reason in itself why a tree should not live forever. The aged man, looking up at it, finds it a synonym for his hopes and speaks of "the tree of life."

The tree accomplishes its increase of stature and wider reach by means of buds and soft, expansible tissue at its extremities. When these tender extensions grow older they harden into wood, and then the terminal buds spring forth again to add to the annual growth.

While a tree agrees with bone in the way of adding girth, and differs from it in procedure at the end of the branches, the roots face a different set of circumstances. A root has to push its way continually through rock and sand and hard impacted earth, and yet it must achieve this growth by means of soft and tender tissues that make such rough contact impossible. In this case there is developed, on the end of the growing tissue, a tough, hard growing-cap consisting of cells that have differentiated in this way, and these serve to protect the cells behind and plough the way for them. The growth therefore takes place in a region a short distance from the end.

III

A tree, like other forms of life, is engaged in the constant circulation of fluid through its tissues. Life processes, animal or vegetable, can go on only so long as each individual cell is surrounded by a fluid containing nutriment. To meet this demand and to provide for a large amount of evaporation, a tree passes up a great deal of water. A fairly large beech tree will use about sixty-five gallons of water on a dry, hot day, while a large oak will require much more. And this water, in the larger species of trees, will have to be lifted two hundred and even three hundred feet.

Anyone who is familiar with pressures in a tall standpipe or water tower, or who has even taken up the problem of raising water to the second story of a country residence, must be interested in asking, How is this supply of water taken to the top of such tall trees? This question, in the present stage of man's knowledge of physics, cannot be answered. We do not know.

I dare say that anyone with an everyday knowledge of physics, such as might be learned from a lamp wick, would be able to suggest ways and means of getting the water up there; but it would be difficult to think of anything that has not already been considered and found wanting. The lamp-wick principle, capillary attraction, will not go far in raising water. Water rises in a capillary or fine tube to a height in proportion to the fineness of the tube; and the viscosity of water is such that if the tube is very fine it would not raise water to the top of even a moderate-sized tree.

Root pressure or osmosis has been taken into consideration. By cutting off a plant near the ground and fastening a glass tube upright on the stem, it is possible to ascertain the height to which its sap will rise by pressure from below. Under favorable conditions a grapevine will exert a pressure sufficient to raise a column 36.5 feet, while a birch has tested as high as 84.7 feet. This might seem a promising line of inquiry were it not that root pressure takes place in woody plants only in early spring, and especially in the morning. It has been found that when the tree is evaporating the greatest quantities of water, on dry, hot days of summer, there is no root pressure whatever. This fact, once it was established, naturally set root pressure aside and left the problem unsolved.

It has been proved beyond question that the rise of water in the tubes of a tree is caused by a pull from above. That there is a strong pull upward can be demonstrated by means of any branch taken from a growing plant.

Such a branch, if its cut end is inserted in an air-tight manner in a glass tube, will draw a supply of water from the tube with such force as to pull a column of mercury up after it. This demonstration, one might suppose, would set us definitely ahead in the solution of the problem. But here a difficulty intervenes.

The nature of the difficulty will be quickly apprehended by anyone who has had to learn the laws of an ordinary cistern or suction pump. A suction pump at its best will lift water but thirty-three feet; consequently it is not advisable to install one in the third story of your house. Since a column of water is not strongly cohesive, and since you cannot take hold of the end of a long pipeful of water and pull up any quantity desired, as if it were a rope, it can be lifted from above only by suction. The pump, by the lift of its piston, removes air pressure from the upper surface and tends to create a vacuum, in consequence of which the water is pushed up the pipe from below by the weight of the atmosphere, a pressure of fifteen pounds to the square inch at sea level. The weight of water being what it is, such pressure will balance a column of thirty-three feet. No invention can be made which will pull more than the laws of physics will enable it to. And thirty-three feet falls far short of reaching the top of a sequoia.

But water has got to go up those tubes to the top of a tree. This being the case, scientists began to consider whether water in thin columns, as in these fine tubes, has not an actual power of coherence, a tensile strength, sufficient to stand a strong pull. Possibly, after all, water may be drawn up from the top as if it were a rope. Strange as it may seem, experimentation has gone quite far in proving this to be the case. It seems that such a column of water has a power of coherence great enough to withstand the pull. And the osmotic force in the leaves, a strong pull of absorption, might be sufficient to raise the columns of water to the necessary height. This is the theory that at present comes nearest to satisfying scientific minds. But further experimentation has caused more difficulty to appear.

The rise of water to the top of a tree is dependent upon evaporation. It is evaporation that makes room for the continual up-flow of water; and it is evaporation that causes the chemical concentration in the living cells which gives rise to the strong absorptive pull, or osmosis. This being true, one thing is evident. If a plant, or a branch of a tree, is placed in an atmosphere so saturated with moisture that evaporation is impossible, it will be unable to keep the water flowing up its stem. Experiment has shown that the intake persists, though it is slowed up, even when the leaves are entirely submerged in water. Everything considered, we may say that the rise of the water is a mystery, provided we do not mean to imply that there is anything mystic about it.

Every cell in the top of a tree continues to be immersed in the life-giving water. Between a cell in the sea and one in the topmost twig there is no essential difference of situation. And the reason is that everything is done to control evaporation and hold it within bounds. Every leaf is coated with a preparation that most effectually seals it. Air can enter and water escape only through microscopic openings called stomates mostly on the under sides of the leaves; and every stomate is capable of being opened or closed according to conditions. The whole trunk and every limb of the tree are jacketed in the protective, suberized bark. There is nothing more waterproof than bark, more stubbornly impermeable. It is because cork is so waterproof that it makes stoppers for bottles and gaskets for engines. It is because it is so impermeable that it is ground up to make linoleum. A tree, from head to foot, is armored against evaporation. Consequently its cells, though they hang in the very eye of the sun, are in water.

A tree manufactures its food direct from earth and air, a thing the animal cannot do; and though it has no lungs, nor anything corresponding to such a mechanical device, it feeds life's constant fires by taking in oxygen night and day. And how can a tree breathe without lungs?

In a tree, the air enters through openings called stomates on the bottom sides of leaves; but there are no air tubes continuing these openings for the reason that the leaf is but a thin sheath of life, only a few cells thick and there are open spaces all through the inner structure in which air may circulate freely. Along the sides of a tree, too, in the bark, are porous openings, and these serve to let in air. The little short marks on the bark of birch, and on the smooth exterior of plum and cherry, are such porous breathing places. While these lenticels are not so evident on the rougher trees, they are none the less there.

From the standpoint of evolution, or even of present-day matter-of-fact, a cell deep in the leg or arm of a man, or hung high on the leaf of a tree, is in essentially the same circumstance as a primitive one-celled animal floating or crawling about and absorbing its food and air direct from the water. All cells, animal or vegetable, are essentially alike in structure; they live on the same sort of food and take it in the same way. It must be in liquid form; not in mere suspension or emulsion, but in true solution. As the cells in a man are confined to one place, and cannot float or wander in a stream or a pond, the nourishing stream is made to flow past them. It all amounts to the same thing. Because our cells are so deep-seated, so specialized, and so far from the free food and oxygen of nature, we have need of all this intricate machinery and this digesting and food-preparing laboratory. But all the time it is the cells that are doing the living, and supporting and cooperating with one another in this strange stock company. It is in this sense that Thomas Edison is speaking when he says that "man is a colony." Being, of all men, mechanical-minded, one might expect him to regard the human animal as a machine. But he is thinking of the builders and operatives—the cells themselves.

QUESTIONS

1. What part of a tree is comparable in function to the skeleton of an animal?
2. Where are the living parts of a large tree?
3. What are some of the factors at work in raising water and minerals to the tops of trees?
4. In what ways are single-celled plants and animals like the living cells in a tissue of a tree?

Henry D. Tiemann

What are the Most Remarkable Trees?

Published with the publisher's and author's permission from The Southern Lumberman, December 15, 1950.

AGE AND SIZE OF TREES

Draw a line ten inches long and mark off one quarter of an inch at the final end. Let the length of line represent the time in years of the life of living redwood trees (say 3,000 years); then the quarter-inch represents the span of a human life of 75 years. These trees living today were a thousand years old when Jesus of Nazareth was on earth—all of which is, of course, trite and has been said again and again; but it is nevertheless impressive to pause long enough to get a graphic picture of what this means.

Geologically sequoias are very old. In the Miocene period, the age when forests reached their maximum development some million years ago, they extended over most of the northern hemisphere, and as far south as Tasmania. The present King William pine (*Athrotaxis selaginoides*), endemic to Tasmania, closely resembles redwood, especially in color and properties of the wood, and is apparently a relic of the early species. Moreover, the metasequoia, recently discovered in the mountains of northern China, long thought to be extinct, is another relic of this ancient race of trees.

But there are other trees, perhaps even older than the redwoods. One is the bristlecone pine (*Pinus aristata*) which is estimated to be 4,600 years old. Still another ancient tree was the "Dragon Tree" of Orotavo in the Canary Islands, destroyed by storm in 1868. This tree (*Dracaena draco*) of the lily family is of slow growth, but was of gigantic size of trunk. Von Humboldt gave its diameter in 1799 as 16 feet, several feet above the roots. In the 15th century an account gives the diameter as 12 feet, at 10 feet above the ground. (See picture in Strasburger's *Text Book of Botany*, p. 541.)

The historic Italian chestnut tree "Castagno dei Cento Cavalli" at the foot of Mt. Etna in Sicily, portions of which are still living (see article in *Southern Lumberman*, Christmas Issue, 1949, "The Lamented Chestnut") may have been several thousand years old. A much-gnarled Western juniper tree in the U. S. Cache National Forest has been estimated as 3,000 years old. (See *Southern Lumberman*, December 15, 1940, for illustration.) No doubt some of the immense kauri trees of New Zealand (*Agathis australis*) with their barrel-like trunks and cabbage heads, are as old as the sequoias. The largest known tree at Mercury Bay, now destroyed, measured 24 feet in diameter and was estimated as over 4,000 years old; but a more recent estimate based on rates of growth, places it as 2,400 years.

As to height of living trees the coastal redwood is supreme. The "Founder's Tree" was accurately measured about 1931 as 364 feet in height. For illustration, see article by the writer in *American Forests*, November 1931, "What are the Largest Trees in the World?" There is evidence, however, that in times past, before destruction by civilization, some of the Australian eucalypts, especially the mountain ash (*E. regnans*), reached a height of nearly 400 feet, but there are none such now in existence.

So much as to age and height. But this is not a sermon on the vicissitudes of life, and I have space to discuss only a few of the many interesting trees of the world. What constitutes a "remarkable" tree? All plant life is indeed remarkable and little understood. No one has solved its mystery. There is a reason for the existence and peculiarities of each species, the result of long descent through geological ages. For instance, the sequoias, as pointed out by John Muir, are taking a final stand in their long struggle for survival since the glacial age, against vicissitudes of climatic changes, on the moraines left by the last glaciers, and also on a narrow strip along the coast where climatic conditions have remained favorable. Others are the recently discovered metasequoias, in the remote valleys of the mountains in northern China. Even more striking in this respect is the Monterey pine, which had become almost extinct, save for a mere speck on the map at Monterey. Yet when this pine has been planted in Australia, New Zealand, and Africa, as has been extensively done, it has exceeded all other pines in the world in its rate of height growth.

FAMILIAR PRODUCTS FROM UNFAMILIAR TREES

Products derived from trees are too numerous to attempt to cover in a short article, yet it would be incomplete without mention of some of the more important ones. In the paint and lacquer industry turpentine from yellow pine resins is, of course, so familiar as to need no discussion, and the crude resin as "naval stores." Tung oil extracted from the nut of the tung tree of China (*Aleurites fordii*) is an oxidizing oil replacing linseed in paints. One of the finest lacquers, as evidenced by the wonderful lacquered furniture from China and Japan, is obtained from the sap of a samach (*Rhus verniciflua*). Until the advent of the innumerable synthetic resins, varnishes were made of gums from trees. Dammar is an exceedingly hard clear gum from the great kauri trees of New Zealand (*Agathis australis*) and resembles amber, which is also the "fossilized" gum of extinct trees. Copal is a similar hard resin from various leguminous trees of Africa and South America, the best coming from Africa. Others are tragacanth, caraya, etc. Ubiquitous rubber is mainly from sap of trees of the euphorbia family, genus *Hevea* of Brazil. Gutta-percha comes from the gutta tree, sapodilla family (*Palaquium gutta*) of the Malay Peninsula. Vegetable ivory, or the ivory nut, furnishes the material resembling the finest ivory, for buttons, etc. The nuts grow in immense globular heads weighing up to 25 lbs. each on a low palm-like tree (*Phytelephas macrocarpa*) of Colombia and Ecuador. Kapok is obtained from the pods of the silk-cotton tree (*Ceiba pentandra*) of the Southern Hemisphere. Cork, as is well known, is the outer bark of cork oak (*Q. suber*) of southern Europe. Chocolate is from the cacao tree (*Theobroma cacao*) family *Sterculiaceae*, of the West Indies and Central America. "Coca-Cola" is made from the cola-nut (*Cola acuminata*) of North Africa, also of the chocolate family *Sterculiaceae*. Chicle, the basis of chewing gums (and incidentally one Chicago's tall buildings!) is from the Yucatan and West Indian sapodilla tree (*Sapota achras*) Sapodilla family. The familiar coconut palm (*Cocos nucifera*) furnishes the copra from which palm oil, soaps and many toilet preparations are made.

A few important medical products should be mentioned before leaving the subject. Indispensable quinine comes from the bark (*Peruvian bark*) of the cinchona trees. The history of the discovery of the medicinal value of Peruvian bark, after its curing the Countess Chinchon in Peru in 1638, and of its introduction into Europe, is fascinating but cannot be dwelt upon here. Camphor, except for the new artificially prepared synthetic, is from the wood of the camphor tree of China (*Cinnamomum camphora*) of the laurel family. The spice cinnamon is the bark of a closely related species (*C. zeylanicum*) from Ceylon and India. Cassia is the dried fruit of the cassia tree (*C. Cassia*) of China. (For an account of spices see *National Geographic Magazine*, March 1949, "Spices the Essence of Geography.") A remedy for leprosy, used for thousands of years in China, chaulmoogra oil, is obtained from the seeds of a handsome tree by the name (*Taraktogenos kurzii*) of Burma, Siam, and Malay. Cocaine is from the coca shrub (*Erythroxylon coca*) of Peru and Bolivia, not to be confused with the coco-nut of the *palm* family (also spelled cocoa-nut), or with the drink cocoa, nor with the cola-nut, both of which are of the chocolate family. So confusing is this that I have tabulated the proper designations of the sources in the footnote.*

The list of dyes, tannins and edible fruits from trees is too long to even epitomize here; and so one might keep on and on in listing of familiar everyday products from unfamiliar trees.

REMARKABLE KINDS OF TREES

Some trees of special interest are worth describing individually. Perhaps the best way to do this will be to imagine taking a trip around the world geographically.

(1) *United States*

Naturally we start from America. I have already mentioned the sequoias and the Monterey pine. The Joshua tree (*Yucca brevifolia*) and the giant cactus or Saguaro (*Cereus giganteus*) deserve mention, but there is not time to describe them now.

(2) *Mexico*

In Mexico there is a cypress (*Taxodium mucronatum*) of prodigious age and diameter. It is growing thriftily at Santa Maria del Tule, in the state of Oaxaca. This tree was visited by Alex. von Humboldt, the noted botanist, in 1803. He stated that the trunk then measured 118 feet in circumference, but a careful measurement in 1840 gave the figure as 112 feet, four feet above

* Product	Common Name	Scientific Name	Family
Cocaine	Coca	*Erythroxylum coca*	Coca
Coco-nut or Cocoa-nut	Coco-palm	*Cocos nucifera*	Palm
Cocoa or Cacao (drink)	Cacao	*Theobroma cacao*	Chocolate
"Coca-Cola" (drink)	Cola-nut	*Cola acuminata*	Chocolate

the ground. In 1903 Hermann von Schrenk of the Missouri Botanical Gardens measured the circumference at breast height as 126 feet. The trunk appears to be made of several stems, and there is no indication of any decay.

(3) *Central and South America*

In South America are many notable species. A brazilian tree of enormous size is the jequitibá vermelho of the myrtle family, which yields excellent saw-timber of a red color. The species is said to reach a diameter of over 22 feet and a height of 148 feet.

The monkey-pot family (*Lecythidaceae*) contains many curious trees, including the familiar Brazil-nut (*Bertholletia*) and the barringtonias with strange square sectioned fruits. The natives grind these fruits and throw them into the water to stupefy or kill fishes. Another tree of the monkey-pot family is the cannon-ball tree (*Couroupita guianensis*). The huge fruits are as large and round as old-time cannon balls, borne in a tangle of crooked branches at the base of the trunk, while the foliage is high above. They are said to explode with a loud noise when ripe.

I have already mentioned the ivory nut from the tagua palm (*Phytelephas macrocarpa*) of Peru and Ecuador. The hard smooth nuts the size of hen's eggs are composed of a dense white substance much like ivory. They grow in immense round clusters weighing up to 25 pounds.

The cohune oil palm (*Attalea cohune*) of Central America has probably the largest leaves of any plant, the midrib of the pinnate leaf reaching 30 feet or more in length. The leaves arise from near the ground.

Balsa (*Ochroma*) and quipo or bongo (*Cavanillesea*) are well known trees of South America on account of their light-weight wood, and belong to the queer baobab family (*Bombaceae*) of tropical Africa and Australia with absurdly swelled trunks (described later under No. 4).

The silk-cotton tree (*Ceiba pentandra*) is also of the baobab family. Kapok, an excellent, white cotton-like stuffing fiber for pillows and mattresses, is obtained from the seed pods.

The rain tree (*Samanea saman* or *Pithecolobium saman*) is remarkable for its wide spread of crown. The branches of a single tree sometimes cover half an acre of ground. It belongs to the *Leguminosae* and on account of its large pods is called monkey-pod (not to be confused with the "monkey-pot"). See account in *Scientific American,* April 1926. "The Mythological Rain Tree."

(4) *Africa and Adjacent Islands*

The dragon tree of Orotavia (*Dracaena Draco*) in the Canary Islands has already been mentioned for its great age.

The baobab tree (*Adansonia*) already mentioned, is common in northern Africa. Their absurd-appearing, swelled stumpy trunks sometimes are wider than high, even looking like some big fat animal. They measure up to 34 feet in diameter and are not over 60 feet high.

Of all queer trees in the world, the welwitschia (*Welwitschia mirabilis*) is perhaps the most curious. It was discovered on Cape Negro on the southwest coast by the explorer Welwitsch about 90 years ago. Geologically it is an extremely ancient type of plant of the family *Gnetaceae* or joint-firs of the gymnosperms. The queer thing is that the only foliage it has is the two original cotyledons from the seed, which grow to six feet in length spreading over the ground. They are flat and leathery and remain during the entire life of the tree, for a hundred years or more. The trunk seldom grows more than two feet in height, but may become six feet in diameter.

(5) *Madagascar*

The Atlas cedars and the cedars of Lebanon cannot be passed by without notice, as they are of world fame and of Biblical account. There is a full illustrated account in *American Forests*, January, 1941 by W. C. Lowdermilk, "Cedars of Lebanon," which will obviate taking space to illustrate them here.

(6) *India*

We must pass on, skipping over many trees of Asia, and mention only three trees of India and Burma, all of the fig genus. The India rubber tree (*Ficus elastica*), familiar as the ornamental household "rubber tree," from the juice of which caoutchouc or India rubber is obtained, and the banyan. The banyan (*Ficus benghalensis*) forms a forest of its own by sending downward long roots from the branches, which form new trunks. (A somewhat similar system is followed by our southern mangrove (*Rhizophora*) along the Gulf Coast.) They are, indeed, ingenious in their method of propagation. It starts growth as an epiphyte on some other tree and eventually grows into a whole forest, from its multiple trunks.

(7) *Australia*

The eucalyptus trees, as is well known, dominate the Australian "bush." In past generations the "mountain ash" (*Eucalyptus regnans*) was the tallest species in the world. Authentic records give 375 feet, but today all of the tall trees have been destroyed, the tallest living specimens being but little over 300 feet. The eucalypts are endemic to Australia, and there are some 385 different species!

But, of all nature's vegetation, nothing can exceed in beauty the fern-trees. They grow sometimes to a height of over 40 feet in the forests of eastern Australia in among the tall eucalypts, and evidentally live to the same age—several hundred years. They are true ferns, and of two genera, *Alsophila* and *Dicksonia*. I have measured fronds 13 feet in length, giving a spread of crown of 26 feet! I have never seen anything in vegetation as impressive as these fern-trees.

(8) *New Zealand*

At first thought one might expect to find in New Zealand a similar type of vegetation to that of Australia, but it is almost wholly different. Trees of New Zealand are almost exclusively softwoods, whereas in Australia they are predominately hardwoods.

I have already described the giant kauri trees. Before leaving the subject I must mention two other trees. We are accustomed here to think of gymnosperms or softwoods as "needle-leaved" evergreens, except for our bald cypress. The kauri tree, on the other hand, has broad flat leaves. Moreover the tanekaha (*Phyllocladus*) not only has flat leaves but they are pinnately compound. There is also a strangler tree which starts growth as an epiphyte ("air plant") in the branches of some tall tree. It then sends runners down the bark into the ground. These eventually coalesce, completely enclosing the trunk of the host tree, and finally strangle it, forming a cylindrical trunk of its own! The usurping tree grows to immense size and is used somewhat for sawed timber. This unethical performance is accomplished by the rata (*Metrosideros robusta*) and the strangled tree is the rimu (*Dacrydium cupressinum*).

(9) *South Sea Islands*

We must hurry on and skip over some trees of China and Japan and the wonderful bamboos—grasses which grow to the height of trees more than

50 feet, one kind in India reaching 70 feet! But this story would be incomplete without mention of the breadfruit tree (*Artocarpus communis*), native of the Malayan Archipelago, now widely grown throughout the tropics for the food value of its large football-shaped fruits, which when baked taste like something between a loaf of bread and a baked potato. Mention of the breadfruit calls to mind Admiral Bligh's attempt in 1789 to bring seedlings across the Pacific to the West Indies, the mutiny on the *Bounty*, and the colonizing of Pitcairn Island.

Whatever facts of interest one may glean from a study of these and other peculiar trees, one significant impression can hardly be escaped: the more one studies living things in their adaptations to environment, be they vegetable or animal, the greater becomes their mystery and the deeper the conviction of an intelligence beyond the material, manifested wherever life may be found.

QUESTIONS

1. Name a few of the oldest living organisms on earth giving common names and their age in years.
2. Do the same in respect to height.
3. Name the source and use of the following products: turpentine, tung oil, lacquer, rubber, kapok, cork, chocolate, coca-cola, chicle, palm oil, quinine, copra, and cocaine.

Edmund Schulman

Tree-rings and History in the Western United States

Reprinted with the permission of the author and publisher from Economic Botany 3:234–250, 1954.

INTRODUCTION

The common opinion that the rings so obvious on cross-sections of most trees may be counted to give the age of the tree, and that the succession of wide and narrow rings may be interpreted as reflecting the history of favorable and unfavorable growth-years, is indeed old—surely, the statement by

Leonardo da Vinci near A.D. 1500 to this effect is the earliest only because far earlier ones were not recorded or have been lost, perhaps in the disappearance of the Alexandrian Library!

Despite this ancient recognition of tree-rings as an historical index, modern scientific research on ring-growth at first quite properly emphasized botanical and ecological aspects. By the end of the nineteenth century a truly vast amount of work had been done on the nature of such growth layers and their complex relationships to climatic and other factors.

In recent decades, however, many investigators in this country and abroad have sampled various forest stands and have measured several millions of annual rings in an effort to develop long chronologies which might represent, to some extent, histories of past rainfall, temperature, river flow and other climatic variables. The stimulus for this activity arose, in good part, in an astronomical objective!

Quite independently, it occurred to a Dutch astronomer, later renowned for his contributions on stellar statistics, and to an American astronomer, studying variations such as those of the markings on Mars, that the rings of trees might directly or indirectly record year-by-year changes in the sun.

Julius C. Kapteyn, about 1880, examined oak sections from western Germany and Holland and derived a 240-year ring chronology. The later decades of this history corresponded well with rainfall data, and a strong, but quite unexplainable, cyclic variation of 12.4 years was present throughout. Fortunately for astronomy, Kapteyn evidently felt this work to be strictly extra-curricular, for he carried it no further. But his single paper on the subject, a published lecture in Pasadena in 1908, is a delight to read for its simple presentation of essentials and its humility.

In contrast to this somewhat abortive effort, the program of research initiated by A. E. Douglass at Flagstaff, Arizona, in 1904, has been carried on for almost half of a century at the University of Arizona, at Tucson, and has led to important developments in quite unexpected directions. The most spectacular development was a method which made it possible to precisely date many ruins and thus provide a time-scale for the pre-Spanish cultures of the Southwest. This method is based on detailed matching or cross-dating of the patterns in tree-rings—an application of the operation of forecast-and-verification, which is such an integral part of the scientific method. It proved to have far-reaching implications in climatic studies as well, for it was the essential key to the development of highly significant tree-ring histories of rainfall and other climatic variables.

We thus see that modern techniques in dendrochronology find their principle application in two fields of research: (a) dendro-climatology, that is, historical climatology based on fluctuations in ring-growth, and (b) dendro-archaeology, the dating of prehistoric structures and activities by the precise dating of ancient wood.

DENDRO-ARCHAEOLOGY

The method of overlapping patterns by means of which prehistoric beams may be dated is illustrated in highly idealized form in Fig. 1. It is evident that matching the outer rings of an old beam with the inner rings in a living tree serves two purposes, namely, to date the old beam and to extend into earlier times the potential climatic chronology in the living tree.

Those acquainted with the great range of variability, which seems to be one of the universal properties of biologic elements, will recognize that such simple growth and perfect synchrone-

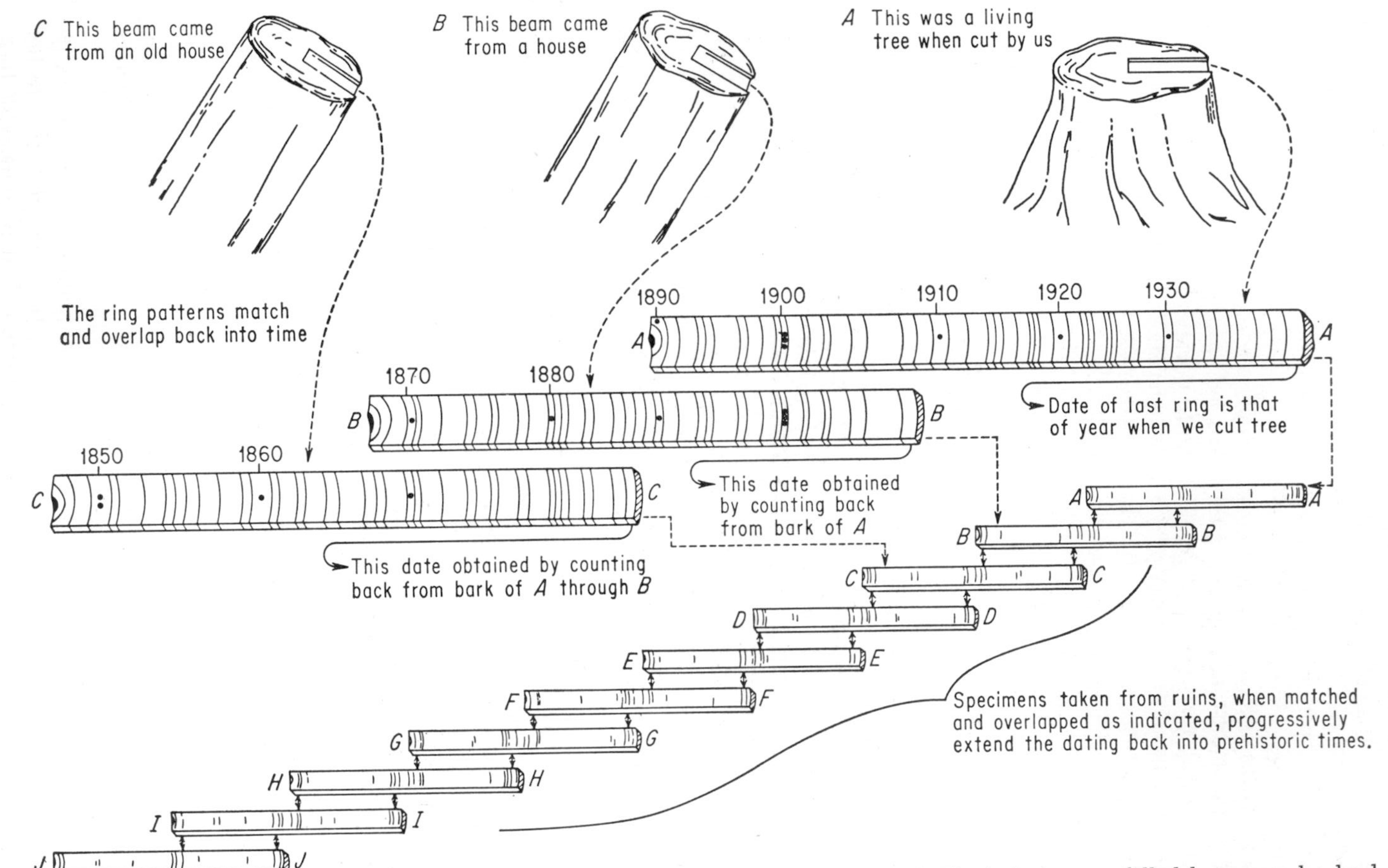

Fig. 1. The matching of ring spectra may not only show when a beam from an archeological site was felled but may also lead to a long backward extension of the ring history of climate in living trees. (From Stallings: Dating Prehistoric Ruins. Courtesy Laboratory Anthropology, Inc.)

ity from tree to tree as shown in the figure is quite unlikely to be found, even in trees of one species and within a small locality.

In many species and individual trees, the rings are so complex and variable that cross-referencing with other rings is not possible. Indeed, the botanist is familiar with so many reasons for such ring irregularity—specific characteristics, environmental influences, accidental events, and so on—that close parallelism in ring fluctuations among different trees might well seem the rare exception. It was fortunate for the pioneer work in dendro-archaeology that it was applied in the Southwest, where species, climate, site and wood collecting by the ancients all so happily favored the research. It should not be supposed, however, from the foregoing that such cross-dating is a characteristic only of certain Southwestern trees. This property has now been found present in many other regions, though nowhere in such good form in so many trees.

The tendency of the ring-widths in dominant conifers of the Southwest—*Pseudotsuga menziesii, Pinus ponderosa, P. edulis*—to show approximately the same patterns over a large area made it significant to take broad-scale averages of many trees and thus derive a so-called master chronology. In this way local peculiarities in growth were minimized and the master chronology served as a general standard, against which beams from widely separated localities could be dated.

The development from living trees and relatively recent house beams of a master chronology which extended back into the time of the prehistoric Pueblos was not accomplished at once—the dating of the Cliff Dweller ruins, announced by Douglass in the National Geographic Magazine in December, 1929, was preceded by over a decade of collection and analysis of archaeological wood. A number of floating chronologies were developed, built up of ancient beams which cross-dated with each other but which could not be joined to the dated rings of the living-tree master record; a gap of unknown length had to be bridged. At last beams were obtained which did overlap the inner part of the master chronology, and immediately dates could be assigned to several scores of ruins in the Southwest. The most magnificent of these, the apartment houses of the "cliff dwellers," as at Mesa Verde National Park, were among the most recent, principally in the 1200's A.D.

The 1929 "Crossing of the Gap" initiated a period of intense activity in dendro-archaeology. Earlier and still earlier ruins were dated in the Central Pueblo area; independent master chronologies were developed for the Rio Grande by W. S. Stallings and for northeastern Utah by Schulman; and now the dates of several hundred ruins and a chronology for the Southwest reaching back 2,000 years have been established. By similar methods dates have been obtained by various investigators for less ancient works of man in Norway, Sweden, Germany, and particularly, by J. L. Giddings, in Alaska.

As an example, we may note a recent application (1952) of this method, namely, the extension of the Puebloan chronology into B.C. times. The ring sequence in a very sensitive and consistent ancient beam of Douglas-fir from Mummy Cave, northeastern Arizona, was definitely dated by comparison with master chronologies and with individual specimens long dated and available for several localities in that area.

This extension of the known chronology then made possible the dating of a number of short charcoal fragments from an early archaeological site near Durango, Colorado. Among these fragments was one with attached bark, the outer ring of A.D. 46 providing the earliest precise culture date presently available for the Southwest.

It will be evident from the foregoing that, in general, the successful application of tree-ring analysis to archaeological dating requires two principal favoring factors which are, unfortunately, by no means widely found:

1. One or more living species must exist in which, on at least some type of site, the annual rings are sharply defined, show fairly high year-to-year changes in ring-width, vary in essentially parallel fashion along different radii and from tree to tree, and provide centuries-long sequences.

2. Available archaeological beams must be of the datable species and from the datable types of sites, in general must overlap the time range of the master chronology for at least 50 years, and must have sufficiently high ring sensitivity to provide unqualified dating. (Since the ring chronologies in any region tend to be much alike over broad areas, the preceding restriction is not so severe as it might otherwise be.)

For specially favored localities of the Pueblo area, ring chronologies in some species are so simple and consistent that reliable archaeological beam-dating, given a sufficiently long master chronology, is an absurdly simple matter. But this is far from true in general. Definitive beam-dating requires, first, a professionally secure solution of all problems, such as those presented by false annual rings, and second, an identification which is not merely probable but absolute with a selected segment of the master chronology.

Absolute identification is possible by the forecast-and-verification method. Given a tentative matching of test specimen and master chronology by some ring characters, corresponding additional characters (locally-absent rings, check-segments of the ring sequences outside the test-dated interval, etc.) are sought; with a sufficient number of verifications the probability of chance correlation becomes vanishingly small. Since such verification depends on fairly close congruence of both ring sequences, such parallelism should appear in the compared growth curves and in the correlation coefficients, especially of the check or forecast intervals.

The unqualified archaeological dating to the year which tree-ring analysis makes possible under favoring circumstances is, from a world-wide point of view, of highly limited application. Even in the Southwest, ruins yielding only juniper or hardwood beams cannot be directly dated; in many other regions the absence of favorable species makes the construction of sufficiently long master chronologies extremely difficult or quite impossible. This deficiency has been met in a most unexpected way.

In the last few years a new method has been devised, by W. F. Libby of the Institute for Nuclear Studies of the University of Chicago, for the dating of wood and other materials by the measurement of the amount of decay in the radioactive isotope of carbon, C^{14}, which these materials contain. This very elegant and powerful technique, now in process of active development, is applicable to a wide range of organic and other material and appears able to provide dates from about 1,000 to some 30,000 years in the past with a probable error that is satisfyingly small. By supplying an absolute time-scale for regions where the construction of a master tree-ring chronology anchored in the present is impossible, C^{14} dating greatly increases the value of possible relative tree-ring dates in some of these regions.

DENDRO-CLIMATOLOGY

Principles. Evaluation of all the influences responsible for the observed absolute growth of trees is obviously a far more complex matter than that of setting up a centuries-long tree-ring index of climate. Nevertheless, even with the latter limited objective, the numerous pitfalls in analysis and interpretation of ring-growth permit no simple generalizations of the results of work in dendro-climatology. It will perhaps be sufficient to sketch certain broad outlines as follows:

1. A most fundamental property of all phases of ring-growth is variability; no conclusions based on one species or stand are necessarily generally applicable.

2. Coniferous species are usually preferable to hardwoods as sources of climatic chronologies because of longevity and ease of sampling and analysis; however, their dominance in the most "sensitive" belts thus far studied may unduly determine this view.

3. As a single meteorological element becomes severely limiting in tree growth—e.g., temperature near the arctic tree line or moisture near the lower forest border on mountain slopes of semi-arid regions—the door seems to close to the entry of numerous random factors which in part control the fluctuations in radial tree growth in mesophytic areas.

4. A powerful tool for the solution of uncertainties and elimination of errors in ring identity is provided by the cross-dating technique already emphasized, in which the sequences of widths are matched ring by ring; only when a general tendency exists for parallelism among the various sequences, whether from a tree, locality or large but climatically homogeneous area, are absolute dating and a significant index possible.

5. The dendro-climatic history of a region, if derivable at all, is an approximation which it is usually possible to replace with a better one. By repeated sampling of trees, selected according to improved field criteria, and by the construction of indices having a wider statistical base, it may be possible to go far towards avoiding or cancelling out the innumerable biotic, climatic and other factors which tend to distort the climatic index in trees.

OVER-AGE CONIFERS AND CHRONOLOGY

The spectacular achievement in archaeological application of a botanical variable was not the only unexpected offshoot of dendrochronologic research. An intensive field search by the writer during the past 14 years for suitable tree sources of climatic data has brought to light a remarkable category of long-lived growth-stunted trees of high index value. These not only provide a unique kind of tree-gage record of past rainfall but exhibit very suggestive properties of growth under extreme adversity.

For many miles bordering the upper Colorado River, as in the area just west of Eagle, Colorado, stunted Douglas-firs and pinyon pines (*P. edulis* Engelm.) dot the steep slopes and are readily accessible from the highway. Standing dead poles are common. That this site happens to be a gypsum formation may have no great significance, since trees of comparable age, sensitivity and slow growth have been found on sandstone or limestone slopes nearby; however, the number of extremely old Douglas-firs per unit area is greater here than at any other site in the Rockies thus far sampled by the writer.

On the basis of several hundred sampled trees which were suitable for chronology studies and which exceeded the commonly assumed maximum age of about 500 years for Rocky Mountain conifers, certain characteristics of these drought-site trees emerge as probably very general in nature: (a) the absolute maximum ages of Douglas-fir, ponderosa-pine and pinyon pine in the Rocky Mountains are of the order of 1,000 years, and for *P. flexilis* (limber pine) in excess of 1,650 years; (b) in addition to the observed tendency for maximum longevity on the most adverse sites, there seems to be a systematic though probably only indirect relation to latitude in the age limits of various stands of a given species; (c) the median ring-width in the lower stem is about 0.30 mm.; (d) this growth rate is often approached by early maturity—two or three centuries—after which the mean growth rate decreases very slowly; (e) the absolute minimum in total mean radial growth of the lower stem for an entire century is about eight mm.; (f) the number of sapwood rings in over-age Douglas-fir does not seem to be significantly related to either the number of heartwood rings or the thickness of heartwood (for relatively young trees a systematic relation has been found by Stallings when groups of five or more trees are averaged); (g) false rings are almost completely absent in these overage trees of all species except the scopulorum juniper, and there is a marked tendency to decreased incidence of locally absent rings in higher latitudes.

GEOGRAPHIC DISTRIBUTION OF DROUGHT CONIFERS

Do over-age conifers providing significant rainfall chronologies exist on other continents? It now seems quite certain that they do.

Along the foothills of the Patagonian Andes of Argentina, between latitudes 38 S. and about 43 S., dry sites comparable to the semi-arid Rocky Mountain margins were sampled in early 1950 by the writer. In two coniferous species, *Araucaria imbricata* Prav. and *Libocedrus chilensis* Endl., the ring records showed the characters of sensitivity and crossdating which are essential for the derivation of climatic chronologies. Since these conifers are developed only in scattered stands in a very thin and short belt between the line of the Andes and the plains, little area is available for development of long-lived strains. Yet the same inverse relation between mean growth rate and age was found for the two Patagonian species as for the conifers of the Rockies. When the analysis of these collections and others in southern Chile is completed, some hundreds of years of climatic chronology for Patagonia should be available.

Xerophytic conifers, and possibly some hardwood species, exist in apparently suitable environments in a number of other regions, particularly in Asia, and will probably be found to provide significant rainfall chronologies; little exploration seems yet to have been made of the extensive Siberian forests as sources of temperature chronologies. In the light of present knowledge, however, it appears that the combination of factors which makes possible long tree-ring histories of climate is particularly favorable and widespread in western North America.

QUESTIONS

1. Explain what dendro-archaeology is and illustrate the subject with a definite example.
2. Name two conditions necessary for the successful application of tree-ring analysis to archaeological dating.
3. Name a dating method that is quite different from the tree-ring analysis method.
4. Illustrate what is meant by dendro-climatology.
5. In addition to its use in archaeology and in climatology, name a third use of tree-ring analysis.

PART THIRTEEN

CONSERVATION

A lad is once reported to have said to his father, "Dad, it seems to me that you older folks aren't doing very well in taking care of the resources that we young folks will have to live on." During the last 100 years, six of the native United States birds have become extinct and others are in jeopardy. Some mammals and plants are also in peril. Heroic efforts are being made, on small budgets, by the Nature Conservancy, Save-The-Redwoods League, Resources For The Future Inc., National Wildlife Federation, The Wilderness Society, National Audubon Federation, The International Union for the Protection of Nature, the Federal Government, and other organizations.

A respectable segment of our population is aware of the necessity of conserving as much of America's beauty as is possible. It is a common feeling that our nation is large enough to have its normal expansion and still have recreational areas set aside for both the present and for future generations. Some of these areas can be for multiple use while others are best held in the primitive condition as "museum pieces." Every American should shoulder a share of responsibility in preserving our natural resources.

Robert B. Gordon

The Conservation of Wild Flowers

Reprinted with the permission of the author and publishers from Bulletin 119, Agricultural Extension Service, Ohio State University, May 1934.

Thousands of people are finding their most healthful forms of recreation in the out-of-doors. The automobile has led directly to the development of a splendid system of highways and the establishment of new state and municipal parks. City dwellers, especially, derive real pleasure from contacts with nature away from the large centers of population. For the first time many of them are brought face to face with old gray beech trees, brilliant scarlet tanagers, orange-colored mushrooms, and large blue lobelias. A thousand objects of interest are certain to arouse an inborn curiosity about nature. Several well-illustrated books have been written to help those who really want information about the abundant wild life which surrounds them.

Perhaps no one needs to be educated to enjoy a gorgeous sunset, an enchanting landscape, or a field of showy flowers. But such scenes may soon become tiresome, if there is not a deeper interest. Some people derive much-needed recreation in the study of minerals and fossils, bird life, insects, or trees. With a little training and encouragement they may become amateur naturalists. They experience thrills of delight when the first warbler arrives in the spring, or when a rare flower is discovered.

So far the enjoyment of nature has been free to all. Nobody needs a hunting license to chase butterflies or to collect insects as a hobby. Only a few states have passed "game laws" protecting wild flowers, and none of us have to pay an amusement tax for watching birds of brilliant plumage in a public park or in a private woodland. It really takes only a little effort to become acquainted with the commoner forms of life, and it pays big dividends in mental stimulation and emotional satisfaction.

The amateur naturalist enjoys nature without destroying it. He is a nature lover as well as a student of nature. He prefers to see wild flowers and wild animals in their natural surroundings rather than to see them carried home as prizes. He desires nature sanctuaries where rare species of plants and animals are free to live their lives without danger of extermination.

WILD FLOWERS AND WEEDS

Flowering plants which grow without cultivation and which we admire because of form and color are called wild flowers. Those which become pests in cultivated fields, pastures, and lawns are called weeds. It presents a problem to the farmer to eradicate such plants from his land. To a city dweller the sight of a field of goldenrod and purple ironweed in late summer may call forth an expression of delight. To the farmer on whose land such plants are growing they may be decidely unwelcome tenants.

On the other hand, the ragweeds (*Ambrosia*), the pigweeds (*Amaranthus*), and the goosefoots (*Chenopodium*) are popular with no one. The ragweeds have been convicted of being the source of much of the "hay fever" hitherto blamed on the goldenrod. For the most part these are weeds of cultivated fields and the farmer knows how to deal with them.

Weeds in pasture land usually indicate low fertility or overgrazing. Where a good bluegrass sod is developed the majority of weeds do not get a start. Those which do become established can be removed with a scythe or cornknife before they go to seed.

Many of the weeds are not so entirely obnoxious as is sometimes believed. A "weed patch" may harbor a number of small but useful songbirds. Song sparrows frequently build nests in clumps of goldenrod. Other species which may nest in low vegetation of this type . . . are the field sparrow, vesper sparrow, grasshopper sparrow, dickcissel, and northern yellow-throat. We can scarcely doubt the distinct value of these birds to agriculture. Do we not go a bit too far sometimes in the spoilage of nature to our own economic loss?

The roadside weeds furnish nesting sites for a number of useful birds. Dr. Lawrence E. Hicks, while employed as a research ornithologist by the Ohio Division of Conservation in 1930, found that game birds are tremendously attracted to roadside situations. A survey made in Union County disclosed that a highway mower, in the distance of 1½ miles, had uncovered six nests of the pheasant and sixteen nests of the bob white. Others may have been missed. All nests found were deserted. Dr. Hicks therefore recommends elimination of all roadside mowing by farmers, county commissioners, township trustees, the state highway department, or other parties, before July 10, in order to protect nesting birds.

USE OF WILD FLOWERS IN DECORATION

A number of our "wild flowers" lend themselves to decorative purposes. Early spring flowers, as a rule do not last long when picked and placed indoors. The common blue violet (*Viola papilionacea*) is an exception, and has merited its popularity because of its long flower stalks.

The oxeye daisy (*Chrysanthemum leucanthemum*) blooms prolifically in June on some of our poorest soils. Because of its abundance, the flowers are often picked in large quantity, and hundreds of blossoms crowded into a pail. This shows poor taste. Fewer flowers, relieved by those of some other color or a bit of green foliage, are far more attractive.

Grasses and sedges, picked just before the seed is ripe, have unlimited decorative value, alone or in combination with a few other flowers.

The coarse brilliant weeds of late summer and early fall include several species of asters and goldenrods, black-eyed-susan, prairie-niggerhead, Jerusalem-artichoke, purple ironweed, Joe-Pye-weed, and boneset; they require judicious treatment to get the proper effect. Cattails are in the same class. A tall, heavy vase is needed for displaying them. All of these plants require water and plenty of light to appear at their best. The water should be changed daily to prevent fouling.

In the winter, dark green stalks of thicket horsetail (*Equisetum prealtum*) may be placed in a tall vase on the floor or on a low taboret. These interesting plants will retain their natural colors without water and without sunlight.

Many of our wild flowers are so abundant that they may be picked in large quantities without danger of extermination. The presence of perennial underground parts, the production of viable seed in large quantities, and the ability to grow rapidly when established are only a few of the characteristics of these plants. Some are foreign . . . having been introduced accidentally, or, in a few cases, intentionally. Under certain conditions they are regarded as weeds. Nevertheless, these plants include many of our showiest wild flowers. Their use in decoration should be encouraged.

SUGGESTIONS ON GATHERING WILD FLOWERS

There is a large group of people who would rather see wild flowers preserved in their natural setting than to see them carried home. A society of large flowered trilliums in a wooded glen is far more pleasing than the same plants in a crockery jar. Complete preservation is most necessary in small woodlots and parks near large cities, where a few wild flower collectors may destroy natural beauty available to thousands.

After all, there are only a few legitimate reasons for collecting wild flowers. The home decorator appreciates the vase of cut flowers on the breakfast table. The artist and the naturalist may require specimens for study. Others keep them as souvenirs of pleasant journeys afield.

If our common flowers were picked in moderation, there would be no occasion for criticism. Wild flowers, like garden flowers, should be picked thoughtfully. Whether intended for home decoration or herbarium specimens, care should be taken in collecting them. A knife or scissors should be used, or else the stems should be broken off sharply, to avoid injuring the roots. Woody stems should be cut off closely to the flowering branch.

One should be careful not to remove all of the leaves in picking flowers from perennials. The green leaves of the plant are its food factories. Unless the plant can manufacture food in excess of its immediate needs, none will accumulate in its storage organs. The next season's growth is very largely dependent on the foods stored in aerial stems, tubers, rootstocks, and bulbs.

It should be borne in mind, also, that picking flowers usually removes potential seed. When a colony of plants becomes reduced to a few individuals the chances for seed production and survival of the colony are very slight indeed. Especially is this true of annuals and biennials. As an arbitrary rule, one should never take a flower out of a woods when fewer than a dozen plants of its kind are present.

Under no circumstances should wild flowers, except the most abundant weedy kinds, be gathered when there is no provision for taking care of them during the journey home. A large market basket containing damp newspapers is a handy container; it will prevent the plants from drying out until they return home. They should be watered and kept cool until the leaves look well. Then the flowers may be arranged to suit the purpose intended.

THE DAMAGE FROM GRAZING IN WOODLOTS

Perhaps the greatest damage to wild flowers has been due not to man directly, but to his domestic animals. Cattle, sheep, and hogs have undoubtedly destroyed far more wild flowers than man himself. Usually the tenderer, more succulent grasses and herbs are eaten first. As the supply of feed plants diminishes, the stock are obliged to eat coarser and coarser plants, comparatively low in actual feed value. It is not uncommon to see small woodlots where hogs have uprooted all the sod and leaf mold, and have eaten every green plant except a few stout jimson-weeds and coarse thistles.

There is no question that, if any of of us had to decide whether to have meat on the table or flowers on the table, we should choose the meat. However, there is a serious question as to whether the sparse grass in a shady woodlot is of much feed value compared with forage crops on the same land kept in pasture, but not overgrazed.

Few farmers who turn stock into a woodlot realize the deleterious effect of overgrazing on the growth of trees. Those who have become interested in the woodlot as a source of domestic lumber and firewood are enclosing their woodlots. The State Forester can furnish the farmer excellent advice on managing his woodlot successfully. An overgrazed woodlot is actually a double liability. Not only does it take up space which might more profitably be used for pasture or field crops, but it is also being rendered unfit for thrifty growth. The changes brought about by the removal of litter, the compacting and puddling of clay soil, exposure of roots, removal of bark, and destruction of young trees in the undergrowth, are such that a forest is scarcely able to grow or to reproduce itself. Placing the fence a rod or two back from the woodlot boundary will protect the interior from grazing and allow some shade for cattle in the adjacent pasture. Incidentally, this will establish a preserve for the forest wild flowers.

In the last analysis each landowner must decide for himself whether to enclose the woodlot and protect it from stock, or to cut down most of the trees and establish a permanent pasture.

LAWS PROTECTING FERNS AND WILD FLOWERS

A Vermont law, enacted by the General Assembly and approved April 1, 1921, provides that "a person shall not take in any one year, except upon lands occupied by him, more than a single uprooted specimen or two cuttings of each of ten kinds of ferns and club-mosses, and then for scientific purposes only." The law also protects some 20 or more species of wild flowers, providing a fine of not more than $10 for each plant or additional cutting taken.

In West Virginia a state law forbids the picking of flowers within a hundred yards of the highway without the written consent of the landowners. The legislature of Illinois has made it a misdemeanor to "knowingly buy, sell, offer, or expose to sale any bloodroot (*Sanguinaria canadensis*), lady's-slipper (*Cypripedium parviflorum* and *Cypripedium hirsutum*), columbine (*Aquilegia canadensis*), trillium (*Tril-*

lium grandiflorum and *Trillium sessile*), lotus (*Nelumbo lutea*), or gentian (*Gentiana crinita* and *Gentiana andrewsii*)" . . . "unless in the case of private land the owner or person lawfully occupying such land gives his consent in writing thereto." An unsuccessful attempt was made in [the Ohio] State Legislature during the spring of 1933 to secure the passage of a bill "to protect native Ohio trees, shrubs, and plants from destruction or removal, without the consent of the owner or agent."

Such laws fail to accomplish their purpose unless rigidly enforced. It becomes increasingly important, then, that people be educated to recognize and appreciate the wild things around them. It is perhaps better that every child should know those truths and beauties which can only come from intimate contacts with nature. The love of nature instilled in the hearts of the children will greatly lessen the problem of protecting wild life, and will later develop an interest in the larger problems of conservation.

QUESTIONS

1. Picture in your own mind, a world with and one without wild flowers. Which one would you prefer and why?
2. List as many benefits as you can that might be derived from wild flowers.
3. What are some of the disadvantages of weeds?
4. Describe one advantage to be derived from weeds.
5. Why should one leave the leaves or most of them when cutting perennial wild flowers for home use?
6. Describe the relation of wild flowers and overgrazing.

Paul B. Sears

What Worth Wilderness?

Reprinted by author's and publishers' permission from Bulletin to the Schools of the University of the State of New York, March 1953.

The state of Ohio, containing about 40,000 square miles, was once a magnificent hardwood forest. The forest types, thanks to the record of early surveyors, have been largely mapped. Yet it is almost impossible to form an adequate picture, from any surviving records, of the appearance of that forest. The state has its full share of memorials—statues, libraries, institutions; some useful, some not; some beautiful, many ugly. But somehow it never occurred to anyone to set aside a square mile, much less a township six miles square, of primeval vegetation for future generations to see and enjoy. Yet this could have been done for less than the cost of a single pile of stone of dubious artistic and cultural merit.

Farther west the "boundless" prairie, that living carpet of wonderful changing colors, is all but gone. Strenuous effort will be required to set aside proposed grassland national monuments. Unless this is done, the prairies will survive only on the pages of travelers' journals and in the descriptions of those who, like Willa Cather, knew and loved them.

We need not, said Darwin, marvel at extinction. But we have reached a point of civilization where we are no longer proud to be the agents of extermination. Once we are reminded that a species—key-deer, trumpeter swan, moccasin-flower or arbutus—is in danger, it is possible although never easy to rally help in preserving it Often, as with the heath hen and passenger pigeon, help comes too late.

The business of preserving game species moves somewhat more briskly, being substantially financed by license fees and insistent sportsmen. But for a long time the conserver of species, whether sportsman or not, missed the point. It seemed enough to slow down or stop the actual killing of individuals. We ignored an ancient rule of warfare, put into effect by Rome against Carthage: if you wish to eliminate, destroy the center of activity, the home.

Now the home of any species is the community of which it is a part. True, by juggling diet we can now get certain wild animals to breed in a zoo, but that is a sorry expedient. As Ding Darling once pointed out, you can always tell a tame mallard from a wild one by its potbelly. If we are really serious about preserving any species we must preserve, in generous measure, its community of plant and animal life. Can we, in our own larger community of fierce competition for space, justify this?

Sentiment, of course, draws scorn from the practical-minded. But I doubt if sentiment is as fragile a defense as we think. How cheaply would the toughest-minded sell the loyalty and pride of those who serve with him in factory, field or countinghouse? How great can a commonwealth become, how long can it endure, if it measures everything by a price tag?

There exists, I suppose, such a thing as fundamental decency and gratitude and there are ways to acknowledge it. The Mormons have their monument to the gulls which saved them from the locusts. The Lord Chancellor sits upon a woolsack, memento of the source of England's early economic power. Many of us have seen the block expressing gratitude to the boll weevil which first obliged the South to begin diversifying its crops—a curious but impressive tribute.

We are, and rightly, generous in our regard for the group of most unusual men who made possible our Nation and planned its greatness. But we ought to remember, too, that in large measure our power and leadership are based upon the lavishness of Nature, building undisturbed through millenniums. The ancients thought it not unworthy to worship the gods who gave them grain—rice, wheat, maize. Is it unworthy in our enlightened day to commemorate, by generous preservation, the natural wealth which has been the lifeblood of our economy? I, for one, do not think so. To me it seems a matter of ethics and national self-respect.

An American commander in eastern Europe told me that he gave permission to the cold and hungry people of a city to help themselves to the trees in their ancient forest-park. This they refused to do, and the hard-headed general was deeply moved by their decision. It will not do to write off sentiment.

There is also, in the need for generous natural areas, the question of important scientific knowledge. The undisturbed community of plants and animals is a beautifully organized dynamic system, employing energy from the sun for the use and re-use of water, air and minerals in sustaining abundant life, while keeping its own organization going. Technically this presents an exceedingly important phenomenon, the approximation of a steady state. Our knowledge of this phenomenon can do with considerable improvement, and again we need generous examples for its study. When men are beginning to talk rather seriously of raising some billions for the exploration of space, we ought not to neglect a more immediate, and definitely hopeful, source of knowledge. Knowledge for its own sake, like sentiment, is not lightly to be written off by a civilized nation.

It happens, however, that although the knowledge thus obtained is not likely to be patentable as a source of direct profit, its benefits diffused over the land-use pattern of our Nation should be very great. The studies of Dr. John E. Weaver of the University of Nebraska, carried on through the years on a pitiful remnant of rented prairie, are of growing significance to the economy of the great grasslands of North America.

Just as the engineer in machine and industrial design must have at hand his theoretical apparatus of calculation, so the biologist and others who would design intelligent land-use, must have their norms or standards of measurement. And these norms, to a large degree, are to be found in the complex pattern of interrelationship represented by the undisturbed natural community. At present we have to rely largely on intuition—a wasteful and dangerous process, as is trial and error. It is a moral obligation to *know,* if we can.

Why are species which have endured for millions of years—the oak, chestnut, elm and beech—suddenly so vulnerable, now that we have disturbed their homes? Introduced parasites are not the entire answer. Why are the second-growth forests which now cover about two-thirds of New England so full of inferior stock that a generation or more must pass before they become reasonably productive? Is it because we have systematically harvested the best and biggest trees, leaving only scrub individuals of bad heredity to reproduce themselves? Four thousand years of corncobs are piled up in Bat Cave, New Mexico, and the ones on top are as scrubby as those at the bottom. Presumably the Indians ate all the big ears instead of saving them for seed. What happened in the cornfield can happen in a forest. We need to know.

Yet neither knowledge nor sentiment alone afford the most powerful justification of ample wilderness or natural areas set aside in perpetuity. Rather it is the mixture of practical, theoretical and ethical symbolized by the question, "What kind of a Nation do we want?" Do we wish to build a future completely and ruthlessly mechanized, standardized and artificial? Do we really mean to crowd back Nature to the utmost minimum, depending upon ingenious artifice at every turn for physical and spiritual sustenance, until we have to eat standing up and the healing which comes of solitude survives only in dreams?

The hour is late, but we still have a measure of freedom to choose.

QUESTIONS

1. Why did our forefathers not preserve tracts of virgin timber, prairie, and shore line when the government was being set up?
2. What are two things which must be done to prevent an animal from becoming extinct?
3. Evaluate the statement "Only resources having a dollar and cents value are worthy of conservation."
4. Extinction of a plant or animal means that its particular and unique genes are lost. Can the scientist ever be sure that he will not need these genes in some future breeding program? Explain.

Marya Mannes

Wasteland

Reprinted with the permission of the author and publisher from More in Anger. Philadelphia, J. B. Lippincott, 1958.

Cans. Beer cans. Glinting on the verges of a million miles of roadways, lying in scrub, grass, dirt, leaves, sand, mud, but never hidden. Piels, Rheingold, Ballantine, Schaefer, Schlitz, shining in the sun or picked by moon or the beams of headlights at night; washed by rain or flattened by wheels, but never dulled, never buried, never destroyed. Here is the mark of savages, the testament of wasters, the stain of prosperity.

Who are these men who defile the grassy borders of our roads and lanes, who pollute our ponds, who spoil the purity of our ocean beaches with the empty vessels of their thirst? Who are the men who make these vessels in millions and then say, "Drink—and discard"? What society is this that can afford to cast away a million tons of metal and to make of wild and fruitful land a garbage heap?

What manner of men and women need thirty feet of steel and two hundred horsepower to take them, singly, to their small destinations? Who demand that what they eat is wrapped so that forests are cut down to make the paper that is thrown away, and what they smoke and chew is sealed so that the sealers can be tossed in gutters and caught in twigs and grass?

What kind of men can afford to make the streets of their towns and cities hideous with neon at night, and their roadways hideous with signs by day, wasting beauty; who leave the carcasses of cars to rot in heaps; who spill their trash into ravines and make smoking mountains of refuse for the town's rats? What manner of men choke off the life in rivers, streams and lakes with the waste of their produce, making poison of water?

Who is as rich as that? Slowly the wasters and despoilers are impoverishing our land, our nature, and our beauty, so that there will not be one beach, one hill, one lane, one meadow, one forest free from the debris of man and the stigma of his improvidence.

Who is so rich that he can squander forever the wealth of earth and water for the trivial needs of vanity or the compulsive demands of greed; or so prosperous in land that he can sacrifice nature for unnatural desires? The earth we abuse and the living things we kill will, in the end, take their revenge; for in exploiting their presence we are diminishing our future.

And what will we leave behind us when we are long dead? Temples? Amphora? Sunken treasure?

Or mountains of twisted, rusted steel, canyons of plastic containers, and a million miles of shores garlanded, not with the lovely wrack of the sea, but with the cans and bottles and light-bulbs and boxes of a people who conserved their convenience at the expense of their heritage, and whose ephemeral prosperity was built on waste.

QUESTIONS

1. Comment on the statement that Americans are said to be the most wasteful people on earth.
2. What might be the relationship between the "permanence" of a country's greatness and the conservation of our natural resources?

PART FOURTEEN

PALEOBOTANY

Someone has said that the past is the key to the future. If we know our fossil forms and compare them with living species, we can then make some valid extrapolations about the future. In other words, the scientific method allows us to make predictions. For example, the study of coal, which is composed of fossil plants, will tell us how much coal remains in the earth's crust, how it was formed, and how much is probably being formed today. This information can then be used to estimate how long our coal will last for home and industry use. We also know how much time we have to develop a suitable substitute before the coal seams are exhausted. Also, the study of fossil algae called diatoms is of great practical value in oil research.

Paleobotanical research also seeks knowledge for its own sake. The study of evolutionary development produces little of monetary value, but it provides concepts of the maximum interest. Who can say when pure knowledge will become useful? The Heliocentric Theory (sun-centered) of Copernicus was strictly of academic interest until man started sending up rockets and satellites. All calculations of the space travelers are predicated on the validity of this theory. What did the first plants on earth look like and when did they make their first appearance? These are also questions with which paleobotanists are wrestling.

Ralph W. Chaney

Redwoods Around the Pacific Basin

Reprinted (abridged) with the permission of the author and publisher from Pacific Discovery **1**(5):4–14, 1948.

On October 10, 1769, members of the Portolá Expedition first sighted the redwoods of North America on the California coast near the present town of Watsonville. More than a century and three-quarters was to elapse before the discovery of redwoods in Asia.

During these years, fossil redwoods were found at many localities over the northern hemisphere. At first the leafy shoots, whose impressions were found in the rocks of France, were thought to be relatives of the yew and were called *Taxites*. With the discovery of fossil cones in Switzerland, the similarity of these fossils to the coast redwood, *Sequoia sempervirens*, of California, was noted by the great Swiss paleobotanist, Oswald Heer. In the past century other fossil leaves, cones and wood of the redwood type have been found throughout most of the northern hemisphere, and all of them have been assigned to the genus *Sequoia*.

Those of us who are concerned with the history of Cenozoic plants, covering the latest sixty million years of geologic time, have long been aware that some of the fossils we have called *Sequoia* have cones different from those of our living coast redwood. These fossil cones are attached to elongate stalks on which there are no needles, and they have been considered a species distinct from the immediate ancestors of the coast redwood. It was not until 1941 that the Japanese paleobotanist, Shigeru Miki, presented the evidence for referring cones of this type to a new genus, to which he gave the name *Metasequoia*. During the war we learned nothing about the progress of science in Japan and it was not until the summer of 1948 that I had an opportunity to read Miki's paper. By that time much had happened.

The first major event was the visit of forester Tsang Wang to the village of Mo-tao-chi, more than a hundred miles northeast of Chungking, in Szechuan Province. Earlier botanists who had visited this part of China all appear to have traveled along the north side of the Yangtse River, and there is no record that anyone other than the villagers had ever seen what caught Wang's eye on the edge of Mo-tao-chi. Here in the midst of the rice paddies rose an enormous tree, with leaves and cones unlike those of any tree previously observed.

The second major event came about when Wang showed the specimens he had collected to Professor Wan-Chun Cheng of National Central University, and to Dr. Hsen-Hsu Hu of Fan Memorial Institute of Biology. Neither of these authorities on the trees of central China had ever heard of a tree with leaves and cones such as these. To them it was wholly new to the living flora of China and the rest of the world. But—and this is the remarkable part of their great contribution to science—they remembered that they had seen leaves and cones of the same sort on fossil specimens; the specimens from the great tree from Mo-tao-chi were an exact match for the fossils which Miki had named *Metasequoia*. Fortunately they had read his paper in 1946, long before it reached the United States. They knew that the tree discovered by forester Wang was a *Metasequoia*.

The third event came about after Dr. Hu had written to me and to others in the United States regarding this remarkable discovery of a living redwood which had previously been known only as a fossil. Dr. E. D. Merrill, of the Arnold Arboretum of Harvard University, had sent funds for additional field work by the Chinese in central China; in 1947 trees of *Metasequoia* had been found growing at several other localities, and many more specimens, including seeds, had been collected. Now, with some of these seeds on the table before me, I realized that a remarkable opportunity was presenting itself to see a forest of long ago, a forest whose principal member had been thought to be extinct for millions of years. In January of 1948, within a few minutes of my first view of these seeds, I was making active plans to visit central China. Dr. Milton Silverman, Science Writer for the *San Francisco Chronicle,* decided to go with me.

Six weeks later, after a flight to Chungking, a journey down the Yangtse to Wan Hsien, and a three-day trip inland over the rocky trails of Szechuan, there came the fourth and culminating event. We stood beneath the great tree growing on the eastern border of Mo-tao-chi, our hands upon its gray, red-flecked bark, our eyes uplifted to branches which rose nearly a hundred feet above. Here was a fossil come to life, a giant whose kind had persisted out of the past to tell us the story of the earth millions of years before man came to live upon it.

Re-examining the large collections of fossil redwoods in our collections at the University of California, the California Academy of Sciences, and the United States National Museum in Washington, I had come to the conclusion that most of the specimens we have been calling *Sequoia,* not only in North America but in Asia as well, are actually *Metasequoia.* It had been a case of mistaken identity. In my study of the forests of the past, I had recognized abundant fossils which I believed were the ancestors of *Sequoia;* now I found they were in many ways unlike it, and were identical with *Metasequoia,* the dawn redwood of China. Clearly some revisions were in order.

When I stood beside the huge tree at Mo-tao-chi, at the end of our third day of travel on foot across the valleys and mountain ranges of Szechuan I realized that its surroundings were not suited to a study of its original environment and associates, for it was growing in a cultivated valley from which all of the original forest had been wholly removed. So we continued on for two more days, trying days with cold fogs in the mountains, almost constant rains, and with inadequate accommodations for foreigners. Finally at Shui-hsa-pa, some 115 miles south of Wan Hsien and across a province boundary into Hupeh, we found small groves of dawn redwoods in ravines, associated with deciduous hardwoods. It was these trees which I had crossed the Pacific and much of China to see, so that I might reconstruct and visualize the forests of ages past. And I was not disappointed. Growing beside the dawn redwods in the valley at Shui-hsa-pa, at an altitude of about 4,000 feet, were birches, chestnuts, sweet gums, beeches, oaks, and at least one large katsura. The Arcto-Tertiary Flora was growing there before me, with essentially the same membership as the group which had its origin to the north millions of years before, and which had migrated southward down both sides of the Pacific. Forests living elsewhere at middle latitudes today include many hardwood members of the Arcto-Tertiary Flora. But these valleys in central China are the only place where the dawn redwood, *Metasequoia*, is known to have survived with them.

We may wonder how long this tree, whose history goes back for a hundred millions years at least, will continue to live in these remote valleys of central China. This is a land of need; fuel and timbers are scarce; land must be cleared for agriculture. Just before our arrival, two of the finest trees at Shui-hsa-pa had been cut down. Others will follow, unless proper steps are taken.

It is gratifying to record the action being taken by the Chinese to meet this problem of conserving one of the most beautiful and interesting trees in the world. A Metasequoia Conservation Committee has been organized, whose membership includes several of the foremost statesmen and scholars of China. Like the Save-the-Redwoods League, under whose auspices my trip was made, this Committee is seeking to preserve some of the finest groves for all time. To this committee go the best wishes of all Americans, especially those of us who may look out across the Pacific, knowing that the scientific problems and the future needs of Asia are essentially the same as our own.

QUESTIONS

1. Recount the three main events in the discovery and recognition of *Metasequoia.*
2. What are some of the hardwood species associated with *Metasequoia* in its native habitat?
3. Does the *Metasequoia* story have any lesson in it for incautious scientists and if so, what might the lesson be?

Allan Sherman and Allen B. MacMurphy

Origin, Nature and Uses of Coal

Reprinted with the permission of the authors from Facts About Coal, U.S.D.I., Bureau of Mines, 1955.

HOW COAL WAS FORMED

Although coal is commonly thought of as a mineral and is classed as a mineral resource, it is not a mineral in the sense that stone, iron ore, and other substances are. This is because coal is of organic origin, which means that it was formed from the remains of living things—trees, shrubs, herbs, mosses, algae and vines—that grew millions upon millions of years ago, during periods of widespread uniformly mild, moist climate. During those periods, there was heavy growth of vegetation in forested swamps and bogs. Century after century, this vegetation died and accumulated. Buried to a gradually increasing depth each year by new accumulations, the remains of roots, trunks, branches, and leaves changed gradually to peat, just as decaying vegetable matter is doing today in the Dismal Swamp of Virginia and North Carolina, and in smaller swamps and bogs in many states.

Peat is the first step in changing organic matter into coal. In a block of peat you can often see, with the naked eye, the woody fragments of stems, roots, and bark. When dried, peat can be burned; but in this country, because better fuels are plentiful, it is used chiefly as an ingredient of fertilizers, as a soil conditioner, and, to some extent, as a packing material for plants, fruits, and vegetables.

As the peat substance was buried, it was cut off from the oxygen in the air, and this prevented rapid decay of its organic matter by slowing bacterial action. The weight of more vegetation falling on the peat helped to compress and solidify it. So did the weight of water if the peat deposit sank below the sea, as often happened. Sometimes mineral sediments settled from muddy flood waters during the period when the vegetable matter was accumulating, and then what we now call "partings," or layers of shale, were formed in the coal vein. During the coal-forming period, the swamps were flooded by sea water for a long time; and earthy sediments were deposited in thick beds over the peat, further compressing it and starting the coal-making process, which is called "coalification."

Coalification was extremely slow when it depended mainly upon the pressure from beds of rock and the temperatures normally prevailing a few hundred feet below the surface. For this reason, many of our coal deposits are still in an early stage of coalification, or "low rank," although they have been buried for millions of years. A few coal deposits, however, were situated where profound movements of the rocks in the earth's crust occurred during periods of mountain building. This rock movement generated much additional heat and pressure, producing our "high-rank" coals, such as medium- and low-volatile bituminous coal and anthracite. Occasionally the movement of molten rock oozing from the deep, hot regions of the earth into its outer crust transformed the adjacent coal beds into coke.

* * * * * *

Bituminous coal is the most abundant and widespread rank of coal in the United States. It is the coal used most commonly for industrial, power, railroad and heating purposes. Bituminous coals may be either coking or noncoking. This property is not based on the rank of the coal, but rather on whether it will produce a coke when processed in a coke oven. Nearly all eastern bituminuos coals have coking properties, but many of the western bituminous coals are noncoking or free-burning.

* * * * * *

Anthracite, sometimes called hard coal, has a brilliant luster and a uniform texture. If you handle anthracite, it will not soil your fingers as does coal of lower ranks. Anthracite has a higher percentage of fixed carbon and a lower percentage of volatile matter than the lower-rank coals. It burns slowly, with a pale-blue flame free from smoke. Most anthracite has a somewhat lower heating value than the highest-grade bituminous coals, but its lack of soot and the fact that it will burn longer without attention make anthracite an ideal domestic fuel, and much of it is used for space heating.

* * * * * *

THE CHEMISTRY OF COAL

Coal, like wood, is made up of the elements carbon, hydrogen, oxygen, nitrogen, a little sulfur, and other elements in minute quantities. The proportions in which the major elements are mixed differ greatly in different kinds of coal, and the chemistry of coal is extremely complicated.

* * * * * *

THE USES OF COAL

You can burn coal; if it is a coking coal you can make coke from it; or you can convert it into gas. These are its three primary uses at present. To them a fourth—the commercial production of synthetic liquid fuels—may some day be added in the United States. Coal already has been used for this purpose in some countries that have little or no oil and a good supply of coal, notably England and Germany.

As fuel, coal is used as a source of heat energy for many things, including:

1. Producing steam for power by electric power plants, industrial plants, and some steam vessels and railroads.
2. Industrial and commercial heating and cooking, such as store and plant heating, bakeries, etc. and coke production.
3. Domestic heating and cooking.
4. Firing ceramic products—brick,

tile, pottery, porcelain, china, and other articles made from clay.

5. Burning cement.

Carbonization of coal produces coke, tar, light oil, ammonia, and gases. When coal is carbonized in an old-fashioned beehive oven, coke is the only product saved. The other products, except for some used for heating the oven, are wasted. But when coal is carbonized in a modern slot-type coke oven, the gas, tar, ammonia, and other chemical products are saved.

QUESTIONS

1. Write a paragraph on the composition and mode of formation of coal.
2. Justify the statement made elsewhere that "coal is fossil sunlight."
3. What are the differences between bituminous and anthracite coals?

G. Erdtman

Introduction to Pollen Analysis

Reprinted with the permission of the publisher from Introduction to Pollen Analysis, Waltham, Chronica Botanica, 1954.

It has been claimed that skillful hunters of old could bring their prey down even if they caught only a fleeting glimpse of its shadow. But still more remarkable appear the performances accomplished today by the pollen analyst. Out of pollen from crumbled clay or minute pieces of peat, taken from bits of earthenware or a stone axe, may be constructed a picture of the primeval forests which flourished in the region at the time when the pot or axe dropped into the bog. This is, however, not the whole story. In a carefully investigated region it is also possible to determine the relative, in certain places even the absolute age of a pollen-bearing sample and to ascertain its place in a system of curves, illustrating changes in vegetation and climate, during ages long past.

Pollen analysis is a young science.

At the sixteenth Meeting of Scandinavian Naturalists in Oslo in 1916 it received its birth certificate by LENNART VON POST who, at that occasion, read a paper on the pollen of forest trees in bogs of southern Sweden. The science of pollen analysis became of age a few years ago, having already made a brilliant record in its childhood and youth. This is amply attested by more than 1500 publications which have been published on the subject to date.

Pollen analysis is essentially founded on the following facts. At the time of flowering many trees shed great quantities of pollen. A single birch catkin may produce in excess of ten million pollen grains. In general, pollen grains are very small, as a rule averaging between one hundredth and one tenth of a millimeter in diameter. Easily carried by the wind, some of them are transferred into higher regions by vertical air currents and remain there for days, weeks, or even months, before they settle back to earth. In the meantime this "plankton of the air" may have moved over great distances. Greenland peats contain pollen grains of pine and spruce, that must have been carried at least 100 kilometers (the distance of the nearest coniferous forest in Labrador). CHARLES LINDBERGH trapped pollen grains and spores by means of "sky-hooks" during a flight over Greenland. In 1937, the author collected pollen grains and spores by means of vacuum cleaners practically the whole way across the Atlantic between Gothenburg and New York. Among the pollen grains thus obtained, American specimens were found at least as far as 700 kilometers east of Newfoundland. For practical purposes of pollen analysis, however, such far-travelling grains are of minor importance. After their aerial journey the pollen grains may settle on the surface of a bog or lake or in a bay, where sediments are deposited, and be embedded in the accumulating peat or ooze and preserved. In this way the peat bogs and the sediment banks on lake-bottoms become archives of vegetational history imprisoning pollen grains, season after season, millennium after millennium.

A trained pollen analyst, studying these forest archives, may not only be able to tell the family or genus to which the pollen grains belong but also the species, and, in some cases, even the subspecies. The identification of the pollen grains is, however, only one side of the matter. Another, and no less important, is the interpretation of the fossil pollen flora. This is sometimes a very difficult problem. Thus a peat sample may provide hazel nuts but no hazel pollen; and bogs within an area with aspen and poplar predominating, may contain much the same pollen flora as bogs of a nearby area with pine and spruce predominating. The latter case may be explained by the fact that the exines of aspen and poplar pollen grains are so thin that they are preserved only in exceptional cases, whilst those of the pine and spruce pollen are very resistant to decay. Furthermore, pine and spruce pollen is easily carried by the wind and may be scattered over considerable areas outside of the coniferous region. Therefore, it goes without saying that the evidence of pollen grains sometimes must be taken with a grain of salt.

The development of pollen analysis might, in a certain sense, be compared to the development of a river system. The Oslo paper was the source and stimulus. Successively, and in ever increasing numbers, tributaries—collaborators—joined the main stream, the course of which was directed by Von Post and his assistants of the Geological Survey of Sweden. At times uncritical overproduction increased the stream more in breadth than in depth.

At present its volume has increased to such an extent, that a cleavage of the stream into different channels must be expected. From these channels an increasing number of fields of scientific activity—from quaternary geology to climatology and archaeology—may be fertilized as a result of a more and more efficient system of irrigation.

Improved research methods have contributed to the present situation. For example, by certain chemical methods it is now possible to dissolve away more of the matrix in which the fossil grains occur, thus greatly facilitating their analysis. Different soils, previously considered more or less devoid of pollen (clay, raw humus, etc.) have become amenable to pollen analysis. And by concentrating the pollen grains of a sample, which in itself is rich in pollen, rare kinds of pollen may be discovered.

To the pollen geologist pollen grains are merely index fossils, by means of which a particular horizon may be traced from one peat deposit to another, from province to province, or even from one country to another. To the pollen botanist, on the other hand, identification is an important consideration. The more pollen species identified, the more complete will be the picture of the former vegetation.

Pollen and spore research is concerned not only with the late Quaternary history of the vegetation, but also with the history of the plant kingdom during more distinct epochs, with the elucidation of the enigma of the origin of the angiosperms, etc. A successful attack on these great problems demands, above all, an extensive knowledge of the pollen and spore types among contemporary plants. Surprisingly little, however, has so far been accomplished in this field.

This outline of the potentialities of pollen analysis may easily be augmented inasmuch as pollen research is not confined exclusively to paleobotany, plant systematics, and plant geography. It is also linked up with many other fields of scientific activity, such as forestry, soil science, limnology, and different geological disciplines. We may also mention archaeology, climatology and aerobiology—with its ramifications in medicine, hygiene, phytopathology, etc.—and even pharmacognosy (the detection of honey and drug adulteration through pollen analysis).

QUESTIONS

1. Name two facts which a pollen analyst might tell us about a pollen sample.
2. What contribution could pollen analysis make to the evolutionary history of the angiosperms?

Anonymous

The Study of Fossil Plants

Amended and reprinted with the permission of the publishers, Leaflet 46, General Biological Supply House Inc.

To the lay person it might, on first thought, seem that an accurate knowledge of the sort of vegetation that covered the earth during remote ages would be impossible. He has heard accounts of dinosaurs, the gigantic reptiles that lived aeons ago, and because of the numerous records of discovery of their fossilized remains, their existence is generally and easily conceded. Because of the relatively few papers that have been presented in a popularized form concerning the discoveries of fossilized plants, there is very little knowledge of this subject, except as possessed by the specialists in our colleges and universities who have fostered the science, Paleobotany. It is hoped that a more general dissemination of this knowledge will be possible in the future, both through popularized publications and through the study of sets of plant fossils which are now available at quite reasonable prices. Through intensive studies of plant fossils, it is now possible to tell just what sort of vegetation covered the earth during different geologic periods. Scenes can now be reconstructed showing whole forests of coal-forming plants. Some large museums now feature such groups and a study of them is not only enlightening but very entertaining. The history of the earth's plant life has been written, indelibly, into the rocks, and science is now beginning to decipher it, much the same as has been done for the Egyptian hieroglyphics.

While many lowly plants, such as bacteria and algae, have been known from Precambrian times, in this article we are devoting our main interest to higher plants, chiefly those that flourished during the Paleozoic era (specifically, the Carboniferous period). These latter plants are preserved for us in such forms as bark, seeds, leaves and stems, so that accurate knowledge is at hand for the gross structure of the coal-forming plants. Not only this, but some of the structures are so excellently preserved that it is possible to prepare microscopic sections of them. The minute anatomy of many of these plants has thus been studied.

The fossils that have made Paleobotany an exact science are found in various kinds of rock formations in all parts of the world. Sandstone, shale and slate yield an abundant supply of fossilized plants. These, being sedimentary rocks, are formed from materials that have been washed down from high elevations and deposited in either fresh or salt water during a great "flood." Just how these "floods" (in some instances they covered relatively small areas) were caused is an interesting speculation. It is thought that due to movement of the earth's crust, the land subsided and allowed the sea to rush in and cover it. The ordinary process of erosion by the rains, winds, etc., also accounts for some inundations that were destined to preserve plant structure for study during later ages.

Fossils are also found in volcanic tuff, which is the rock formed from volcanic ashes. Plants falling into mineral springs were quickly infiltrated with a special kind of limestone and thus were preserved entire. Amber has also been a medium for preserving plants from the far distant prehistoric times. It was formed from the resin of coniferous trees. Parts of plants, and also insects, have been imbedded in the resin which later solidified, thus preserving them intact and in their original state. The color of structures preserved in amber, which is lost through the other types of fossilization, remains unaltered through the ages and gives us our only impressions of the colors in the prehistoric forests.

Many fossil plants are found in the so-called coal balls. These are hard dark lumps which are found in coal seams. They vary in size from small masses approximately one or two inches in diameter to those a foot or more in diameter. On examination these coal balls prove to be masses of plant material saturated with crystallinic lime. The deduction is that at the time the coal seam was formed, some mineral water in the coal swamp precipitated lime crystals or silica about the nucleus of plant matter, which through this process has been preserved almost in its original form.

We cannot, within the limitations imposed by a short article, enter into a detailed account of all of the plants that flourished during the Coal Age. However, we will give below a brief description of some of the major forms.

SPHENOPSIDA

This group includes among others, the Paleozoic Calamites, the remote ancestors of our present day horsetails or scouring rushes. Quite in contrast with the small American scouring rushes, which are to be found early in the year along the banks of brooklets and other moist places, were the giant Calamites, which in general appearance resemble extant horsetails but which attained heights of a hundred feet. They bore narrow lance-shaped leaves arranged in whorls at the nodes, just as the present forms possess scale-like leaves in a circular arrangement about the nodes. The stems of these giant horsetails were hollow. Most of the plants of this group must have been arborescent although there must have been herbaceous species as well.

Calamites are found in the Pennsylvania deposits and are very abundant in the coal deposits in the eastern United States. They disappeared in the Permian.

LYCOPSIDA

The surviving genera of this order are our present day club mosses *Lycopodium* (commonly called ground pine), *Selaginella, Isoetes* and others. *Lepidodendron* and *Sigillaria* are the principal genera of Paleozoic Lycopsida, about 100 species of each having been described. Both of them attained a height of about a hundred feet. What a contrast with their descendants of this age!

Lepidodendron means "scale tree," and this name was assigned these plants since the bark on the trees was covered with scales. Representatives of this form are found as far back as Devonian times. It was during the Permian that their dominance gave way.

The trunks of *Lepidodendrons,* some of which were four feet or more in diameter (and which grew to a height of a hundred feet or more), were straight and palm-like, and bore toward the top a crown of branches. The stems were clothed in long simple leaves which, being needle-like, resembled roughly those of the pine. In some forms the needle leaves attained a length of six or seven inches. The tips of the slender branches bore cones which sometimes reached a length of 20 inches and a diameter of 2 inches. There were huge underground parts, very much like roots in appearance, but without the structure of roots, to which the name *Stigmaria* has been applied. These root-like structures are marked with circular scars where the "rootlets" were attached. These root-like organs were possessed both by *Lepidodendron* and the closely allied form, *Sigillaria.*

Sigillarias were also found along with the *Lepidodendrons.* The word *Sigillaria* means "sealtree" and is appropriate because the impressions on the bark frequently resemble the wax seals which were used by our forefathers to close their letters. Like the *Lepidodendrons,* these trees attained a great size but most of them were unbranched. There are accounts of some of these trees that were only 18 feet in height but were 6 feet in diameter. The leaves were varied in size, some resembling closely those of the *Lepidodendrons,* while others were long and sword-shaped being three feet long. *Sigillarias* bore their cones in vertical rows or in a whorl about the stem and the cones were usually much smaller that those of the *Lepidodendron* cones.

The propagation of both of these trees was accomplished by means of spores. Quantities of big spores are found in coal, and naturally enormous masses must have been shed in the swamps where coal was formed; but only a few, relatively speaking, ever germinated. The first food of the embryonic plant was contained in the spores, hence they were rich in oils and other fats. The coal made up of these spores is oily and is commonly referred to as "cannel coal."

PTEROPSIDA

In this category we place the true ferns, the gymnosperms and the angiosperms. The true ferns trace their history back to the middle of the Devonian period. They increased in species and numbers of individuals during the Carboniferous period. During the Jurassic they showed some tendency to decline but they are apparently "holding their own" with some 10,000 species known.

Fossil gymnosperms may be illustrated by the Pteridosperms and the Cordaitales. The first group was characterized by fern-like foliage but they were true seed plants. Some of them grew to 60 or 70 feet in height and had trunks with diameters of about two feet. The Cordaitales includes several groups. One of these groups contains the genus *Cordaites.* The genus was very common in the Carboniferous period. The slender leaves frequently were three feet in length, the stem had secondary wood and a pith and the male and female inflorescences were in the form of strobili.

ANGIOSPERMS

It is in this group that the bulk of our familiar living plants belong, so that it is obviously unnecessary to go into any detail concerning them. Angiosperms represent the culmination of the much branched plant line of ascent. They were the latest to come upon the earth and some are perfectly adjusted to a terrestrial existence. Angiosperms appeared during the Lower Cretaceous and have been dominant among plants since Tertiary times. It is estimated that they are represented by about 300,000 living and several thousand fossil species. The rapid rise of Angiosperms is thought to be due in part at least to the development of the flower-loving insects such as the bees, wasps, and butterflies in the Jurassic, the period just preceding that which marks Angiosperm beginnings.

QUESTIONS

1. What importance does Paleobotany have for students of earth history?
2. How are plants preserved as fossils?
3. What were the fossil relatives of the "horsetails"?
4. Mention two fossil relatives of our lycopodiums and selaginellas.
5. What groups might be included in the Pteropsida?
6. Name and characterize one of the fossil gymnosperms.
7. Trace the history, geologically speaking, of the angiosperms.

PART FIFTEEN

CYTOLOGY

Some years ago, the late Dr. Milliken is reported to have said that all of the major facts of physics had been discovered and that all that remained was the refinement of measurements. Shortly thereafter the dissection of the atom began and we suddenly had a "new" physics. Cytology was, at one time, in a sort of doldrum period until refined chemical and miscroscopic methods enabled men to make a real breakthrough. Strasburger's paper represents the old frame of refer ence whereas the other papers have a more modern "flavor." The revolution came, in brief, with the discovery that chromosomes contained super molecules of deoxyribose nucleic acid arranged in a double helix. It was further discovered that the amount of this substance, DNA, in gametes was half the amount contained in the regular cells. These facts led to the prediction that the DNA was, in fact, the material known as the gene. Genes of DNA have been transferred from some forms to others leading to all sorts of interesting predictions about making new species at will.

The above development was cyto-chemical. Cytotaxonomy, as Dr. Anderson points out, attempts to deduce the relationships of organisms by studying the numbers and kinds of chromosomes in parents and their probable hybrids. This, too, is a highly exciting and rewarding type of endeavor.

For more papers in this area, read The Cell *by Carl P. Swanson.*

Eduard Strasburger

The Periodic Reduction of the Number of the Chromosomes in the Life-history of Living Organisms

Reprinted with the permission of the publisher from Annals of Botany 8:281–316, 1894.

The simplest organisms with which we are acquainted reproduce themselves in only an asexual manner. It would appear that it is only in the lowest organisms that the absence of sexual differentiation is possible, and that this differentiation necessarily accompanies a certain definite degree of organization: it is, in fact, as if this differentiation must manifest itself at a certain stage of phylogenetic evolution in virtue of certain properties possessed by organized matter as such. It is true that many highly organized plants are asexual, but comparative investigation proves that this is due to a gradual loss of sexual differentiation, as in the great group of the fungi, and doubtless also in the apogamous ferns.

It appears that the sexual act has always given a powerful impulse to phylogenetic evolution; and that, on the other hand, all advance in development was in abeyance so long as sexual differentiation had not been obtained. From the phylogenetic standpoint, we must assume that all sexually differentiated organisms are descended from asexual organisms.

Our insight into the nature of the process of fertilization was very materially promoted by the discovery, made by Edouard van Beneden, that the number of the chromosomes is the same in both the conjugating nuclei. Further investigations established the fact, for both animals and plants, that a reduction to one-half of the number of the chromosomes in the generative nuclei precedes the sexual act, and that, in consequence of the coalescence of the male and female nuclei, the nucleus of the fertilized ovum possesses the number of chromosomes characteristic of a vegetative cell.

Guignard and I established the

fact that the number of chromosomes characteristic of the generative nuclei of angiosperms, is determined in the mother-cells of the embryo-sacs. The investigations of the zoologists have also shown that this determination is effected in the mother-cells of the ova and of the spermatozoa of animals, by two successive cell-divisions, which give rise, in the one case, to four spermatozoa, and in the other, to the ovum and to three so-called polar bodies.

But what is the significance of this reduction in number of the chromosomes in the sexual cells, and of the equality of their number in the male and female cells? The physiological utility of the arrangement readily suggests itself: for were it not so, the number of chromosomes in the nuclei of each generation would be twice as great as in the preceding; and again, by this means each parent is represented in the offspring by an equal number of chromosomes, and thus equally transmits its hereditary characters. The morphological cause of the reduction in number of the chromosomes and of their equality in number in the sexual cells is, in my opinion phylogenetic. I look upon these facts as indicating a return to the original generation from which, after it had attained sexual differentiation, offspring was developed having a double number of chromosomes. Thus the reduction by one-half of the number of the chromosomes in the sexual cells is not the outcome of a gradually evolved process of reduction, but rather it is the reappearance of the primitive number of chromosomes as it existed in the nuclei of the generation in which sexual differentiation first took place. Viewed from this standpoint, many facts become more readily intelligible: for instance, the immediate and sudden occurrence of the reduction, the developmental stage at which it takes place, and the varying length of the interval which separates it from the sexual act.

The number of chromosomes determined in the mother-cells of the pollen of the angiosperms persists up to the formation of the spermatic nucleus in the development of this nucleus: two divisions take place in the mother-cell resulting in the formation of four pollen-grains; then there is the division in the pollen-grain by which the generative and the vegetative cells are respectively formed; and, finally, there is the fourth division, the division into two of the generative cell in the pollen-tube. The number of chromosomes determined in the mother-cell of the embryo-sac persists through a series of divisions, the number of which varies with the species of plant, until it attains functional importance in the ovum. As a rule, the mother-cell of the embryo-sac divides twice, and the lowest of the resulting daughter-cells develops into the embryo-sac. In the embryo-sac three divisions succeed each other before the nucleus of the ovum is formed. In this case five divisions, and not four as in the development of the spermatic nucleus, intervene between the reduction and determination of the number of the chromosomes, on the one hand, and the constitution of the sexually functional nucleus on the other.

The reduction of the number of the chromosomes in the pollen-mother-cells of angiosperms, which has been adduced as an example, is therefore not to be regarded as a preparation for the sexual act; it really marks the beginning of the new generation which comes into existence with the primitive number of chromosomes. This primitive generation has, however, undergone great limitation before it attained the reduced ontogeny which it now exhibits in the angiosperms. In the first place it developed sexual dimorphism, so that it was represented by two parallel developmental series, a male and a female. The phylogenetic course along which this reduction, as also the development of the dimorphism, proceeded, can be traced backwards.

The constancy of the number of the chromosomes in the nuclei of the sexual cells is doubtless of great importance, for it ensures the equal influence of the two parents in the sexual act: and the act of fertilization is, in all the higher organisms, the centre of gravity of the maintenance and development of the species.

It is established that, in the higher plants, all the nuclear divisions which lead up to the formation of the sexual cells are normally attended by longitudinal splitting of the chromosomes, so that the number of the chromosomes remain the same throughout. There is no such thing, among plants, as nuclear divisions resulting in the reduction by one-half of the number of the chromosomes. Such a conception involves the assumption that the entire, not longitudinally split, chromosomes of the mother-nucleus become separated into two groups, each of which goes to form a daughter-nucleus. If this be so, then each daughter-nucleus must contain only half as many chromosomes as the mother-nucleus; and, in the next generation, each nucleus must contain only half as many chromosomes as a daughter-nucleus: but nothing of the kind can be observed among plants, a fact which has to be taken into account in a consideration of the phenomena of heredity.

I have rejected the view of the hereditarily unequal division of nuclei on the ground that it is contrary to the facts ascertained by direct observation, and I am equally unable to admit that theories of heredity are justified in reconstructing the nucleus with the object of finding in it all the structures which are necessary to them: the only legitimate point of departure is afforded by the actually observed facts of nuclear structure. I consider Weismann's conception of the id, as an element in the nucleus which is charged with all the hereditary characteristics of the species, to be felicitous, because it appears to me that it can be supported by direct observation. I regard as ids the discoid segments of the chromosomes, which are all exactly similar in form and structure, and are serially arranged with such remarkable regularity in the chromosomes of nuclei about to divide.

It is by their simultaneous activity that the constancy of the species is proportionately maintained: for the co-operation of so many ids must produce a resultant effect which would be a mean between the individual variations of the successive generations. If, however, in consequence of the repeated union of individuals presenting a similar variation, the number of ids representing this variation be increased, the variation must become permanent.

At each longitudinal splitting of the chromosomes during nuclear division, all the ids are halved and are equally distributed to the succeeding generations of nuclei. The number of the ids would, however, become doubled at each sexual act, were it not for the reduction which takes place at the initiation of each sexual generation. Since this reduction is not due either to extrusion or to an absorption of the chromosomes, at least in plants, the only remaining explanation is that it is due to the fusion in pairs of the ids and therefore also of the chromosomes.

It is now known that the chromosomes of the two parents do not lose their independence in connexion with the sexual act. Hence in hybrids the chromosomes of both father and mother continue active; and the behaviour of hybrids shows peculiarities which are very instructive for the comprehension of the phenomena of heredity in the offspring of legitimate unions. Hybrids may exhibit in all their parts a combination of the characters of the two parents; or they may show this only in certain parts, whilst other parts present the distinct characters of one or other of the parents; or they, on the whole, resemble one parent more than the other; or, finally, they may altogether resemble one of the parents. Naudin has drawn attention to the fact that, in some hybrids, the characters of the two parents, instead of being blended, are manifested in patches; this may occur in all parts of the plant, but it is especially marked in flowers and fruits. In such a case the hybrid is a sort of mosaic made up of portions of the two parents. Millardet has recently given an account of hybrids which are more like, or, in the extreme case, exactly resemble either the father or the mother.

The process of reduction of the number of the chromosomes by half takes place, in the Muscineae, Pteridophyta, and Phanerogamia, in the spore-mother-cells, that is, at the close of the generation developed from the fertilized ovum; but in the lower Cryptogams, where the cell produced by the sexual act does not give rise to a definite organism representing the asexual generation, the reduction probably takes place on the germination of this cell.

The reduction in number of the chromosomes takes place, among the higher plants, in the mother-cells of the spores, and it is consequently these which must be regarded as the first term of the new generation. They assert this their true significance in that they usually isolate themselves from cohesion with other cells and become independent, although this independence is only of practical utility in the case of the products of their division, that is, of the spores. Hence the centre of gravity of the developmental processes which take place in both micro- and macro-sporangia of Cryptogams and Phanerogams, does not lie in those cells, cell-rows, or cell-aggregates, which give rise to the sporogenous tissue and have been designated 'archesporium' by Goebel. The archesporium still belongs to the sexually-developed asexual generation; it is only the spore-mother-cells which initiate the new sexual generation: consequently the presence or absence of a well-defined archesporium is not a matter to which importance should be attached. For the archesporium is merely the merismatic tissue from which the spore-mother-cells are derived, a tissue which is frequently, but by no means necessarily, differentiated from the surrounding tissues at an early stage; so that its differentiation cannot be of fundamental importance.

QUESTIONS

1. Can you name any plants that reproduce entirely by asexual means?
2. What does Dr. Strasburger believe to have been the course of evolution? Did it proceed from asexual to sexual or from sexual to asexual?
3. Can you think of any advantage in propagating apple trees asexually instead of using seeds?
4. What phenomenon takes place in the chromosomal mechanism preceding the formation of male and female sex cells?
5. What is the practical advantage of this phenomenon?
6. Are Strasburger's ideas about the steps leading to the formation of the sexual generation (gametophyte) essentially

modern? Consult a textbook if necessary.

7. To what modern term do the "ids" most closely refer?

8. Are the parental chromosomes present in a hybrid? What is the significance of this?

George A. Baitsell

The Cell as a Structural Unit

Reprinted with the permision of the author and publisher from the American Naturalist **74**:5–24, 1940.

Year by year since 1828 when Wöhler synthesized urea in the laboratory and showed that organic chemistry, the chemistry of life, was merely a greatly complicated inorganic chemistry, that the difference between the compounds formed in the living organism and those existing outside the living organism was not one of *kind* but of *degree of complexity*, the boundary wall between the chemistry of life and non-life has been repeatedly shattered. As a result it is now apparent that the plan of organization exhibited in the living world, with the cell as the basic unit, does not differ intrinsically from that exhibited by inorganic materials, but is a plan which has become amazingly elaborated and of extreme complexity.

The phenomena characteristic of life are only possible when a tremendously complex association of certain elements is present. But the materials used in the life stuff, protoplasm—the atoms of carbon, hydrogen, nitrogen, oxygen, sulfur, and various other elements—are the same in living materials as elsewhere. Since every element has its own unchanging characteristics, the structure and behavior of a carbon atom or the atom of any other element is not changed when it is temporarily built into the protoplasm of a living organism. But the almost incomprehensible complexity of living materials, constructed from a wide assortment of elements, is accompanied by unique phenomena maintained by the ultilization of radiant energy e.g. the characteristics of the living state—which are beyond and different from those of the individual elements or from any known association of elements existing outside the living organism. Even at the present time the scientist has nothing definite to offer as to when or where or how protoplasm and the associated living phenomena originated, and comparatively little as to the basic features of the complex chemistry of metabolism essential to life.

THE USE OF THE X RAY IN THE DETERMINATION OF MOLECULAR PATTERNS

The structure of any crystalline substance as revealed by the X rays is essentially uniform, that is, there is a definite characteristic unit pattern formed by the constituent atoms and molecules which is continuously repeated throughout the substance; a pattern which, though ultramicroscopic, may be determined by the proper treatment of the data obtained from the diffraction of the X rays as recorded on a photographic film. This condition may be visualized by comparing the ultramicroscopic pattern in a crystalline substance with the visible repeat pattern in wall paper or in a woven textile. A regular arrangement of the molecules in a substance constitutes a crystal and it will diffract X rays in a definite pattern which is continuously repeated and can be identified. This repeat pattern in a crystalline substance is the "unit-cell, that is, the size of the smallest area containing the unit of atomic or molecular pattern which is repeated from end to end of the crystal."

The molecule of the chemist is usually defined "as the smallest portion of an element or compound that retains chemical identity with the substance in mass." As such, the molecular unit of inorganic substances or even that of a much more complex organic substance is far below microscopic visibility. But X ray studies first revealed the basic fact that the molecules do not exist as independent units in solid or crystalline substances. The constituent atoms are all bound together to form larger units of the crystal pattern without molecular separation.

It should be recognized that the association of the independent molecules in the development of a characteristic crystal pattern occurs only in solids. In a gas the unit molecules are entirely independent except for chance contacts in their rapid movements. Molecules in a liquid are more closely associated than in a gas but even so are not bound together in a rigid crystalline pattern; they are, in general, free to move in any direction and accordingly are uniformly dispersed in a solution.

Increasingly in recent years X rays and polarized light have been used to study the ultramicroscopic structure of various organic materials, particularly the proteins. It now looks as if the situation in the study of proteins, the protoplasmic building materials may be compared to that in the physical sciences in earlier years at a time when the results from the early X ray studies were first considered. The results already obtained are of basic importance to workers in the physical and biological sciences and also to the economic world as well. The most extensive researches in the structure of the organic substances by X rays have been made by the textile industry in the studies of cotton, wool, silk, and other fibers essential to this great industry.

It is also clearly established that not only are the nonliving organic materials, such as cellulose and keratin, crystalline in nature, but protoplasm itself, as found in various types of highly differentiated cells such as those of muscle and nerve, has a basic structural plan extending from molecular levels to a visible crystalline pattern in the cell units. Even before the basic revelations of the X rays the geneticists had established a definite linear pattern of the particulate hereditary units, or genes, in the chromosomes of the germ cell nuclei. Apparently the actual gene particle is below the resolving power of the electron microscope, though some authorities are convinced that in certain instances genes may actually be seen. At all events, it is definitely established that the genes in a chromosome are arranged in a precise pattern.

Thus the present situation relative to the structural pattern of protoplasm may be summarized by saying that in essentially all instances, where the new methods have been used, evidence has been obtained of an inherent crystalline pattern just as is found in inorganic solids. It therefore becomes evident once more that the difference between inorganic and organic substances lies primarily in the much greater complexity of the latter rather than in a different method of construction. Many major details of the crystalline patterns of the varied lifestuffs are still undisclosed, but a firm foundation has been laid, and the years ahead will undoubtedly record substantial progress.

MOLECULAR SIZE IN THE PROTEINS AND VIRUSES

The data accumulated has made it possible to determine the molecular weights and dimensions of a wide range of proteins and viruses for comparison with cellular units of living organisms. The data on particle size may be arranged to show a gradual increase, beginning with the smallest ultramicroscopic protein molecules and continuing with the virus and bacteriophage units up to the cell of the smallest known bacterial organism and, finally, to cellular units of microscopic visibility.

THE CELL AS A STRUCTURAL UNIT

Turning our attention to the cell of the biologist, it is important to inquire whether the fully established facts of organic structure, as just outlined, give any grounds for bringing cellular organization, which is almost universally associated with the living organism, into direct relationship with the structural patterns of the elemental materials from which it is built. In other words, is the cell considered purely as a structural unit an entirely distinct and unrelated entity in the material world, or does it represent the climax of a gradually increasing complexity in pattern having direct continuity with the structural forms of less complexity associated with the materials of the nonliving world? May it not be possible that the cell is essentially a protoplasmic crystal in which an almost infinite number of protein molecules, beginning with the genes in the chromosomes, are associated in a specific ultramicroscopic pattern characteristic of a particular type of cell? In such a condition independent protein molecules are not present, but all are organized to form the complete cell unit exhibited in the crystalline pattern of a specific type of protoplasm.

In a very real sense, therefore, the cell may be regarded as a molecule of protoplasm; the least amount of this lifestuff which will exhibit the characteristics of the living state, just as a single molecule of sugar or hemoglobin is the indivisible unit of these substances. This condition becomes particularly evident in the enormous protein molecules of the virus and bacteriophage particles which have the greatest molecular weight of any known protein.

There is a difference of opinion

among biochemists as to whether the unit particles of the viruses and the bacteriophages are enormous protein molecules equipped in some way for propagation by autocatalytic reactions or whether they are elementary living units. Stanley, from his extensive studies on the viruses, has taken a position which to some extent favors the view that viruses are living agents, though possibly of a retrograde nature. Apparently the evidence at hand does not afford indisputable proof that the virus particles are either living agents or non-living proteins. However, the evidence is conclusive that the functional characteristics of the tobacco mosaic are "part and parcel" of the protein molecule. They reproduce, they adapt themselves to certain variations in different types of living cells, exhibit "heritable" permanent changes or mutations, and are destroyed by certain conditions fatal to living cells.

It has been extraordinarily difficult for the cytologist to get a clear vision of the cell as a structural unit because he has been blinded by the brilliance of its functional features and also because he has been unable to penetrate through the ebb and flow of the heterogeneous mixture of complex organic substances which are necessarily accumulated within the cell boundaries to keep the "wheels of life turning." The behavior and appearance of protoplasm indicates superficially that it is an emulsion, but this is illusory; there is an underlying ultramicroscopic substance—protoplasm itself—now revealed by use of the X ray and other experimental methods, a substance which is continuous and highly organized.

All protoplasmic phenomena have their source in this ultramicroscopic organization from the complex chemistry of life to structural formations of incredible beauty and exactness, from the diatom shell to identical twins. Furthermore, each living cell, as it periodically divides by mitosis, reveals a temporary stage of crystallinity at the levels of microscopic visibility with both nuclear and cytoplasmic elements united in the complete pattern. The protoplasm in a cell in the intermictic periods is not less uniform in its organization; the cytoplasm and karyoplasm are only woven into an ultramicroscopic pattern of different design. The proteins of cell protoplasm, which are essential to the maintenance of life phenomena, form a perfect whole; all the molecules are associated to form a microscopically visible macromolecule, the cell.

Geologists long held to the Catastrophic Doctrine, the primary assumption of which was that "natural forces were more active and powerful in the past geological ages than they are now; that great convulsions of nature had riven the crust asunder into valleys and elevated other portions into mountains." But by the middle of the last century the Uniformitarian School gained the ascendancy, largely through the influence of Hutton and Lyell. According to this view geological processes in past ages had never differed intrinsically from those of the present day. And why, we now ask, should it ever have been thought otherwise since the same primary forces and elemental materials were at work? Clearly biology at the middle of the twentieth century is in much the same position as was geology a hundred years ago in failing to observe that there is a Uniformitarian Principle pervading all types of organization whether in the inorganic realm or in the organic.*

The basis of separation between life

* There is a little bit of catastrophism, however, in the thinking of most geologists.—Ed.

and non-life is dependent on the *degree of complexity* rather than on a difference in *kind,* because the same elements are used in both domains, and they must conform to the same elemental patterns. From the simplest substance in the inorganic world to the most complex patterns of living substance there must be a graded series.

Finally, there is the possibility that a living organism is something more than the sum of its parts. Such being the case, it is not to be expected that "continual fragmentation will of itself necessarily reveal the true inner meaning of life processes." Is there not the possibility that there is something deeper and more fundamental than cells and molecules that contains the key to the mystery of life, some as yet undiscovered common factor which underlies all living phenomena and which, in its effect, might be compared with the molecular theory that brought the diverse phenomena associated with the solid, liquid, and gaseous states of matter into a unified whole?

QUESTIONS

1. What significant change took place in our thinking when an organic compound was synthesized by Wöhler?
2. What part do X rays play in discovering the structure of living matter?
3. What are some of the reasons why viruses may be considered living and what is one reason why they may not be living?
4. Has the crystalline, molecular theory answered the question, "What is Life?"

Ralph E. Cleland

Cytology: the Study of the Cell

Reprinted with the permission of the author and publisher from American Journal of Botany **43**(10):870–881, 1956.

In their efforts to learn about life and living beings, biologists have developed many specialties, for although they know but a tiny fraction of what they need to know in order to understand fully what life is and how it functions, the sum total of biological knowledge is already far too extensive and complex for any one man to grasp it all. And so, some biologists have concerned themselves primarily with the identification and recognition of the different kinds of organisms, others with the manifold structures which these organisms have developed; still others have sought to analyze their activities, how they nourish themselves, grow and reproduce, how they behave in their native surroundings, and under controlled conditions.

Most of these and other specialties, however, attack the problem of the nature of life only indirectly, by studying the varied manifestations of life, the results of life activity. It is only by a study of that part of a living organism which is itself alive (the so-called protoplasm) that one can hope to gain an understanding of what life is in essence, what lies at the bottom of and is responsible for the phenomena which together make up what we call life. To achieve this goal, one must turn to the cell, for protoplasm exists, with very few exceptions, not in large masses, but in minute units which are called cells. Cytology is the study of the cell, and it is, therefore, of all fields the one which comes closest to the heart of the major quest of biology—the understanding of life in its essence.

The cell is a marvelous microcosm, extremely small, yet unbelievably complex. Although protoplasm is incomparably the most complex system known, it is organized into units whose size, or lack of size, is difficult for the average man to grasp. As the late Professor Sponsler has pointed out, the average-sized cell has a volume about one-millionth that of the average raindrop. It might seem that a unit of matter so small would be incapable of containing a substance as complicated as protoplasm. The complexities of protoplasm, however, are at the molecular level. It is an organized system of molecules of myriad kinds, some simple, some ranging up to the most complex molecules known, each kind of molecule having its own chemical properties, the sum total of all these properties adding up, when the molecules are organized in just the right way, to what we call life.

That there is plenty of space for a system as complicated as protoplasm in the cell is shown by a comparison of the size of an average cell with that of the various molecules which make up protoplasm. Protoplasm is composed of a skeletal framework made up of protein molecules, to which molecules of other kinds are attached, the whole suspended or dissolved in water. One of the substances found in some abundance in the cell is sugar. As Sponsler has pointed out, there is room in an average-sized cell for 64 trillion molecules of glucose (grape sugar), each with a molecular weight of 180 (i.e., it is 180 times as heavy as a hydrogen atom). The protein molecules, which form the structural framework of the protoplasm are much larger than glucose molecules, averaging about 36,000 molecular weight. A cell with a volume a millionth that of the average raindrop is large enough to accommodate over 60 billion such protein molecules of average size (about 25 times as many as there are people on the face of the earth). Some of the protein molecules in the cell, however, may have molecular weights as high as 6 million. There would be room for as many as 500 million molecules of this size in such a cell. It is evident, therefore, that a cell could even be much smaller than a millionth the size of an average raindrop and still be abundantly able to enclose an enormous number of molecules of all sizes and sorts, and to permit a molecular organization so complex that its properties would total that of life itself.

The cell has been known for a long time, but its nature, its organization and the ways in which it functions have only recently begun to be elucidated. Back in 1665, Robert Hooke, an Englishman, constructed one of the first "microscopes," and with it saw many things never before seen by the eyes of man—among them, the box-like structure of cork. The compartments which he found to compose the structure of cork he called "cells"—he thought that they were empty compartments, as indeed, in cork they were, since cork cells die soon after they have been formed and hence lose their contents. It was not until nearly 200 years after Hooke that it became evident that living cells are not walls surrounding empty spaces, but are masses of material surrounded by walls or membranes. The 1870's and 1880's were especially significant in the history of cytology. It was during this period that chromosomes were discovered, that the details of cell division were worked out, that the foundations for the study of the structure, chemical composition and behavior of protoplasm were laid.

If one were to ask why it took so long after the cell was first seen for the science of cytology to be born, the answer is easy. Cytology, dealing as it does with units of microscopic size, had to await the development of magnifying apparatus of sufficient strength and resolving power to enable objects as small as a cell to be studied in detail. Such instruments were not developed until the latter third of the 19th century.

Ever since its birth, cytology has been limited in its achievements by the instruments and methods at its disposal. On the observational side, it has been limited by the ability of available equipment to magnify and resolve. The microscope which uses ordinary light can only magnify in a really satisfactory manner up to about 2500 diameters, and this result has only been achieved by the use of special types of optical materials, such as fluorite. At higher magnifications, the image begins to lose definition, to become more and more fuzzy.

Various improvements have been made from time to time on the light microscope. Quartz lenses have permitted the use of ultraviolet light which, because of its shorter wave lengths, permits a higher resolving power than does visible light. An ultraviolet microscope, however, can be used only photographically, since ultraviolet light is invisible to the human eye.

Dark-field microscopy has provided another useful supplement to the light microscope. It depends upon visible light which is introduced obliquely into the material being studied and is reflected off the surface of particles to the eye of the observer. When light from below is cut off and only the light reflected from the surfaces of particles is seen, the presence of particles too small to be resolved by the ordinary miscroscope is revealed.

In recent years, other mechanical developments have been added to the cytologist's arsenal of weapons. One of the most serious sources of error in cytological study stems from the fact that protoplasm in its living state is so transparent that one can look right through it with the ordinary microscope and fail to see most of the structures which it contains. This has made it necessary to use dyes which will stain different structures differently or stain particular structures and leave others unstained. Such dyes, however, will function as a rule only after the cell has been killed. The cytologist is compelled, therefore, to kill the cell first, then stain it. This necessity introduces into the work an element of uncertainty, for one is confronted with the possibility that the killing process has altered the fine structure of the cell or has rendered parts of the cell soluble in the reagents that must be used in the staining and mounting process. He now has two new kinds of microscopes, the phase-contrast microscope and the interference microscope, which utilize certain optical principles hitherto unused in microscopy to make many of the constituent parts of the cell stand out from their surroundings when the protoplasm is still living, so that they can be studied in respect to both their structure and behavior.

Perhaps the most spectacular mechanical development which in recent years has become available to the cytologist is the electron microscope. This instrument is capable of providing sharply resolved images at magnifications 10 times that of the light microscope. Although there are certain drawbacks to its use, the greatly increased magnification which it affords has brought it into great prominence as a cytological tool. The drawbacks to its use, beside the great cost of the instrument, are the fact that it must be used primarily as a photographic instrument; the fact that the material studied must be very thin, since electrons will not pass through thick layers of matter; and the requirement that material must be studied in a vacuum, since electrons will not penetrate air. The use of the electron microscope as a photographic instrument is in one respect an asset; for it is possible to take pictures at magnification of 15,000 diameters or more on fine grained film, from which enlargements can be made which retain sharp definition up to magnifications of 50,000 or more.

The electron microscope is making as drastic a revolution in cytological knowledge as did the light microscope in the 1870's and 1880's. It is revealing an amazing intricacy of structure in the cell beyond anything dreamed of a few years ago. Resolving powers as low as 8 Angstroms are being achieved, i.e., it is possible to reveal particles as small as one 30 millionth of an inch in diameter.

At its inception, cytology was a distinct science which showed relatively little relationship to other sciences. Cytologists did not need to master the techniques of other sciences, nor were these sciences in turn concerned with the findings of cytology. In only one direction was cytology a science which involved more than one discipline. It was equally a botanical and a zoological field. Plant and animal cytologists had much more in common than either of them had with other branches of botany or zoology. Except for this one relationship, however, cytology remained a science apart for some decades.

The position of cytology changed, however, as it began to feel the need for techniques from the other sciences to supplement its own, and as other sciences began to discover that the solution of their own problems required going back to protoplasm itself, where alone the answers to the really fundamental questions are to be found. On the one hand, cytologists began to utilize for their own purposes the techniques of genetics, biochemistry, and histochemistry. On the other hand, they found themselves helping to furnish the answers to the questions the geneticists, the biochemists, the taxonomists, and the evolutionists were raising. Cytology rather suddenly became, therefore, an experimental, as well as an observational science, and it became a fundamental contributor to, if not an integral part of, other important branches of biology.

This transformation of the science of cytology began at the turn of the century with the rediscovery of Mendel's work. This discovery marked the birth of the science of genetics and immediately this new science found a use for cytology. When Mendel's work was finally brought to light in 1900, cytological analyses had reached a point where the parallelism between chromosome behavior and gene behavior could be appreciated. It was Sutton who was the first to make this parallelism clear and to show convincingly that hereditary determiners are distributed among the chromosomes and carried by them. From this time on, cytology became a handmaiden of genetics, and its importance to genetics soon became so apparent that the two sciences became to a considerable extent fused into the new synthetic science of cytogenetics.

As a result of these developments, cytologists can no longer confine their interests and competencies to the killing, sectioning, staining and observing of cell structures. And he must in addition become almost inevitably a biochemist and preferably a biphysicist as well, for many of the most intriguing problems of cytology now have to do with the identification and analysis of key chemical compounds in the cell and the roles which these specific compounds or classes of compounds play in heredity and other cellular activities.

Again, cytology has proved in recent years to be of marked use in the solution of the problems of taxonomy and evolution. Much can be learned regarding the relations between species or races by a comparative study of chromosomes, with respect either to their numbers or their structures. It has been discovered that evolutionary development often involves alterations in chromosome number or structure, so that analysis of these cytological characteristics may shed important light on evolutionary history and on species relationships.

In still another direction, cytology has proved to be of fundamental importance, namely in the solution of physiological problems. Physiology has become increasingly concerned with something more than the functions of tissues and organs, the behavior of organisms and their reactions to environment. When one has analyzed these activities he is still confronted with the question as to the basic causes of these phenomena and is inevitably forced back to the protoplasm itself—to its chemical and physical properties, to the way in which the cell and its constituent parts behave, to the question as to what parts of the cell initiate the processes which eventuate in physiological activity, how these essential ingredients in the cell maintain and reproduce themselves and become distributed to the daughter cells when a parent cell divides. Cytology has thus found itself concerned with the most fundamental questions which a biologist can ask.

A modern cytologist, therefore, must be a man of parts—a broadly trained person—ideally a biologist with chemical, physical, mathematical and statistical competence. Many eminent cytologists have utilized a wide variety of materials, plant and animal, in the course of their experiments.

One of the fundamental problems upon which marked emphasis is now being placed relates to the nature of the gene. Mendel long ago showed that heredity is based upon the existence of separate and distinct determiners which are transmitted from parents to offspring through sperm and egg. The characteristics of an individual depend upon what determiners of heredity it receives from its parents. These determiners have become known as genes. What, then, is a gene? What is it composed of? Where is it situated in the cell? How does it produce its effects? How is it distributed from one generation to another? Do all cells in a body contain full sets of genes? If so, how do genes multiply, so that the two daughter cells derived from a single cell will each have all the genes which the parent cell had? Can genes change? If so, what is the nature of these changes, and how are they accomplished? Are genes discrete chemical entities? There are some biologists who claim that they are not.

The first problem relating to the gene is its location in the cell and its cytological identification. Much progress has been made along this line in recent years. Genetical methods have demonstrated the fact that, as a rule, genes are duplicated every time a cell divides so that each daughter cell receives a full set of the genes which the parent cell had. The geneticist has shown that genes are associated in blocks, which tend to be inherited together, and they have found that the genes are associated within each block in linear order, like beads on a string, each gene having its particular position in the string between specific neighbor genes. They have also found that genes may occasionally change their position and a variety of ways have been discovered by which this can be accomplished. A section of the gene string in a given block of genes can become inverted in position, the genes in this section coming to lie in reverse order; or a group of genes may be moved to a different position in the block; or different blocks may exchange sections of their gene strings. Sometimes genes seem to vanish completely, or they may be duplicated so that a gene is represented more than once in a set of genes. All these facts regarding the arrangement and order of the genes and possible rearrangements of this order have been detected by genetic means, but such findings have not in themselves related the genes to any particular structure or region in the cell as observed microscopically. This has been accomplished by cytological investigation. When Mendel's paper was discovered in 1900 and the laws of the distribution of hereditary determiners were thus brought to light, the cytologists found that they had already seen with the microscope structures in the cell whose behavior exactly corresponded to the behavior of the genes. It had been found that certain bodies which had been termed chromosomes were indeed divided equally whenever a cell divided, each chromosome becoming split longitudinally, one half going to each daughter. These and no other bodies in the cell were distributed with exactitude to the daughter cells. It was found that the number of chromosomes in a cell corresponded exactly to the number of blocks of genes existent in that cell, that larger blocks of genes corresponded to larger chromosomes and vice versa. The behavior of the chromosomes at the time of reproductive cell formation also fitted exactly that of the genes, so that the chromosomes were distributed to the germ cells according to the same rules which governed the distribution of the genes. Furthermore, whenever a case was found where the chromosomes behaved in an unorthodox manner in this regard, it was found that the genes behaved in corresponding fashion, and whenever genes were found to have changed places, via inversion or transfer of segments, cytologists were able to demonstrate that corresponding segments of certain chromosomes had suffered the same alteration.

All of this has demonstrated beyond question that the genes are carried in the chromosomes and that the laws of the distribution of genes from parent to offspring are in reality the laws governing the distribution of the chromosomes from one generation to the next.

The biochemical approach has shown that the chromosome is composed of two principal classes of substance, nucleoproteins and a globular type of protein. Nucleoproteins are composed of nucleic acids, associated with protein. The protein associated with nucleic acid seems to be of a relatively simple type—mostly histone. Nucleic acids exist in the form of complicated molecules, each composed of units known as nucleotides: each nucleotide consists of a purine or pyrimidine base attached to a sugar, which is in turn attached to a molecule of phosphoric acid. The nucleotides are arranged in parallel, somewhat like the rungs of a ladder, which are attached to each other, but only at one end. The rung consists of the base and sugar, the part which attaches the rungs together at one end is the phosphoric acid. The latter also attaches the nucleic acid to the associated protein.

Considerable progress has been made in recent years in the field of nucleic acid chemistry. The work of Watson and Crick, for instance, suggests that nucleic acid molecules exist in pairs, the two molecules wound around one another, with the nucleotides extending horizontally inward. Each nucleotide is attached to a nucleotide of the other nucelic acid molecule by its base, in a very precise manner, the two nucleic acid molecules together thus resembling a twisted ladder. It used to be thought that the nucleotides containing the two purine bases adenine and guanine and the two pyrimidine bases thymine (or uracil) and cytosine were present in a nucleic acid molecule in equal numbers and arranged in a regular sequence. This is no longer found to be true. Not only are the various nucleotides present in varying proportions, but there are also more than four kinds of nucleotides now recognized. Far from there being but a single pattern of arrangement of four nucleotides, a very great variety of arrangements of an unknown number of different nucleotides is indicated.

The question of first importance in this study of chromosome chemistry is what part of the chromosomal structure constitutes the gene? Genes show great diversity in their functional activities. Not only are there thousands of different kinds of genes in a single organism, doing thousands of different things, but the genes in different organisms differ, at least in part, from each other. The total number of different genes in all of the species of plants, animals and microorganisms is undoubtedly very great. What part of the chromosome is capable of existing in such myriad forms? Apparently not the histones, for they are relatively simple structures, probably not the globular proteins, which constitute such a small proportion of the chromosome. The suspicion falls on the nucleic acids which recent students have shown are capable of an enormous variety in their structure. This surmise is strengthened by the finding that self-duplicating bodies in the cell seem all to contain nucleic acid: since one of the chief characteristics of the gene is its ability to reproduce itself, this suggests that nucleic acid is tied in with its structure in some way. It is probable, however, that not all nucleic acid is genic in character. Some organisms, such as members of the lily family, for instance, have relatively enormous chromosomes, and the chromosome set has a relatively huge amount of nucleic acid compared with such organisms as the fruit fly or man. It is not likely, however, that the lily has more genic material than the latter organisms. The quantity of nucleic acid present in a set of chromosomes, therefore, is probably not a measure of the number of genes present. We are not justified in exactly equating genes with nucleic acid. It is likely that genes are not pure nucleic acid but a combination of nucleic acid and protein, the nucleic acid imparting to the gene its specificity.

Another focus of interest which is occupying the attention of many cytologists at the present time is the cytoplasm—that portion of the cell which lies outside of, and surrounds, the nucleus with its chromosomes and genes. For a long time cytologists tended to place relatively little emphasis on the cytoplasm, largely because there seemed to be so little that could be observed microscopically in this portion of the cell. Bodies as striking as chromosomes were seldom present, very few definitive activities seemed to accompany cell division, in contrast with nuclear division. Some bodies, to be sure, were to be seen, but except for plastids (chloroplasts, etc.) none of these were large enough to show much structure under the ordinary microscope, and none seemed to undergo any sort of marked change or cyclical modification. There seemed little, therefore, that the cytologist could learn about this portion of the cell.

This situation is rapidly changing, however, in view of the discoveries by both the geneticists and the biochemists. The geneticists have discovered that the cytoplasm has a role in heredity which is far larger than had originally been suspected. The plastids, for instance, have been shown to have hereditary characteristics of their own which to a degree are independent of those of the genes. To be sure, the genes set up the conditions under which the plastids operate, and if the wrong genes are present, a given kind of plastid may not be able to function successfully. There are also cases where a gene may succeed in bringing about a more or less permanent change in the structure or function of a plastid. On the other hand, cases are known where plastids remain uninfluenced by foreign genes, in whose presence they are unable to function, but to whose influence they fail to yield—so that if they are removed from the presence of the uncooperative gene and find themselves again in a congenial genic environment, they can again function normally, unchanged in their fundamental characteristics by having been associated with the wrong kind of gene. Hence, plastids seem to have a degree of independence of the gene.

Plastid inheritance is therefore a well known phenomenon and has been studied intensively in a number of organisms. Since plastids or their precursors are usually transmitted through the egg but not the sperm, their inheritance is usually maternal in character, i.e., the offspring receives its plastids only from the mother. There are exceptions, however, where plastids may also be introduced into the offspring along with the sperm. But it is not only the plastids which are of interest from the standpoint of cytoplasmic inheritance. The work of Sonneborn and others has drawn attention to the fact that certain hereditary characteristics require the interaction of both the genes and certain elements in the cytoplasm. The "killer" characteristic in *Paramecium*, a one-celled animal, is a case in point. Some individuals in *Paramecium aurelia* are capable of excreting a substance into the surrounding water which will kill other "sensitive" animals. To be a "killer" a cell must have a certain gene (K) and in the cytoplasm it must have minute particles which are known as kappa particles. If both are present, the animal is a killer. If, however, the K gene is present and the kappa particles absent, the cell cannot produce the killer substance. Kappa particles are self-reproducing bodies, but they can live and reproduce only in the presence of the K gene. In the absence of this gene they soon vanish. The K gene, on the other hand, cannot synthesize new kappa particles. If none of the particles are present in a cell possessing K, none can be formed. In other words, kappa particles must come from preexisting kappa particles. The conditions under which these particles can divide and function are set up by the K gene, but the K gene cannot create new particles. The particles are therefore dependent upon the gene for the proper environment in which to continue existence, but not for their origin; the gene is dependent on the particles to carry out the process of killer substance formation. Thus a Mendelian or hereditary character is dependent for its expression on both a gene and a type of cytoplasmic particle. A number of other cases of this type of inheritance are known.

Another type of particle in the cytoplasm is the chondriosome, or mitochondrion. Chondriosomes have been known for 50 years or more but they have not received much attention until recently. They are ordinarily minute spherical or rod shaped bodies, about the size of bacteria, with which they have been confused by some investigators. For a long time their function remained obscure, although their universal presence in all plant and animal cells indicated that they had a vital role to play. In recent years, however, a combined biochemical and cytological approach has shown that they are the chief centers of respiration, the regions where most of the enzymes are situated which together bring about the liberation of the energy needed by the protoplasm. This discovery has added a new importance to the chondriosomes and has focused renewed attention upon them.

The renewed interest in the cytoplasm has resulted in an increased use of the electron microscope in order to learn more about the structure of the bodies found in this region. Since these bodies are so small their structure is beyond the capabilities of the ordinary microscope to elucidate, and electron microscopy seems the only feasible way now available to get at the details of their architecture, The results of recent studies by such workers as Frey-

Wyssling, Steinmann, and Sjöstrand have revealed an amazing complexity of organization in bodies which had previously been considered to be essentially structureless. Chloroplasts, which can often be seen under the ordinary microscope to be filled with granules or "grana" are now found to present a finely layered appearance, the grana as well as the surrounding material having such a structure. The grana, which contain the chlorophyll, seem to be composed of alternate layers of protein and fatty material and, since the tadpole-shaped chlorophyll molecule is attracted at its head end by water and at the tail end by oil, it takes up a position with its head in the protein layer and its tail in the lipid layer. Thus the chlorophyll becomes oriented in a very orderly and precise manner.

Chondriosomes also appear to have a very intricate and precise structure. The work of Sjöstrand and others shows that they have a double membrane with cross membranes extending part or all the way across the body. Like the chloroplasts, therefore, they also have a form of lamellate structure.

A third center of interest among cytologists arises from the fact that cytological studies can throw considerable light on the relationships of species and races, and can furnish clues as to the paths along which evolutionary progress has been made. The nature of the evidence which cytology is able to present varies with the material. In some cases, a comparative study of chromosome structure will indicate relationship. Chromosomes have definitive shapes and sizes, and it is often possible to recognize particular chromosomes under the microscope. In many genera, it is possible to compare the various species or subspecies from the standpoint of chromosome structure. Species which have similar or identical chromosomes so far as morphology is concerned are considered to be more closely related than species whose chromosomes differ in these regards.

In other cases, relationships can be determined or confirmed by analyzing the structural alterations which have occurred in the evolution of the group. Thus, in certain species of *Drosophila*, the fruit-fly, inversions of chromosome segments have occurred with relative frequency. In some cases, sequences of inversion can be followed, especially where a portion of a previously inverted segment becomes involved in a second inversion. In other organisms, other types of structural alteration have proved of value. For instance, in the evening primrose (*Oenothera*), the author and his students have found that exchanges of segments between non-corresponding chromosomes have occurred with unusual frequency and it has been found possible to analyze many races from the standpoint of the interchanges which have occurred. Races which show evidence, at least in part, of the same interchanges are considered, other things being equal, to have been derived from common ancestors in which these interchanges occurred. The more closely races resemble one another in respect to the interchanges which have occurred in the course of their evolution, the more closely related they are considered to be, and vice versa. As a result of cytological and genetical techniques, the evolutionary story of the evening primrose is being revealed, and this in a genus which has for many years been the despair of taxonomists who have tried to ferret out the relationships by strictly taxonomic methods.

In plants another cytological phenomenon has proved to be of great importance in determining relationships. It not infrequently occurs in plants that the chromosome number becomes altered. Chromosomes may occasionally be lost, or additional chromosomes may be added. Of greatest significance are the cases where the ordinary or diploid chromosome number becomes doubled, producing what is known as a polyploid. It has been found that polyploidy has been a major factor in plant evolution. A polyploid does not produce fertile progeny easily when crossed with its parental diploid, because the progeny will have an odd number of chromosome sets, and will fail to a large extent to produce sperms or eggs with complete sets of chromosomes. A polyploid, therefore, has a degree of reproductive isolation which enables it to carry on an independent existence and to evolve along its own line. A very large number of species of plants show evidence of chromosome doubling in their evolution—in fact, doubling has occurred more than once in the ancestry of many plants. A curious fact has been discovered in the course of studies of polyploidy: if doubling occurs in a plant whose parents were very closely related, the resultant polyploid is likely to be more sterile and less able to maintain itself than if its parents had been very unrelated. This fact, the reason for which we cannot go into here, is of great practical value. It is often advantageous to combine the desirable traits of different varieties or species, but when one crosses these, the resultant hybrid proves to be sterile—the chromosomes of the two species are too unlike to pair and separate properly during the process of germ cell formation. Such a cross would not be able to propagate itself, therefore, were it not for the possibility of polyploidy. If one induces the chromosomes to double in such a hybrid (and this can be done easily with the use of colchicine or other chemical), the resultant polyploid, which will still possess the desired combination of characters, will be found to be perfectly fertile and capable of passing its desirable combination of genes to succeeding generations. The wider the cross and the more sterile the hybrid, the more likelihood that a polyploid derived from it by chromosome doubling will be perfectly fertile, and vice versa.

In the course of evolution, chromosomes are apt to suffer various major or minor alterations in structure. They may lose small segments, or certain segments may become duplicated. They may experience inversions, or they may exchange segments with other chromosomes. As a result, chromosomes in races which were originally derived from a common ancestor may become very different in structure, so different that if they are brought into the same plant by appropriate crossing they can no longer associate in pairs as corresponding chromosomes are supposed to do at the time when germ cells are produced. Cytologists can study the behavior of chromosomes in hybrids and from their behavior at this stage judge as to their similarity of structure and hence their evolutionary relationship. By techniques of this sort, much has been learned about the ancestry of plants important to our economy, such as wheat and oats.

Cytology demonstrates in unusual degree the essential oneness of living nature. The average person is apt to be impressed more with the diversity than with the unity of life. Plants seem so different from animals. Bacteria seem so different from either plants or animals. The millions of different species of animals and plants, and the range from amoeba to man, from the microscopic alga to the sequoia tree, are evidence of the ability of protoplasm to take on myriad forms, to adopt multitudinous variations of structure without losing that structural key which makes it alive. Truly the diversity of living material is a profoundly impressive fact. And yet, it is also an amazing fact that through all this diversity there runs a unity of structure and function which is equally impressive, and most of this unity reveals itself at the cellular level. It is a striking fact that practically all organisms, plant or animal, follow the same laws of heredity, based upon the presence of genes carried in chromosomes. These chromosomes divide and are transmitted, when cells divide, to the daughter cells by the same process of mitosis, and are parcelled out to the individual reproductive cells by the same mechanism of meiosis. The deviations have involved relatively unessential aspects; the essential features of living protoplasm have been retained by all organisms—otherwise they would not have been able to survive.

This fact has very important practical applications. Cells have the same fundamental attributes, whether they belong to bacteria, the higher plants, or animals. An agent or condition which effects the functioning of one kind of cell is likely to have similar effects on other cells. Many of our most pressing biological problems involve the cell and the behavior of protoplasm. Cancer, for instance, is a condition in which cells have lost the inhibitors which retard and control growth and cell division. The brakes have been released and the processes of growth and multiplication are unrestrained. The solution of the cancer problem will not be achieved by attempts to cure cancer, nor will it necessarily come by the study of human tissues, since cancers are found in many other organisms, even in plants. It will not be found until we know what makes cells grow and multiply, what controls and regulates these processes, what substances are capable of throwing a monkey-wrench into the regulatory machinery, and what part of the machinery they effect.

From this brief discusion it is evident that cytology deals with the most fundamental properties of living beings—how the living material is organized and constructed, how it carries on its multitudinous processes, how it is governed, how it reproduces and transmits to successive generations the powers which it possesses. The answer to all the basic riddles of living nature, so far as they are capable of solution, are to be found in the cell, the happy hunting ground of the cytologist.

QUESTIONS

1. Why is cytology closely allied to the search for the nature of life?
2. What is one disadvantage of staining cells when one is studying protoplasm?
3. How did Sutton's work verify the findings of Mendel?
4. Describe the Watson-Crick model of a chromosome core.
5. What is plastid or cytoplasmic inheritance and of what significance is it?
6. What was Sonneborns' work on cytoplasmic inheritance?
7. How can chromosomes play a part in deciding relationships between organisms?
8. How does Dr. Cleland think the cancer problem will be solved?

G. W. Beadle

What is a Gene?

Reprinted with the permission of the author and publisher from the A.I.B.S. Bulletin 5(5):15, 1955.

A series of recent developments in biology and chemistry has greatly increased our understanding of the structure, function, replication and mutation of genetic material.

Beginning with the work of Avery and his collaborators on pneumococcal transforming principles, evidence that the primary genetic information is carried in the form of desoxyribonucleic acid (DNA) has become quite strong.

The most compelling of the several arguments for assigning this important role to DNA comes from the experiments of Hershey and co-workers (Cold Spring Harbor Symp. Quant. Biol. 18:135, 1953) with bacterial viruses in which the protein coat is labelled with sulfur-35 or the DNA core labelled with phosphorous-32. The course followed by these radioactive tracers through the virus life cycle indicates that only the DNA enters the host cell. Since genetic studies show quite clearly that the virus has linearly arranged hereditary material that behaves in several respects like that of higher organisms, the indicated conclusion is that this material in the virus must consist solely of DNA.

Perhaps of greater significance to biology than any advance of recent decades is the proposal of a specific structure of DNA by Watson and Crick. (Cold Spring Harbor Symp. Quant. Biol. 18: 123, 1953.) This structure, which consists essentially of a pair of complementary polynucleotide chains hydrogen bonded together through purine and pyrimidine bases, provides a basis for genetic specificity in the order of base-pairs along the molecule. Separation of the complementary chains, followed by directed synthesis of new complementary partners by the single chains, is presumed to be the basis of replication of the genetic material. Mistakes in nucleotide sequence, made during replication, provide one plausible basis for gene mutation.

It has been suggested that gene function involves a transfer of DNA information or specificity to ribonucleic acid (RNA) and thence to such macromolecules as proteins. Since no structure of RNA comparable in plausibility to the Watson-Crick DNA structure has been proposed, the nature of the transfer of DNA specificity to RNA remains a key problem. In the same sense, the precise way in which RNA directs the synthesis of specific proteins remains to be discovered. One possibility that has several times been suggested is that segments of RNA serve as templates against which protein molecules are constructed from their constituent amino acids.

Using the Zinder-Lederberg technique of transduction in *Salmonella* (transfer of small chromosome segments from one bacterial cell to another by means of a virus capable of being carried in a latent form in the recipient cell), Demerec and his associates (Proc. Nat. Acad. Sci. **41**:359, 1955) have developed what appears to be a powerful method for investigating the fine structure of the gene.

Defining functional units of the genetic material of this bacterium both in terms of their control of single chemical reactions and by their genetically determined positions, it is found that for each such unit mutant changes are possible that can be shown to the nonidentical (often complementary) in cross-transduction tests. In terms of the Watson-Crick structure these are presumed to consist in substitutions, deletions or rearrangements of base-pairs at various positions along the functional unit.

Using a special technique for detecting rare recombinations, Benzer (Proc. Nat. Acad. Sci. **41**: 344, 1955) has presented evidence for the existence of similar functional units in bacterial viruses. Again mutational changes of independent origins within a single such unit are often recombinable in "crosses."

It is not yet clear what the relation of these results is to the so-called pseudoalleles of higher forms (Lewis, Amer. Nat. **89**: 73, 1955). Neither can it be said with certainty how they are related to the remarkable phenomenon reported by M. B. Mitchell in *Neurospora* (Proc. Nat. Acad. Sci. **41**: 215, 1955) in which there appears to be rare transfer of a limited amount of genetic material from one chromosome to its homolog without conventional crossing over.

In higher plants and animals, in which the chromosomes are several orders of magnitude larger in cross-sectional area than are the DNA strands of bacterial viruses, Mazia (Proc. Nat. Acad. Sci. **40**: 521, 1954) presents evidence indicating that the chromosomes are made up of DNA-protein segments about 4000 Å long bound together end-to-end by divalent calcium and magnesium ion bridges. It is possible that these units consist of bundles of identical DNA segments, somehow combined with protein, that correspond to the functional units of genetics. If the breaks of crossing over occur only between such segments, they would also correspond to the genetic units of recombination. But such a structure does not exclude the possibility that crossing over is sometimes or even always intragenic.

Despite these many important unanswered questions, the main lines of evidence suggest, or are consistent with, the following hypothesis:

Segments of DNA of perhaps several hundred nucleotides make up the primary functional genetic units. In bacterial viruses these appear to be transferred to the host without accompanying protein. In higher forms, on the other hand, there is no convincing evidence that they ever become separated from protein. Genetic specificity (information) is dependent on proportions and sequences of base-pairs in these DNA segments. In gene mutation base-pair proportions and sequences are altered by substitution, deletion or rearrangement. Replication of genes is accomplished by separation of complementary nucleotide chains followed by synthesis of complementary daughter chains. Functional units of DNA in some manner transfer specificity to RNA units which in turn serve as templates in protein synthesis.

It is conceivable that the transfers of information from DNA to RNA and from RNA to protein are under some circumstances reversible processes. Such reversibility would allow for the storage of genetic information in the form of RNA in those viruses that appear to contain no DNA. Since such viruses replicate their genetic information only in a host cell containing DNA and protein, it is not necessary to assume that RNA is self-replicating in the same sense in which DNA is postulated to accomplish this remarkable feat.

On this hypothesis, what is a gene? Is it a functional unit carrying the information necessary for the synthesis of a specific macromolecule? Or is it the unit of recombination? If it is the latter, the evidence from viruses and bacteria suggest that the ultimate unit might well be a single nucleotide. If it were necessary to define a gene without additional information, the choice would have to be an arbitrary one. It may well be that the time is near for a reconsideration of terminology. Until then it is particularly important to make perfectly clear in particular cases just what one has in mind when such terms as *gene*, *locus*, and *allele* are used.

QUESTIONS

1. Describe the Watson-Crick model of DNA.
2. What is the relationship existing between DNA and RNA?
3. What is transduction?
4. Would you say that Dr. Beadle is entirely satisfied with current definitions of the gene?

Edgar Anderson

Cytotaxonomy

Reprinted with the permission of the author from Chapter 4 of Plants, man and life. Boston, Little, Brown and Co., 1952.

Cytologists are microscopists; they study plant and animal cells under high magnification. Their commonest technique has been to take some easily accessible portion of a plant or animal (in plants it is frequently the tip of a rapidly growing root) and immerse it in various successive solutions to preserve and stain its essential features and then to study these pickled remains enlarged a thousand times or more under the microscope. Who would have supposed that men of this sort would have new clues to the origin and history of the plants so closely associated with man? Yet it is they who, though generally ignorant of prehistory, knowing little or nothing about taxonomy and usually so scornful of its innate conservatism that they did not wish to learn any more, have made the most startling discoveries in this field in the last few decades. It is they who have produced exact evidence as to which kinds of primitive grasses were combined in the Stone Age to produce our wheats. It is they who can prove without the shadow of a doubt that the Asiatic cottons (perhaps the wild ones, perhaps the cultivated ones) somehow crossed the Pacific or traveled around it by slow stages and played a definite role in establishing American cultivated and weed cottons. It is they who narrowed down the problem of where tobacco might have originated and explained such modern miracles as the loganberry. Nor have they been content merely to launch fantastic hypotheses; by further developments of their techniques and with the help of plant breeders they have been able to re-enact these hypothetical histories and actually (as we shall see) to recreate such crop plants *de novo* from their primitive ancestors. Brilliant as this new evidence is, it tells us about only one or two details in the origin and development of certain crops and weeds—nothing about the rest of their histories, and nothing at all for many other crops and weeds. If we revert to our previous conception of the history of these important plants as a complex detective story with many kinds of clues, then cytology furnishes a disconnected set of brilliant flashlight photographs, illustrating with tantalizing clarity just one or two phases of the mystery. . . .

Most of our cultivated polyploids are of ancient origin. Take the cultivated wheats. It had been known for years that the wheats of the world were more than just a large number of varieties of wheat. They belonged in three or more great groups; crosses between some of the groups were hard to make and such hybrids were more or less sterile. The cytologists showed that there was a very real background for these groupings. Einkorn wheat, an ancient cereal of Neolithic times, now practically disappeared as a crop plant, was a diploid; all the other cultivated wheats were polyploid. Some of them were tetraploid, including those protein-rich varieties which make a sticky flour and are known as "the macaroni wheats." The most important wheats of all, the bread wheats, were hexaploid, that is, they had six full sets of chromosomes. If each of the capital letters A and B and D designates a set of seven chromosomes, then the einkorns were of formula AA, the emmer and the macaroni wheats were AABB, and the bread wheats were AABBDD. Presumably the einkorn wheats had evolved out of the wild wheats of the Near East, since some of these were also simple diploids of the constitution AA, but where did the BB's and the DD's come from? This fascinating puzzle is not yet solved down to proving the last detail, but we are already reasonably certain of the general outline of the story and even have exact experimental proof for some of it. It is clearly apparent that the cultivated wheats did not spring from the wild wheats alone; the BB's and the DD's must represent other distinct genera of plants. BB may well be a quack grass, *Agropyron triticeum*, which is wild in the eastern Mediterranean region. A polyploid of it and einkorn back in Neolithic times may well have produced the first of the tetraploid AABB wheats from which emmer, the Persian wheats, and other modern teraploids were eventually bred. The hexaploid (AABBDD) bread wheats were most probably produced from accidental hybridization between the AABB tetraploids, and a bristle-headed little weed of the Near East, *Aegilops squarrosa*, which supplied the necessary DD for the finished hexaploid.

One of the most brilliant pieces of current biological research has been the proof by two American scientists that *Aegilops* played a leading role in the evolution of our modern bread wheats. From evidence too technical to discuss profitably here, a Texas wheat breeder named McFadden came to the conclusion that *Aegilops squarrosa* was the probable source of the DD chromosomes. He accordingly took emmer, one of our most primitive tetraploid (AABB) wheats, and crossed it with the diploid (DD) *Aegilops squarrosa*. He eventually produced, as one might have predicted, a sterile hybrid of the formula ABD. It had three sets of chromosomes, AB from emmer and D from *Aegilops*. Like most plants with three sets of chromosomes it was sterile, though otherwise it looked like a primitive bread wheat.

At this point a Missouri cytologist, Dr. Ernest Sears, joined in the work. He took McFadden's sterile hybrids and treated them with colchicine, a drug which if carefully regulated can prevent cells from dividing when their nuclei divide. With patience and good luck one may get a sector of a plant and eventually a whole plant which has developed from these affected cells and in which consequently the chromosome number has been doubled. By this technique Sears produced a hexaploid AABBDD from McFadden's sterile ABD triploids. As might have been predicted it was fertile and true-breeding. Furthermore, it was virtually identical with a primitive hexaploid wheat, known as spelt, which has been a minor European crop since Roman times. The spelt artificially produced by McFadden and Sears is fertile with European spelt and that the latter is a polyploid of *Aegilops squarrosa* and some simpler wheat may be taken as proved.

Only one thoroughly familiar with the literature on the history of wheat can realize how completely the work of McFadden and Sears causes a realignment of the facts and theories in that complicated field.

We now learn that our commonest wheats belong to the genera *Agropyron* and *Aegilops* quite as much as they do to the genus *Triticum*. Were it possible to sacrifice convenience to accuracy, our bread wheats could more fiittingly be designated as *Aegilotriticopyron sativum* than as the currently accepted *Triticum sativum*. McFadden even thinks it likely that a fourth genus, *Haynaldia*, by simple hybridization without any polyploid realignments, may have contributed some of the distinctive characteristics of our tetraploid macaroni wheats. *Haynaldia*, growing as a weed in primitive grainfields, might well have crossed with some of the wheats. These hybrids, crossing back to the wheats again, would bring a little *Haynaldia* germ plasm into the wheats. In other words, we now realize that if we are to understand the wheats of the world, either as a key to prehistory or as the staff of life for a good portion of the human race, we must study a whole group of quack grasses and other weeds from the Near East and Asia. For the purpose of practical plant breeding the world now finds itself needing to know in detail about several humble weeds, plants so far removed from our ordinary lives that we have no common English names for them and must resort to such unwieldy technical vocables as *Agropyron*, *Haynaldia*, and *Aegilops* in discussing them!

This example by no means exhausts the new evidence that has been turned up by the cytologists in the last few decades concerning the origins of cultivated plants. There are new facts and new insights into the origin of tobaccos, of white potatoes, of citrus fruits, of bluegrasses, of apples and pears, of roses, chrysanthemums, dahlias, and many other ornamentals, and of such modern domesticates as blueberries and strawberries. But quite as important as any of the specific information which it contributes to the problem of the origin of cotton or the origin of tobacco, is the bearing of the cytological evidence on the general problem of cultivated plants as a whole.

In the first place it gives us a wholly new appreciation of the importance of hybridization. After reviewing the cytological and breeding evidence, hybridization seems to have been a really major factor in establishing our crop plants. Fifty years ago any scientist who would have dared to suggest that our common wheats are quack grasses quite as much as they are wheats, or that seedless bananas could only be produced by crossing certain kinds of wild, seedy bananas, would not have been taken seriously. The modern plant breeder not only makes such suggestions, he goes ahead and proves them. The fortunate thing for our understanding is the way in which polyploidy preserves for centuries clear cytological evidence of certain hybridizations. The whole set of chromosomes is still there and with luck and perseverance it may be identified, even though the original cross took place in the Iron Age or earlier. Without polyploidy this clear evidence would have been lost. Those of us who are familiar with the cytological facts and have speculated about their over-all meaning, have suggested that hybridization was probably just as common among the diploids and may well have involved rare crosses with other genera. Such hypotheses can be proved for diploid crops but it takes much more time and requires more elaborate research programs.

In the second place the cytological evidence demonstrates the intimate connection between crop plants and weeds. Einkorn, our most primitive wheat, was essentially built up into a world crop by hybridizations with its own weeds, *Aegilops*, *Agropyron*, and *Haynaldia*.

Most important of all, the cytological evidence demonstrates that the history of any major crop is a long involved affair. There was a time when anyone with a good general background in biology could look up the scientific names of our major crop plants (if he did not already know them), ascertain what parts of the world they were said to come from, and write a definitive article concerning the origin of agriculture. That time is past. One of the chief services of the new evidence from cytology and genetics has been to show up the experts.

QUESTIONS

1. Explain how cytologists can tell us something about the (1) origin of a plant, (2) its relationship to other plants.
2. Describe briefly the origin of cultivated wheat.
3. How is colchicine valuable to the plant breeder?
4. How does hybridization speed up evolution?

PART SIXTEEN

GENETICS AND PLANT BREEDING

Plant breeding depends upon a knowledge of genetics. Together these two disciplines have great significance in light of the population explosion. Increasing the food supply must go hand in hand with birth control. More acres can be planted or new crops can be developed. Corn, wheat, and other plants have been greatly improved by the plant breeder. Corn now produces about 30 per cent more per acre than it formerly did. Other crops are being studied in various university and government establishments. It is interesting to point out that the practical applications in this area had their start in the little-publicized pure research of Gregor Mendel circa 1865.

False prophets have occasionally appeared in genetics. For an example of this, the article on Lysenko should be read. Fortunately for the Soviet Union, the influence of Lysenko has been greatly curbed as this book goes to press.

For more information on genetics, read Classical Papers in Genetics *by James A. Peters and* Heredity *by David M. Bonner.*

Bentley Glass

Genetics in the Service of Man

Reprinted with the permission of the publisher and author from The Johns Hopkins Magazine 6(5):2–5, 12–16, 1955.

Human power, which mounted slowly indeed through the eons of prehistory and somewhat more rapidly after the advent of the sword and pen, has gathered momentum with logarithmic sweep since the dawn of modern science. Today it seems to be rocketing into outer space with the incredible energy of atomic fission.

I would be the last to imply that the principal value in the pursuit of scientific knowledge is the ultilitarian one—that society should nurture science only because of its fruits. Yet the fruits are of undeniable importance, and before we eat, it might be well for us to see upon which side of the tree of good and evil they are borne. Power, especially unlimited power, can be more danger than blessing, and what foresight and intelligence we do possess ought to be exercised in safeguarding and channeling it into wise uses. Mankind was not prepared to use and control nuclear power. Today we stand on the verge of biological discoveries of an equally revolutionary and potentially devastating kind, which it will require all our wisdom to control.

A century ago, when my grandfather was born, the life expectancy of the average male infant was forty years. At the turn of the century, it was still only forty-eight years; but by 1930 it had jumped to fifty-nine years, and today stands at the amazing average of seventy years. Whatever we may think about the wise use made of those extra thirty years of life by the average American man, surely this achievement of medicine and biology has been spectacular.

Without recounting here the several steps in the advancement of health and longevity, I wish merely to point out that genetics has contributed its share to this progress. You are certainly aware of the tremendous role of penicillin in virtually wiping out many infectious diseases. In the course of the enormous wartime effort that went into the attempt to produce penicillin on a large scale, one serious difficulty was met.

The highest-yielding strains of the mold *Penicillium* would grow only on the surface of the culture medium in the great vats, and strains that grew well when submerged were poor penicillin producers. Applying the methods of inducing mutations already known to geneticists at the time, Milislav Demerec and his coworkers at the Cold Spring Harbor Laboratory of the Carnegie Institution of Washington undertook to irradiate with high doses of x-rays some *Penicillium* strains that grew well when submerged, and to look for mutations that would permanently affect the yield of penicillin. Among 504 selected products, one was found that doubled the production of penicillin over that in the original strain. This high-yielding strain became the basis of the enormous production of penicillin that within the last nineteen years has contributed so much to our national health.

Even more significant than the production of this strain, however valuable, was the insight gained in the studies by Demerec and others into the fluctuating relations between virulent, disease-causing bacteria and viruses and those agents that may be used to combat them. It was discovered that the infectious agents have powers of mutation too; and among the mutations that can be induced by x-rays or by chemical compounds, or among those that are always arising spontaneously in any large population of organisms, there are some mutations that confer resistance to the sulfonamide drugs, to penicillin, to streptomycin, in fact, to the killing effects of radiation itself. Learning this, geneticists at once made dire predictions about the consequences of an overenthusiastic use of the wonder drugs and the antibiotics. But it seems that their medical colleagues failed to understand the danger, while the clamor of those who were ill led to the widespread use of such agents even for the common cold. Millions of doses were given to soldiers as mere prophylaxis, in the hope of warding off some possible infection. The result, now well known, was a near-disaster. People began to say, "The miracle drugs don't work any more. Penicillin has lost its punch. Streptomycin is no good." What had happened was exactly what the geneticists had predicted. Mutant strains of infectious germs had arisen that were now resistant to our drugs and antibiotics, just like the now all-too-common houseflies that seem to thrive on DDT. As a matter of fact, there is in existence at least one bacterial strain that actually *requires* a supply of streptomycin in order to grow.

New kinds of antibiotics had then to be discovered and put into mass production. Yet the race was a losing one, for the mutational powers of the infectious organisms seem virtually unlimited and permit change far more rapidly than scientists can discover and produce new agents.

Here again the geneticist may interpose a prediction. The simultaneous coincidence of two mutations, say to penicillin resistance and to streptomycin resistance, is of an order of probability so low (about 10^{-16}) as to be truly negligible. Start out with two antibiotics to which the infectious agents have never been exposed, and use them together; and use a high enough initial dose to leave no survivors—except, of course, your patient. In this way the antibiotics may continue to serve mankind in the future. But meanwhile, penicillin and streptomycin must be given a rest.

In recent decades the shade of Malthus has once again risen to trouble us.

Clearly, if the general life expectancy doubles, then even without any increase in births at all there are twice as many mouths to feed at any one time as there were before. But there are also more than twice as many adults with unmodified (or but slightly moderated) yearning to have children and rear families. The world population has soared, in spite of wars and famines, from one and a half billions of people, a century ago, to two and three-fourths billions today. Fertile land is almost fully occupied. How can we feed another billion people, whom we may expect inevitably to arrive before the slowly dropping birth rate overtakes the still declining death rate? The immediate answer, if there be one, lies in the almost unheralded achievements of geneticists in increasing the food supply.

On September 28, 1954 there died in Princeton, New Jersey, a geneticist who never received a Nobel prize or made a fortune. To most Americans George H. Shull remains completely unknown. Yet this man, together with a few others who made his theoretical achievement a practical possibility, has brought about a 20–30 per cent increase in the United States yield-per-acre of corn crop with no further requirement for labor, and has added literally billions of dollars to the income of our nation.

In fact, a true agricultural revolution, though scarcely recognized, has resulted from the discovery of hybrid corn. During the war years 1942–44, in the face of acute shortages of labor and of bad weather, and at a time when the corn acreage of the United States was still only about one-half planted with hybrid corn, the increased yield amounted to approximately twenty per cent—a total of 1,800,000,000 bushels worth two billion dollars. Hybrid corn thus in a sense paid for the entire development of the atomic bomb. Even more important, it was a large factor in preventing this time the aftermath of hunger that followed the end of the first World War; for the amount of food we were able to ship to the desolated countries of Europe in 1946–47 was more than equalled by the increase in the corn crop attributable to the planting of hybrid corn. The hunger and chaos of Eastern Europe in 1918 and 1919 furnished Communism with the seedbed in which it first rose to political domination in Russia. The curbing of the spread of Communism in Western Europe after the more recent World War may in a very considerable measure have been due to the boon of hybrid corn, as Paul Mangelsdorf of Harvard University has claimed.

It is of some interest, therefore, to see just what G. H. Shull did with his corn plants. He started out with the intention of studying the inheritance of quantitative characters, such as yield, in order to see whether these followed the laws of Mendelian inheritance; and he began by inbreeding his lines. He found that this inbreeding brought out a number of hidden, deleterious hereditary characteristics, and that the inbred strains showed a marked loss of both vigor and productiveness. Eventually he obtained very pure strains of great uniformity, though from the point of a farmer totally worthless, runty, and weak, with small ears bearing few seeds, and of course very low in yield. When, however, two of these inbred lines were crossed together, there was a phenomenal improvement in the hybrids.

In 1917 Donald F. Jones, at the Connecticut Agricultural Experiment Station, invented the so-called "double cross," with quite the opposite effect from that of the usual connotation. By crossing together the two hybrids produced from the single crosses of four different inbred lines, A, B, C, and

D, Jones obtained seed that, when planted, considerably exceeded in vigor and yield even the hybrids of the first crosses, of A with B, and of C with D. Seed produced by Jones' method is the present-day hybrid corn, and later efforts have been devoted simply to finding the best inbred lines to combine for a particular purpose or area, and to producing the hybrid seed in a quantity great enough to plant some sixty million acres.

The same hybrid corn that is best suited for growth in Iowa is not adapted to Texas, and assuredly not to Mexico. Hence the extension of the benefits of hybrid corn to the entire nation, and then to foreign countries, requires a repetition of the process while utilizing native strains of maize. This takes time, but requires no essential modification of theory or method.

Eventually we may have to subsist on great quantities of yeast or some microscopic alga like *Chlorella* that can be raised by the ton in tanks of nutrient solution, but these answers to the world's hunger are not yet ready. Meanwhile the geneticist must continue to breed strains resistant to the latest mutant forms of wheat rust, and more productive fruits, vegetables, and field crops like hybrid corn. Even when the day of mass-produced yeast and algae does arrive, the geneticist will have had to make an essential contribution in finding palatable, productive, and disease-resistant strains.

The geneticst can even create new species—in fact, he has already done so. He can, in short, control the course of evolution.

The evolutionary process is conceived today in somewhat different terms from those of Charles Darwin, although his ideas have been supplemented rather than superseded. In a population that is breeding quite at random with respect to certain alternative characteristics, the gene frequencies underlying those characteristics will remain in equilibrium, unchanging from generation to generation. In other words, the hereditary nature of the species, the make-up of the population, will change only if some factor upsets the equilibrium and favors one gene over another.

Four major factors contribute to evolutionary change. Only these four, and no others, can be shown to be effective in altering the frequency of particular genes in populations. The first of these factors is mutation, the rare but permanent change of individual genes or chromosomes. This is the process fundamental to all the others, for it provides the variety of hereditary material upon which the other factors can act. The second factor is natural selection, which is today regarded simply as the differential reproduction of genetic types rather than as that ruthless competition embodied in the classic phrase, "the survival of the fittest." The third factor is genetic intermixture, brought about by means of the migration and interbreeding of individuals from populations that have been to some degree isolated in the past and have become genetically differentiated, like the several races of mankind. The fourth factor is chance itself, which in populations of very small size may result in statistical fluctuations about the expected composition of the population.

Human control over the mutation process began in 1927 and 1928 when my former teacher H. J. Muller and my later friend and mentor L. J. Stadler, working quite independently, the one with fruitflies and the other with maize and barley, succeeded in demonstrating that exposure to x-rays enormously increases the frequency of all kinds of mutations. Other kinds of potent radiations, and even ultraviolet rays, were found to do the same.

Most of the mutations produced

are harmful to their carriers, as might be expected from a blind interference with the delicately balanced mechanisms of life. Most mutants have a lower viability and a poorer fecundity than the types they are derived from. Yet this is not always so. Sometimes a new mutant type may be poorer than the original type under the existing conditions of life, but may prove itself superior when these are altered. Flies dependent on garbage pails do better in the city of Baltimore if they have wings, but on the storm-swept island of Kerguelen in the southern Indian Ocean the only flies to be found creep about without wings, or with little stubby vestiges of wings. Natural selection, as Darwin pointed out, determines the differential survival of various hereditary types, and natural selection is but a name for the complex combination of conditions under which each population lives and reproduces, and which is different, at least somewhat different, in every other time and place.

The third evolutionary factor is genetic intermixture, certain possibilities of which have already been indicated in what has been said about hybrid corn. Intermixture may, however, be extended to wider limits, to encompass crosses between different geographic races of even different species. The latter have evolved to a point where the hybrids between them are commonly highly sterile—witness the mule. Yet just here, by an odd chance, there emerges the very mechanism that has enabled the geneticist to create his first true new species. For if in some way the chromosomes of a sterile hybrid can be doubled, its self-fertility is often completely restored, although it remains infertile when crosses are made with either of the parent species. If, for example, one could double the chromosomes of the mule, the latter would have two sets of horse chromosomes and two sets of ass chromosomes. Hybrid sterility is often due to the inability of the chromosomes of different species to pair with one another during the formation of the sex cells; but after doubling, one set of horse chromosomes could pair with the other and likewise for the ass chromosomes, so that each egg cell or each sperm cell would possess when mature a full set for both kinds. No one has yet succeeded in doing this to a mule, or in breeding two mules together afterwards, but exactly this feat has been accomplished a number of times in the plant world.

The first and most famous instance was performed by a Russian geneticist, G. D. Karpechenko, in 1927. Karpechenko crossed two different genera, the radish (*Raphanus*) with the cabbage (*Brassica*), and obtained a sterile hybrid. He then succeeded, with some difficulty, in getting the chromosomes to double, following which he could self-pollinate the hybrid and obtain in the next generation a perfectly fertile form which he named *Raphanobrassica* and which, according to the same etymological principle, should in English be called by the common name of "rabbage." Since it could be crossed with the original radish or cabbage parent species only with a resultant almost-complete breakdown of fertility, Karpechenko rightly regarded this as a new species, the first man-made one in history.

But unfortunately for Karpechenko, the new rabbage species combined the prickly inedible leaves of the radish with the miserable root of a cabbage. Although he received worldwide fame among geneticists for his feat, it was scarcely an achievement to impress the makers of agricultural five-year plans. Karpechenko was later liquidated. The method is nonetheless one of great promise, for in some instances the valuable characteristics of two species may thus be combined in a single new one;

and today, by means of the drug colchicine, it has become easy to double the chromosomes of a hybrid, just the step where Karpechenko met his greatest difficulty.

There is, at any rate, no difficulty in controlling the amount of genetic intermixture by performing, on the one hand, the desired crosses, and on the other by isolating and otherwise preventing intermixture, just as man in the past has controlled the interbreeding between different breeds of dogs or cats. As to the fourth factor, this too is under human control because it depends particularly on the size of population, which may be readily regulated.

At this point one might feel like singing, with Swinburne, "Glory to Man in the highest, for Man is the Master of things." But one had better be wary. Problems aplenty remain just as soon as one begins to consider the application of this newfound genetic power to Man himself.

QUESTIONS

1. Comment on two of the major biological discoveries made in recent years.
2. What problem does mold mutation present to the scientist and to the physician?
3. What two men have done most toward warding off the Malthusian threat of an inadequate food supply? Briefly describe their work.
4. Discuss the four major factors contributing to evolutionary change.

M. B. Crane

Lysenko's Experiments

Reprinted with the publisher's permission from Discovery, February 1949.

Are Lysenko's claims to success in breeding and grafting unaccountable in terms of scientific genetics? The author of the following review examines Lysenko's evidence and weighs it against his own experience in this field. Mr. Crane is a Fellow of the Royal Society of London and geneticist in the John Innes Horticultural Institution.

The address by Academician T. D. Lysenko to the Lenin Academy of Agricultural Sciences reports results so remarkable that they raise questions beyond the scope of an ordinary review. Most writers on biology, especially when dealing with their own work, freely and clearly give all relevant details of their experiments so that the reader can decide whether or not the results and conclusions the author arrives at are justified. It is regrettable that so often in this book and in earlier publications by the author and his associates, such details are not adequately given. We have, however, heard so much about the work of Lysenko and Michurin that all biologists—and especially those engaged in growing, grafting, and breeding plants—will, I feel, be impelled to read this latest account of biology in the Soviet Union. There are five points which will doubtless attract attention and at the same time puzzle the critical reader:

I. breeding grafted plants;
II. vegetative hybridization;
III. improving plants by grafting—Michurin's so-called 'Mentors';
IV. the inheritance of acquired characters;
V. the rapid conversion of "hard" wheat *Triticum durum* into winter wheat *T. vulgare*.

These five points, and especially the first three, I shall attempt to analyze in detail.

I

The first experiment involved the grafting of a tomato shoot with "pinnate leaves" and yellow fruits on to a plant with potato-like, non-pinnate leaves and red fruits. Seeds were sown from the red fruits of the latter part and we are told that most of the resulting plants "did not differ from the initial strain." "Six plants, however, had pinnate leaves, and some had yellow fruits." Lysenko concludes that this result is due to both the leaves and the fruits having changed under the influence of the yellow-fruited, pinnate-leaved shoot grafted upon it.

In this experiment and indeed in all the experiments referred to in the book, Lysenko and his associates seem to have had no scientific method. At least we are left in the dark on many important points. It would have been of value if we were told if all the six pinnate-leaved plants had yellow fruits, and, if not, how many were yellow, and what was the color of the remainder. Also, if control plants were grown and whether the two plants used to make the composite grafted plant were homozygous or not.

The inheritance of leaf-shape and fruit color in tomatoes has long been known. The pinnate cut-leaf character *C* is dominant to the non-pinnate potato-leaf *c*. Two major genes *R* and *Y* are concerned with fruit color; *RY* is bright red as in the common tomato of commerce, *Ry* is dull red, *rY* deep yellow, and *ry* pale yellow. Since no mention is made of control plants, the first question which arises is, were the plants, and especially the red-fruited plant, used in the grafting homozygous or heterozygous. That is to say, was it of the constitution *RRYY*, *RrYY* or *RrYy*, for although the fruits of all three would be red and indistinguishable, seeds from the latter two would give a proportion of plants with yellow fruits, but we should expect them to have the recessive potato-leaf character. If, however, a few grains of pollen from the pinnate-leaved upper part of the composite grafted plant came in contact with the female organs of the potato-leaved lower part, then plants with pinnate leaves and yellow fruits would arise.

Admittedly natural cross-pollination in tomatoes is rare between separate undisturbed plants, but it is not unknown and where, as in this grafted plant, two forms are growing together and are probably being interfered with by the experimenter, the chance for cross-pollination is greater than between separate plants.

There is another possibility which we may consider. As shown by Jorgensen and Crane (1927), plants grafted together, and especially solanaceous plants, frequently develop tissues in which the two components are intimately combined. The most common development is the so-called periclinal chimera where even only a small area of one component may be over the other. If such an area is two layers thick, resulting seeds and offspring will be like the component of which these layers are composed. On the other hand, if the outer component is only one layer thick—then the offspring would be like the inner component. In this way seeds from a single fruit could give both pinnate and yellow and non-pinnate and red-fruited plants. With two varieties of tomatoes, especially if only a small area of a flower was involved, such a development could be passed unnoticed. Periclinal tissue has occurred from time to time in other plants such as apples, medlars, and roses following the common horticultural practice of grafting, but without any other interference.

Later, Lysenko refers to a tomato plant which had one yellow and one red fruit. When we consider the numerous recorded and well authenticated examples of spontaneous somatic variations in plants, see for example Darwin (1899) and Crane and Lawrence (1947), involving all kinds of characters including the color of flowers and fruits, this tomato plant does not stand out as a very wonderful happening. In my own work with tomatoes I have had a fruit partly red and partly yellow and it is only a small step from this to wholly red and wholly yellow fruits on one plant.

In Lysenko's *Heredity and its Variability* translated by Dobzhansky (1946) it appears that the yellow tomato used in the grafting experiments was the double recessive *rryy*. Plants are also mentioned where the fruits were pale yellow or slightly reddish. In *The New Genetics in the Soviet Union* by Hudson and Richens (1946) tomato fruits pale yellow with pink stripes are described. Since such fruits may appear new and unusual I will point out that these descriptions appear to correspond to the fruits of a variety named "Blood Orange" which has been known in England for ten years or more. In this variety individual fruits vary. At one extreme the fruits appear almost wholly yellow and at the other they are appreciably reddish. Between these extremes fruits with intermediate amounts of red occur, i.e., yellow with irregular blotches or stripes of red.

II

The so-called "Mentors" elaborated by Michurin receive much attention. Lysenko tells us I. V. Michurin not only recognized the possibility of obtaining vegetative hybrids, but he elaborated the Mentor method. This method consists in the following: by grafting scions (twigs) of old strains of fruit trees on the branches of a young strain, the latter acquires properties which it lacks, these properties being transmitted to it through the grafted twigs of the old strain. That is why I. V. Michurin called this method "Mentor." We are also told: "When grafted, organisms which have not reached the stage of full development, i.e., have not completed their cycle of development, will always change their development as compared with the plants which have their own roots. In the union of plants by means of grafting the product is a single organism with varying strains, that of the stock and that of the scion. By planting the seeds from the stock or the scion it is possible to obtain offspring, individual representatives of which will possess characteristics not only of the strain from which the seed has been taken, but also of the other with which it has been united by grafting."

I have been profoundly interested in the growing, breeding and grafting of plants and trees for nearly fifty years, and have raised thousands of fruit trees from seed; grown many both on their own roots and on the roots of others. I have also grafted twigs of an old variety on a young seedling on its own roots and also twigs of young seedlings on to old varieties. I have raised peach seedlings from peaches growing on plum roots; plum seedlings from *Prunus domestica* growing on *P. cerasifera* roots; pear seedlings from pears growing on quince, on pear-stocks, and also on their own roots. In the same way I have used as parents apples growing on widely different root-stocks. In all these there has not been the slightest indication of the different roots having had any influence on the seedlings. That is to say in my experience no vegetative hybridization occurred.

I have also compared numerous seedlings on their own roots with the same individuals grafted, at an early stage, on other roots. Those which were good on the grafted tree were also good on their own roots and those which were inferior on the one were also inferior on the other.

III

I am often asked the question, what are these "Mentors" and how do they work? We have just read one account of them in *Soviet Biology*, but Lysenko says: "The best way for scientific workers in various departments of biology to master the theoretical depths of Michurin teaching is to study Michurin's works, to read them over again and again, and to analyze some of them with a view to solving problems of practical importance."

We will take Lysenko's advice and refer to "The use of 'Mentors' in raising hybrid seedlings and examples of definite changes induced in fruit tree varieties by various external factors." This was written by Michurin in 1916 and published in 1939. Here Michurin says the "Mentor" method works as follows: "Supposing we have a well-developed six- or seven-year-old hybrid seedling, which has not started fruiting, we know that it will not start fruiting before some ten years have elapsed since in some cases the parent varieties do not normally start to fruit until their twentieth year (*sic*). Yet by grafting close to the base of the lower branches of the crown several scions taken from the fruitbearing tree which is known to be of a high-yielding variety the seedling can be induced to bear fruit within two years."

Further we are told: "In three further instances the method was used for the improvement of the quality of hybrid fruits, namely, for development of certain storage characters, for improvement in color of the fruits, for increase in sugar content in fruit flesh. In these instances the "Mentors" were employed after the hybrids had already fruited once"; and again: "It is quite apparent that the method can be used to effect various other changes in the properties and characters of hybrid varieties, such as the increase of fertility, attainment of larger size fruits, etc."

Now I have had many families of cherries in which the earliest seedlings fruited in their fourth year and the latest in their eighth year. These were grown on their own roots without any interference apart from ordinary common-sense cultivation. Amongst tree fruits pears are most delayed. A few fruit in their eighth year, about 50 per cent in their ninth year and then there is often a small proportion which have not fruited until their fifteenth year. The point is that as far as I can see Michurin used no controls; indeed the only way to get real control would be to multiply an individual seedling vegetatively and use some as control and some for experiment. Otherwise if observations are confined to a single or very few trees one might mentor trees which will fruit early and compare them with others which normally fruit late.

In this country we are of course well aware of certain root-stock effects, but these, important as they are to commercial growers, are indeed trifling when compared with the claims of Michurian mentors.

We are also aware of the so-called juvenile period of pears and other fruits and of the practice of bark-ringing to bring fruit trees into flower, but neither these nor the root-stock effects are quite as mysterious as "Mentors." Incidentally, it is just conceivable that several grafts at the base of branches might have a similar effect to bark-ringing, but Michurin does not make any such suggestion.

The claims of "Mentors" for improving size, color, sweetness, fertility, etc., are no more convincing than the others. They are, however, very remarkable, the inferior seedlings developing fruit with qualities akin to those of the highly desirable mentors grafted upon them.

There is much more in this paper of Michurin's written in the same loose and, I fear, lightly-judged way, which to some extent has flowed over into Lysenko's *Soviet Biology*. Thus Michurin writes: "As to the famous pea laws of Mendel, only very ignorant people may think that they may prove useful to the breeder of new hybrid varieties of perennial fruits. Mendel's law is not applicable to perennial fruit trees, nor does it apply to annual hybrids, or if you wish, to kitchen garden crops themselves." This is, of course, rather an ironical statement. I have always considered the garden pea a kitchen garden crop, and we know many annuals whose characters behave the same as those in peas. As to only very ignorant people, it would indeed be a very ignorant person who would expect vegetatively-propagated perennials, such as fruit trees, which are invariably heterozygous, commonly self-incompatible, and hence cross-pollinated, to behave in inheritance precisely the same as peas which are self-pollinating, reproduced sexually annually, and, in consequence, in the main homozygous. Nevertheless my work and that of my colleagues and others has shown that there are many characters in various perennial fruits, such as raspberries, peaches, pears, etc., which in inheritance behave the same as those in peas.

This paper also describes experiments in breeding pears. One of the most successful varieties used as a parent appears to be the variety *Beurre Diel*. Thus we are told: "This combination was a cross between *Beurre Diel* and a young seedling of the wild usuri pear flowering for the first time. Of the hybrids raised, two-thirds bore fruits maturing in summer or autumn, and one-third were hybrids producing fruits that ripened in winter"; I read this to mean that 100 per cent of the family were fertile, and if so this again conflicts with my experience. *Beurre Diel* is a triploid variety, and hence with me it has not been a desirable parent; on the contrary, and as one would expect it has proved a bad parent.

Following Lysenko's advice I have read all that has come my way on the teachings of Michurin including *Voks Bulletin* (1945). Here a certain Professor Yakovlev, a Stalin Prize Winner and Manager of the important Michurin Nurseries, writes: "In his science of vegetative hybridization which is now being developed and expanded by his talented follower T. Lysenko—Michurin dealt a decisive blow to the metaphysical views of the geneticists Mendel and Morgan." There is nothing, however, in his article which supports this now familiar and somewhat vindictive statement.

Professor Yakovlev then goes on to what he calls intergenal hybridization and writes, "for the first time in world practice such fruit-bearing hybrids have been produced in Michurinsk as hybrids of apples and pear trees (by T. R. Gorshkova), plum and peach (by V. N. Yakovlev), cherry and plum, red and black currants." I would point out that Professor Yakovlev is not correct in this statement—plum-peach, gooseberry-currant, pear-quince, peach-almond and other hybrids have long been known.

The plum-peach hybrid I have referred to was raised by Messrs. Laxton of Bedford, and was described by them in the Report of the Third International Conference on Genetics (1906). It was raised from *Prunus triflora x Amygdalis persica*. I grew it for over thirty years, and it was quite sterile. I have also grown the peach-almond for over thirty years; it crops well in favorable seasons and produces good seeds. The pear-quince was raised in this country in 1895; in Algeria it produces fruits abundantly but they are entirely seedless. I have made cross-pollinations between apple and pear, but without success.

I wonder why in this article we are, as is usual in Soviet writings, left so much in the dark and not told the things we are eager to know. You will note Professor Yakovlev says his hybrids are fruit-bearing. An account of the parent varieties and details of the flowers and fruits of his apple-pear hybrids would, I am sure, be of intense interest to horticulturists and biologists not only in this country but throughout the world. The same applies to his plum-peach hybrid. Soviet biologists should realize that if they would only take the trouble to give us such details we would then be able to appreciate their work much better, and many misunderstandings might be swept away.

On page 28 of his *Soviet Biology* Lysenko says, "altered sections of the body of the parent organism always (*sic*) possess an altered heredity. Horticulturists have long known these facts. An altered twig or bud of a fruit tree or the eye (bud) of a potato tuber cannot as a rule influence the heredity of the offspring of the given tree or tuber which are not directly generated from the altered sections of the parent organisms. If, however, the altered section is cut away and grows separately as an independent plant, the latter, as a rule, will possess a changed heredity, the one that characterized the altered section of the parent plant." This, like so much in the book is very far from the truth, for we know beyond any disputation that an alteration of the body cells of an organism does not always result in an altered heredity.

Now one of the most brilliant and informative investigations on this subject was carried out by Lysenko's country-woman T. Asseyava, and if he refers to her publication, Asseyava (1928), or better still discusses the problem with her, he will find that far from such alterations *always* having a changed heredity, most often and, as a rule, it remains the same.

Asseyava investigated many such body alterations, i.e. somatic mutant alterations, in potatoes, and in all cases she says "the characters of the mutant are not transmitted through seed, and its offspring are exactly similar to the progeny of the original variety." The reason why there was no changed heredity, although the altered potatoes had for long been grown as independent plants and were so distinct that they had different varietal names, is simple and clear. The alterations did not penetrate as far as the germ-tract, and hence could not change heredity. With body alterations it does not matter whether or not they are removed from the parent organism; if the alterations go as deeply as the germ-tract they will be inherited, otherwise they will not. This of course applies to twigs and buds of fruit trees, etc., as well as to potatoes. With such a lamentable lack of horticultural and biological knowledge, it is perhaps not surprising that *Soviet Biology* contains so many loose statements and inaccurate conclusions.

IV

Lysenko brings in Michurinism in connection with the inheritance of acquired characters and he states, "the well-known Lamarckian propositions, which recognise the active role of external conditions in the formation of the living body and the heredity of acquired characters, unlike the metaphysics of Neo-Darwinism (or Weismannism) are by no means faulty. On the contrary, they are quite true and scientific." I cannot find anything in the book which proves that the inheritance of acquired characters is true.

V

The hard and soft wheats provide my last point. Agriculturists, plant breeders, and cytologists alike will, I feel, ponder long over the rapid conversion of *Triticum durum* into *T. vulgare*. Lysenko writes; "Michurinists have mastered a good method of converting spring into winter wheat." "When experiments were started to convert hard wheat into winter wheat it was found that after two, three, or four years of autumn planting (required to turn a spring into a winter crop), *durum* becomes *vulgare*, that is to say, one species is converted into another. *Durum*, i.e., a hard 28-chromosome wheat, is converted into several varieties of soft 42-chromosome wheat; nor do we, in this case find any transitional forms between the *durum* and *vulgare* species. *The conversion of one species into another takes place by a leap*." Biologists are familiar with new species arising more or less by a leap, *Primula kewensis* being a notable example, but the conversion of a tetraploid wheat into a hexaploid species is indeed remarkable, and I have no explanatory comments. Perhaps, however, I may be pardoned if this brings to mind some mishaps I have experienced in a long association with seeds and plants. In our pre-soil-sterilization days, I have seen elderberry plants germinate and grow where only gooseberry seeds were sown, also a proportion of red currants *Ribes rubrum* among a sowing of black currants *Ribes nigrum*.

Throughout this small book much space is devoted to various philosophical and political themes and materialistic arguments. I have not attempted to discuss them; as they have not, or should not have, anything to do with biology. I have, however, taken space in this review to give my experiences in the growing, grafting, and breeding of plants and trees to show how they have so often differed from those of the Lysenko-Michurin school.

I have also given some account of the Soviet "Mentors" and other things, having done this I will leave it to the reader himself to decide what "Mentors," vegetative hybridization and the like are, and how they work.

QUESTIONS

1. Why is it necessary to know something about the hereditary composition of plants used for breeding purposes?
2. What is meant by vegetative hybridization and what is the author's feeling about it?
3. What is meant by a "control" and how would it work in a "Mentor" experiment?
4. What opinion does Lysenko have about Lamarckianism and what is the general feeling among biologists regarding this theory?

Joshua Lederberg

Genetic Transduction

Reprinted with the permission of the author and publisher from American Scientist 44(3): 264–280, 1956.

The recombination of genes stands on a par with mutation and selection as a cardinal element of biological variation. In the laboratory, recombination furnishes the experimental test of mutational change in genetic units. In nature, it leads to their fulfillment by generating a multitude of different combinations which are then sifted by natural selection. Until recently, genetic recombination has been closely identified with sexual reproduction: indeed geneticists consider it to be the principal biological function of sexuality, but other processes are now recognized as alternative means to the same end. In sexual reproduction, the fertilization of one intact cell or gamete by another precedes the formation of the new zygote and assures the union of a full complement of genes from each of two parents. In *genetic transduction*, by contrast, one cell receives only a fragment of the genetic content of another. As we shall see, the fragment can be defined not only in genetic but also in physical, chemical, or virological terms. That is, the fragment may be associated with subcellular constituents of DNA (desoxyribonucleic acid). So far genetic transduction is only known, with certainty, in bacteria but whether this limitation is one of fact or of technology must still be found out.

HISTORICAL BACKGROUND

Scattered observations that might be attributed to transduction have been recorded since the infancy of modern microbiology in the last century but could not be understood or coordinated in the incomplete genetic theory of the time. During the past twenty years, however, an infusion of quantitative method has nourished bacterial genetics, and this discipline has enlarged that basic concordance of all living forms which comparative biochemistry had firmly substantiated.

In higher plants and animals, the concept of the gene originated from recombination studies, but in bacteria it arose and for some time depended exclusively on mutation studies. This concept simply states that the hereditary quality, the intrinsic differences of organisms, can be analyzed in terms of unit factors, markers or genes. Detailed factorial analysis of bacterial heredity has, of course, had to wait upon the recognition of recombinational techniques, be they sexual or transductional. Unit factors that are subject to mutation, and can be used for genetic studies of bacteria, are related to such diverse traits as pigmentation, resistance to antibiotics and to bacterial viruses, biochemical aspects of nutrition and fermentation enzymes, cellular morphology, and antigenic specificity. . . .

The idea of transduction of hereditary fragments is still difficult to reconcile with our well established knowledge of highly organized chromosomal systems of heredity, but the problem can now be stated in terms clear enough that the synthesis, if not yet certain, can at least be experimentally sought. . . .

THE "PNEUMOCOCCUS TRANSFORMATION"

A new turn of events was marked by Griffith's announcement in 1928 (the same year as Muller's proof that X-rays caused mutations) of the transformation of serological types in the pneumococcus. He had been working for some years on the serotypic classification of pneumococci, which was important for therapy as well as for diagnosis, since antiserum was almost the only specific treatment known at that time. The most prominent antigen of virulent pneumococci consists of a polysaccharide capsule that envelopes each cell, and is readily detected by an apparent "Quellung" (swelling) reaction in the presence of specific antiserum. . . . The presence of the capsules conditions not only the high virulence of these organisms, but also the appearance of their colonies on agar media, whence these are called "smooth" types. "Rough" variants are also known: these are relatively avirulent and lack the specific capsular substances. Some rough variants were more or less unstable and would occasionally revert to the parental smooth form; others appeared to be absolutely stable. Griffith was impressed by the occasional occurrence of more than one serotype in a single sputum, and speculated on the possible interconvertibility of the types. His experimental design was fundamentally similar to that of earlier attempts at transduction: he prepared heat-killed suspensions of smooth bacteria, and inoculated mice with a mixture of this vaccine and some living, rough cells. Neither the killed vaccine nor the rough bacteria, separately, would be expected to generate an active infection in the mice, and none did in control experiments, but in a few inoculations, the mixture of the two gave a virulent infection from which living smooth pneumococci could be isolated. In further experiments, he also showed that the serotype of the recovered bacteria depended on the type of bacteria used to prepare the vaccine, rather than on the parentage of the rough cells. He had therefore justified the claim that rough bacteria, originally of one type, had been transformed to a different smooth type. The mouse played the part of a selective agent in obtaining a specific genotype, namely a new virulent form. To explain this transformation, Griffith did not use genetic language, but adopted what amounts to transduction hypothesis, namely that the substances responsible for the formation of the specific capsules had been transferred via the vaccines to the deficient, rough cells.

Fortunately, Griffith's observations were saved from limbo by their prompt trial in several other laboratories where they could be confirmed and extended. The problem was taken up in the laboratories of the Rockefeller Institute by a group of workers under the leadership of the late O. T. Avery. Their extensive researches culminated in the report in 1943, that the active material in the "pneumococcus transformation" was a macromolecular form of desoxyribonucleic acid, DNA, a substance that had already been found to occur characteristically in the nuclei and chromosomes of the cells of higher organisms, and was therefore believed to be intimately connected with the stuff of heredity. Griffith had been rather lucky in his earlier experimental design. The living mouse proved to have two functions: a selective action, as already mentioned, and to furnish protein adjuvants from its serum that play an obscure part in conditioning the bacteria to enable them to take up the DNA particles.

Considerable progress has been made recently in the chemical analysis of DNA, and it is known to consist of extended chains of nucleotide units. Each unit contains phosphoric acid; a five-carbon sugar (desoxyribose); and a purine or pyrimidine base (adenine, guanine, thymine, or uracil). The specificity of DNA is believed to depend on the sequence of these four alternatives; it is not surprising that very large molecules are required to store biological information of ultimate complexity in a language with such a simple alphabet. Actually, the true molecular size of pneumococcal DNA is not accurately known, for such long linear macromolecules are the most difficult to study by the physicochemical methods that have been developed for the proteins. It is generally accepted, however, that the material extracted from the pneumococci is a mixture of active and inactive material, and that the active constituents would consist of chains with hundreds or thousands of nucleotide units. The same difficulties have stood in the way of rigorous proof that only DNA is involved in the transforming substances, though this has been established to the limits of current analytical methods. . . .

The success of Griffith and Avery has, of course, inspired many investigators to look for genetic effects of DNA with other bacteria. The greatest success to date has been met with in the influenza bacillus (*Hemophilus influenzae*) where again a capsular antigen and streptomycin resistance proved to be useful markers. This system is closely parallel to the pneumococcus transformation, a result which is important, in itself, in confirming the generality of the potency of DNA in transducing activity. On the other hand, many trials with other bacteria have been definitely unsuccessful, though negative results do not, of course, receive equal attention.

TRANSDUCTION BY PHAGE

A second mode of transduction, mediated by bacterial viruses rather than chemically extracted DNA, was discovered independently of the pneumococcus researches in the course of studies on *Salmonella*. This group of bacteria is of medical interest because of their connection with diseases such as food-poisoning and enteric and typhoid fever. However, they are closely related to *Escherichia coli*, a species which has been shown to undergo recombination by a sexual mechanism, that is one that involves intact cells and the exchange of large blocks of genes. Originally, sexuality could be demonstrated in only one bacterial strain (K-12) but after suitable methods were developed, the same process could be found in many different strains of *E. coli*. It was therefore natural to extend these researches to other related organisms, of which *Salmonella* was a choice.

The principal criterion for sexual rather than transductive recombination is the concurrent exchange of several factors, a result that was also considered technically more reliable than the change of a single marker, for which simple mutation must always be considered. This caution led to many indecisive experiments: indications of exchange with single markers could not be confirmed in multi-factorial experiments. We eventually realized that genetic exchange was taking place in certain combinations of *Salmonella* strains, but in a different pattern from crossing in *E. coli*, as only single markers were being exchanged at each event. This realization was promptly followed by the corollary discovery that filtrates of certain mixed cultures could be freed of intact cells, and still transform individual traits of a recipient strain. The term "transduction" was introduced at this point for the hypothesis that genetic fragments were being transmitted from one strain to another, via cell-free filtrates, as seemed to occur in the pneumococcus too. However, *Salmonella* proved to be far more amenable to genetic study than the pneumococcus, and generalizations on this transduction could be based on studies with thirty or forty different markers in a relatively short time. The advantages of *Salmonella* in genetics were, however, compensated for in biochemistry. At first, the most important information about the transforming substance of *Salmonella* was that its activity was not destroyed by desoxyribonuclease, in distinction to the pneumococcus experiments. Filtration and sedimentation experiments then connected the activity with particles about 0.1 micron in diameter and hence just beneath microscopic visibility. (For comparison, an *E. coli* cell is about 1 micron wide and 3 to 5 microns long.) These particles were later identified as bacteriophage, or bacterial virus. The lack of effect of desoxyribonuclease was then easily explained, if the true agent of transduction were protected inside the skin of the virus particle. The inner agent might very well be DNA—but chemical studies so far cannot distinguish the bacterial genes from the DNA nucleus of the virus itself, and we must rely for this guess on the analogy with the pneumococcal transduction.

But where did the virus come from in these bacterial filtrates? One of the *Salmonella* strains proved to be "lysogenic," that is to say is infected by a latent virus. The latent virus, or "prophage" is ordinarily transmitted as a hereditary quality, during the multiplication of the lysogenic cells. Once it is freed, the virus can infect other cells. Here it may behave alternatively as a typical lethal parasite, and grow rapidly at the expense of the host, or re-enter its latent form, and render the bacterium lysogenic.

The conclusion may be simply stated that the pneumococcus and *Salmonella* both manifest types of genetic transduction. In the latter, bacteriophage acts as passive carrier of the genetic (DNA?) fragments, but the viral nucleus has no other demonstrable relationship with its host companions. In both cases, any genetic marker that could be tested for was amenable to transduction.

APPLICATIONS AND PROSPECTS

The study of transduction in bacteria has been the labor of many scientists of whom only a few are listed in the references here. But the story has only well begun. Of the thousands of bacteria species, only a few have been examined at all, and each study has revealed a new facet. So far, only a minority of attempts to demonstrate recombination mechanisms (sexual or transductive) in bacteria have been successful. It is a fair caution that the first essential is a selective technique, a workable means of detecting new types even when they are extremely rare. Partly for this reason, and partly because the experimental organisms have usually been economically unimportant, recombinational techniques have had more analytic than practical utility. (Artificial serotypes in *Salmonella* have been of some use in the preparation of diagnostic serums.) The vast applications of genetics in practical agriculture are, however, a sufficient portent of what may be accomplished in due course with the microbes that are important in medicine and industry.

Some of the hopes that have been expressed, however, are too extravagant in the light of present knowledge, for example for the massive transformation of virulent or drug-resistant bacteria in an infected host to more innocuous forms. To be therapeutically effective, such transformations would have to involve virtually every bacterium, which is too much to ask of a recombination process (barring the exceptional examples of lysogenic conversions). A similar misconception has provoked the suggestion that transduction could account for the spread of drug-resistance from one mutant cell to a large population (a result that needs no elaborate explanation other than selection). In every case so far, genetic transduction is achieved at the expense of the life of the donor cell: in the most favorable cases, the DNA or the lambda from one or a few bacteria has been enough to transform a single recipient, which speaks for the recovery of much of the original genetic material.

So far, no definite case of transduction has been reported for higher organisms. Claims that DNA from tumor cells would induce tumors in normal mouse tissues are controversial but they do illustrate the impact of transduction on experimental cancer research. The concept may also have some bearing on mysterious changes in tumor cells that are transplanted to new hosts. And speculations correlating the pneumococcus transformation to embryonic inductions perhaps have to be inverted and reviewed with the genetic understanding of the former. However, before a convincing search for transduction in higher organisms can be executed, efficient selective methods will have to be developed as they have been for bacteria.

The question of whether transduction is unique to the bacteria, or occurs more generally, is important for its bearing on general genetic theory. It has been suggested that the postulated "chromosomes" of bacteria and viruses are chemically and structurally less elaborate than the cytogenetically verified chromosomes of higher plants and animals. However, the generalization of concepts and techniques learned from these organisms has been the most productive approach to the analysis of transduction in bacteria. Conversely, transduction has pointed up the weaknesses of some traditional formulations of chromosome behavior. In crossing-over, for example, can we believe that two chromosomes will regularly break at precisely corresponding points? The impending translation of genetic differences as chemical (or grosser structural) differences in DNA has also provoked a re-examination of the concept of the "single gene." We are reminded again of the first principle of genetics, that we cannot recognize genes directly but only their differences. In turn, we should not insist on genes as self-reproducing units, but as units or markers of a more complex self-reproducing system. Nevertheless, the representation of genic differences in chemically purifiable DNA is the closest approach to the reduction of genetics to biochemistry, an enterprise which can challenge the skills and imaginations of specialists in a dozen sciences.

QUESTIONS

1. What is the difference between sexual reproduction and genetic transduction?
2. Of what substances does DNA consist and why is an understanding of DNA important to us?
3. How does phage transduction seem to operate?

W. Gordon Whaley

The Gifts of Hybridity

Reprinted with the permission of the publisher and author from The Scientific Monthly **70:** 10–18, 1950.

In the year 1932 corn was planted on 113,024,000 acres of United States farm land. The total yield for that year was 2,930,352,000 bushels, an average of 25.9 bushels per acre. In the year 1946, 3,287,927,000 bushels were harvested from plantings on 90,027,000 acres, representing a per acre yield of 36.5 bushels. The difference in yield was due in greatest measure to the use of hybrid corn on a large scale. The production of 36 bushels to the acre instead of 26 represents nothing short of a revolution. The importance of the revolution extends even further than the increased yield figures indicate, for it has freed approximately 23,000,000 acres of land for the growing of other crops or for inclusion in a hedge against soil fertility exhaustion.

These developments suggest startling potentialities for other crops, and they may be a consideration pointing the way out of the dilemma of increasing populations and decreasingly fertile farm lands with which most of the Temperate Zone countries of the world are faced.

The superiority of hybrid corn has its basis in a little-understood phenomenon known to biologists as heterosis. Whatever may be involved, heterosis gives to hybrids a developmental vigor which makes them larger, higher-yielding, improves the quality of their products, or otherwise renders them more desirable than their parents. The occurrence of this hybrid advantage, generally referred to as hybrid vigor, provides one of the most intriguing of biological puzzles.

Our discussion of it must be prefaced with a note about the use of the word "hybrid." In a narrow sense, a hybrid is an offspring of two different species. In the broader sense in which we shall use it here, hybrids are the offspring of genetically different types. These may be species, varieties, or lines, types which differ too litle to be called separate varieties.

The discovery that among both plants and animals certain cross-fertilizations result in the production of progeny more vigorous than either parent was made long ago. There are records of plant hybridizers taking practical advantage of hybrid vigor as early as the last quarter of the eighteenth century. The value of the mule, which is often, though perhaps not correctly, cited as a classic example of hybrid vigor, was recognized by the contemporaries of Moses. Through the years it has been learned that hybrid vigor is the result of interbreeding within plant genera as diverse as corn and oaks and within animal genera as different as fruit flies, fish, cattle and man.

THE BASIC PROBLEM

There is a vast literature on the subject of hybrid vigor. Part is devoted to the usefulness of hybrid vigor as a manageable biological occurrence, and part is devoted to the opportunities that hybrid vigor presents for approaching certain complex questions of inheritance and development. When one examines the results of research, it becomes apparent that there is no single definition of what constitutes hybrid vigor. Different plant types exhibit hybrid vigor in different ways. For example: In corn, in which greatest practical use has been made of the characteristic, the hybrid advantages are generally recorded in terms of total yield, weight, length of the ears, number of grains per row on the ear, and number of nodes per plant. There appear to be "quality" factors involved also, but these are much more difficult to evaluate. Among them are likely to be differences in chemical composition, making for differences in nutritive value. In the tomato, on the other hand, the effects are mostly in increasing the number of parts rather than the size of the individual parts.

The differences in manifestation of hybrid vigor in corn and tomato are related to differences in growth habit. Corn is a determinate plant in which, after a certain number of internodes have been formed, the growing shoot apex matures as a flower structure. Tomato is an inderterminate plant which forms an indefinite number of lateral branches and bears lateral rather than terminal flowers. Apparently, in determinate plants like corn, added vigor increases the magnitude of the parts, the number of which is more or less fixed by the genetic pattern. In indeterminate plants like tomato, added vigor results in faster or longer-continued production of the new parts. There may be an important clue as to the nature of hybrid vigor in these differences in expression, for they seem to suggest that we are not dealing so much with a change in the basic genetic pattern as with an increase in the efficiency of growth and development.

Hybrid vigor in corn presents the best example for consideration. Corn has been grown in the Western Hemisphere for hundreds of years. It has been subject to so much artificial selection that it was long ago modified to the point where it can now exist only in cultivation. The fact that a plant with such a long history of use could be so greatly improved in the short space of a few decades is pertinently suggestive for our handling of other plants and animals with much shorter histories of domestication.

Despite much research and a great deal of speculation, we still have no certain knowledge as to the ancestry of the modern cultivated type of corn. It is clear, however, that corn early became distributed over a fairly wide range. It was grown by most of the American Indians. As a basic Indian food crop, the distribution of corn was over a number of areas more or less sharply isolated from one another. In each of these there appeared much variation, some of which has long since disappeared. Some of it has been preserved in the germ plasm of corn. Because the corn-growing areas were more or less isolated from one another and represented different environmental conditions, different sets of variants have been preserved in the different areas. It is an ancient observation that corn tends to gain in vigor as diverse kinds are combined. Both the Indians and the early white settlers frequently made a practice of planting blue grains and red or yellow grains and white grains together, or making other combinations which tended to result in a mixing of kinds, because the yields in such mixed plantings were higher than those obtained when a single type of corn was planted by itself.

With the advent of scientific plant breeding came efforts to produce true breeding stocks of plants. It was early discovered that when corn is self-fertilized there results a segregation of lines, often with quite different characteristics. Repeated self-fertilization of these lines ultimately produces stable or nearly stable stocks, although generally a great number of the lines are lost during the inbreeding operations. It is a universal observation that inbreeding in corn to produce pure lines is attended by marked degeneration.

When different surviving inbred lines of corn are crossed they most frequently produce hybrid progeny which not only exceed their parents in vigor, but generally are more vigorous than the stocks from which the inbred lines were originally derived.

Hybrid corn is valued first of all for its relative vigor, which not only makes for greater yield, but which also, apparently, provides better adaptability to environmental conditions. Too, being a genetically uniform stock, hybrid corn grows and develops much more uniformly than do randomly pollinated stocks.

Recently the techniques of hybridization have been extended to produce what are known as double hybrids, or sometimes "double-crossed" corn. Inbred A is crossed with inbred B to produce the hybrid AB. Inbred C is crossed with inbred D to produce the hybrid CD. The two inbreds are then crossed to produce the double hybrid ABCD. In many instances such double hybrids have certain added advantages. Occasionally they are more vigorous than their immediate hybrid parents, but more usually their advantages are found in somewhat greater uniformity of growth and development and a little wider range of adaptability, probably brought about by the combination of four rather than two selected germ plasms.

The hybridization of corn has now reached practically an assembly-line stage. The production of hybrid corn seed is a big business, with competitive aspects which will keep alive attempts to produce new and better hybrids. Like any strain of plants, the efficiency of a hybrid is dependent upon a proper balance of inherited characteristics, the soil, climate, and other factors which constitute the environment. A hybrid which will grow well and produce large yields in one locality may be distinctly inferior in another. This feature of hybrid corn production gives the problem some local flavor and makes it necessary to study the behavior of individual hybrids under given sets of conditions before their adaptability and usefulness can be determined.

To whichever of the genetic bases heterosis is related, it has its roots in the changes wrought by evolution. The phenomenon presents an attractive field for investigation of the part played by specific factors in evolutionary change. Our studies of heterosis contribute to several fields of knowledge. In addition, the practical usefulness of these effects of hybridity is tremendous. Can we but learn enough of their nature and development we can make available the gifts of hybridity in many important crop plants and domestic animals. The bequest might go far toward meeting the food and energy demands which increasing populations are imposing upon the world.

QUESTIONS

1. What is meant by heterosis?
2. What has heterosis contributed to the world's food supply?
3. Describe the "double cross" in corn.
4. Why did the Indians plant variously-colored corn grains together?

PART SEVENTEEN

EVOLUTION

Few, if any, subjects have generated as much controversy as evolution. Millions of words have been written about it, starting with the early Greeks. Both scientists and clergymen have touched on it. Even today, the word "evolution" is a fighting word in some circles.

Evolution usually means the development on the earth of living things, from simpler forms, through time. It is a grand concept, and being based upon natural laws, it is the only concept that the scientist can deal with in his day by day work. It should also be borne in mind that Charles Darwin did not originate either the Theory of Evolution or the Theory of Natural Selection. What he did was to assemble a tremendous amount of data which made the Theory of Natural Selection likely as the mechanism *of organic evolution. Darwin did not know the source of the variation which was the cornerstone of his theory. Today we know that variation originates as a result of gene or chromosomal changes.*

There is also the feeling that some characteristics of organisms have no selective value, as far as we can tell, and that these are passed on by chance (genetic drift).

Another clarification that has come about in recent years is the difference between speciation and evolution. The major steps in phylogenetic evolution presumably occurred in the Pre-Cambrian period and what has mostly happened since then is speciation or the elaboration of taxa within each phylum.

In recent years, animals and plants thought extinct have come to light in the living state. One is the fish known as the Coelocanth and the plant is the Metasequoia. Every year we learn more and more about evolution. If the history of science can tell us anything, it is that gradually we reduce the percentage of error in our theories and approach closer and closer to the truth.

Alfred Russel Wallace

The Debt of Science to Darwin

Reprinted with the permission of W. G. Wallace and the publishers from Natural selection and tropical nature. London, Macmillan Co., 1895.

The great man recently taken from us had achieved an amount of reputation and honour perhaps never before accorded to a contemporary writer on science. His name has given a new word to several languages, and his genius is acknowledged wherever civilization extends. Yet the very greatness of his fame, together with the number, variety, and scientific importance of his works, has caused him to be altogether misapprehended by the bulk of the reading public. The best scientific authorities rank him far above the greatest names in natural science—above Linnaeus and Cuvier, the great teachers of a past generation—above De Candolle and Agassiz, Owen and Huxley, in our own times. Many must feel inclined to ask—What is the secret of this lofty pre-eminence so freely accorded to a contemporary by his fellow-workers? What has Darwin done, that even those who most strongly oppose his theories rarely suggest that he is overrated? Why is it universally felt that the only name with which his can be compared in the whole domain of science is that of the illustrious Newton?

It will be my endeavor to answer these questions, however imperfectly, by giving a connected sketch of the work which Darwin did, the discoveries which he made, the new fields of research which he opened up, the new conceptions of nature which he has given us.

THE CENTURY BEFORE DARWIN

Almost exactly a hundred years before Darwin we find Linnaeus and his numerous disciples hard at work describing and naming all animals and plants then discovered, and classifying them according to the artificial method of the great master, and from that time to the present day a large proportion of naturalists are fully occupied with this labour of describing new species and new genera, and in classifying them according to the improved and more natural systems which have been gradually introduced.

But another body of students have always been dissatisfied with this superficial mode of studying externals only, and have devoted themselves to a minute examination of the internal structure of animals and plants, and early in this century the great Cuvier showed how this knowledge of anatomy could be applied to the classification of animals in a far more natural manner than by the easier method of Linnaeus.

Down to the middle of the present century the study of nature advanced with giant strides, while the vastness and complexity of the subject led to a constantly increasing specialization and division of labour among naturalists, the result being that each group of inquirers came to look upon his own department as more or less independent of all the others, each seemed to think that any addition to *his* body of facts was an end in itself, and that any bearing these facts might have on other branches of the study was an altogether subordinate and unimportant matter. For while there was much talk of the "unity of nature," a dogma pervaded the whole scientific world which rendered hopeless any attempt to discover this supposed unity amid the endless diversity of organic forms and structures. This dogma was that of the original diversity and permanent stability of species. Although the doctrine of the special and independent creation of every species that now exists or ever has existed on the globe was known to involve difficulties and contradictions of the most serious nature, although it was seen that many of the facts revealed by comparative anatomy, by embryology, by geographic distribution, and by geological succession were utterly unmeaning and even misleading, in view of it, yet, down to the period we have named, it may be fairly stated that nine-tenths of the students of nature unhesitatingly accepted it as literally true. Holding such views of the absolute independence of each species, it almost necessarily followed that the only aspect of nature of which we could hope to acquire complete and satisfactory knowledge was that which regarded the species itself. This we could describe in the minutest detail. But, as soon as we attempted to find out the relations of distinct species to each other, we embarked on a sea of speculation. We could, indeed, state how one species differed from another species in every particular of which we had knowledge, but we could draw no sound inferences as to the reason or cause of such differences or resemblances, except by claiming to know the very object and meaning of the Creator in producing such diversity.

The majority of naturalists openly declared that their sole business was to accumulate facts. Year after year passed away, adding its quota to the vast mass of undigested facts which were accumulating in every branch of science. And thus, perhaps we might have gone on to this day ever accumulating fresh masses of facts, while each set of workers became ever more and more occupied in their own departments of study, and, for want of any intelligible theory to connect and harmonise the whole, less and less able to appreciate the labours of their colleagues, had not Charles Darwin made his memorable voyage round the world. Others have added greatly to our knowledge of details; he has given us new conceptions of the world of life, and a theory which is itself a powerful instrument of research; has shown us how to combine into one consistent whole the facts accumulated by all the separate classes of workers, and has thereby revolutionized the whole study of nature.

Let us first glance over the *Journal of Researches*, in which are recorded the main facts and observations which struck the young traveler, and see how far we can detect here the germs of those ideas and problems to the working out of which he devoted a long and laborious life.

THE JOURNAL OF RESEARCHES

The question of the causes which have produced the distribution and dispersal of organisms seems to have been a constant subject of observation and meditation. At an early period of the voyage he collected infusorial dust which had fallen on the ship when at sea, and he notes the suggestive fact that in similar dust collected on a vessel 300 miles from land he found particles of stone above the thousandth of an inch square, and remarks: "After this fact, one need not be surprised at the diffusion of the far lighter and smaller sporules of cryptogamic plants." He records many cases of insects occurring far out at sea, on one occasion when the nearest land was 370 miles distant. The remarkable facts presented by the Galapagos Islands brought out so clearly and strongly the insuperable difficulties of the then accepted theory of the independent origin of species, as to keep this great problem ever present in his mind, and, at a later period, led him to devote himself to the patient and laborious inquiries which were the foundation of his immortal work. He again and again remarks on the singular facts presented by these islands. Why, he asks, were the aboriginal inhabitants of the Galapagos created on American types of organization, though the two countries differ totally in geological character and physical conditions? Why are so many of the species peculiar to the separate islands?

He remarks on the occasional blindness of the burrowing tucutucu of the Pampas as supporting the view of Lamarck on the gradually acquired blindness of the aspalax; on the hard point of the tail of the trigonocephalus, which constantly vibrates and produces a rattling noise by striking against grass and brushwood, as a character varying towards the complete rattle of the rattlesnake; on the small size of the wild horses in the Falkland Islands, as progressing toward a small breed like the Shetland ponies of the North; on the strange fact of the cattle having increased in size, and partly separated into two differently coloured breeds. While collecting the remains of the great extinct mammals of the Pampas, he was much impressed by the fact that, however huge in size and strange in form, they were all allied to living South American animals, as were those of the cave-deposits of Australia to the Marsupials of that country.

Soon after his return home in 1837, it occurred to him "that something might be made out on this question by patiently accumulating and reflecting on all sorts of facts which could possibly have any bearing upon it." He tells us that he worked on for five years before he allowed himself to speculate on the subject, and then, having formulated his provisional hypothesis in a definite shape during the next two years, he devoted another fifteen years to continuous observation, experiment, and literary research, before he gave to the astounded scientific world an abstract of his theory in all its wide-embracing scope and vast array of evidence, in his epoch-making volume, *The Origin of Species*. This work was the outcome of *twenty-seven* years of continuous thought and labour, by one of the most patient, most truth-loving, and most acute intellects of our age.

STUDIES OF DOMESTIC ANIMALS

Although, as we have said, Darwin had early arrived at the conclusion that allied species had descended from common ancestors by gradual modification, it long remained to him an inexplicable problem how the necessary degree of modification could have been effected and he adds: "It would thus have remained forever, had I not studied domestic productions and thus acquired a just idea of the power of selection." These researches were published at length in two large volumes, with the title *Animals and Plants under Domestication.* In order to determine the nature and amount of the variability of domestic productions, he prepared skeletons of all the more important breeds of rabbits, pigeons, fowls, and ducks, as well as of the wild races from which they are known to have been produced. Another set of experiments was made by crossing the different breeds of pigeons and fowls which were most completely unlike the wild race, with the result that in many cases the offspring were more like the wild ancestors than either of the parents. These experiments, supported by a mass of facts observed by other persons, served to establish the principle of the tendency of crosses to revert to the ancestral form, and this principle enabled him to explain the frequent appearance of stripes on mules, and occasionally on dun-coloured horses, on the hypothesis that the common ancestor of the horse, ass, and zebra tribe was a partially striped and dun-coloured animal.

It was proved that the parts most selected or which had already most varied were most subject to further variation. Once a part had begun to change, variations became more abundant. It was found in many cases, when much variation occurred, that there was a tendency to a difference in the sexes which had not before existed. Another curious fact is the correlation of parts which occurs in many animals, such as the tusks and bristles of swine, and the hair and teeth in some dogs, both increasing or becoming lost together; the colour and size of the leaves and seeds changing simultaneously in some plants.

The effect of disuse in causing the diminution of an organ was exhibited. The sternum, scapulae, and furcula to which the muscles used in flight are attached, are found to be diminished in domestic pigeons, as were the wing bones in domestic fowl, the capacity of the skull in tame rabbits, and the size and strength of the wings in silkworm moths.

Still more remarkable, perhaps, is the collection of facts afforded by plants. Notwithstanding the enormous mass of facts and observations given, the portion relating to plants is often but an abstract of the results of his own elaborate experiments, carried on for a long series of years, and given at length in three separate volumes on *The Fertilization of Orchids, On Cross and Self-Fertilization of Plants,* and on *The Forms of Flowers.* These works may be said to have revolutionized the science of botany, since, for the first time, they gave a clear and intelligible reason for the existence of that wonderful diversity in the form, colours, and structures of flowers. The investigation of the whole subject of crossing and hybridity had shown that, although hybrids between distinct species usually produced sterile offspring, yet crosses between slightly different varieties led to increased fertility. A long series of experimental researches established the important proposition that cross-fertilization is of the greatest importance to the health, vigour, and fertility of plants. In the case of orchids, it was shown that those strange and beautiful flowers owed their singular and often fantastic forms and exceptional structure to special adaptations for cross-fertilization by insects, without the agency of which most of them would be absolutely sterile. It became evident that every peculiarity of these wonderful plants, in form or structure, in colour or marking, in the smoothness, rugosity, or hairiness of parts of the flower, in their times of opening, their movements, or their odours, had every one of them a purpose, and were, in some way or other, adapted to secure the fertilization of the flower and the preservation of the species.

RESEARCHES ON THE COWSLIP, PRIMROSE, AND LOOSESTRIFE

The cowslip (*Primula veris*) has two kinds of flowers in nearly equal proportions: in the one the stamens are long and the style short, and in the other the reverse. This fact had been known to botanists for seventy years, but had been classed as a case of mere variability, and therefore considered to be of no importance. After a considerable amount of observation and experiment, Darwin found that bees and moths visited the flowers, and that their probosces became covered with pollen while sucking up the nectar, and further, that the pollen of a long-*stamened* plant would be most surely deposited on the stigma of the long-*styled* plants, and *vice versa.*

The same thing was found to occur in the primrose, and in many other species of *Primulaceae,* as well as in flax, lungworts, and a host of other plants.

Still more extraordinary is the case of the common loosestrife (*Lythrum salicaria*), which has both stamens and styles of three distinct lengths, each flower having two sets of stamens and one style, all of different lengths, and arranged in three different ways: (1) a short style, with six medium and six long stamens; (2) a medium style, with six long and six short stamens; (3) a long style, with six medium and six short stamens. These flowers can be fertilized in eighteen distinct ways. The exact correspondence in the length of the style of each form with that of the stamens in the two other forms ensures that the pollen attached to any part of the body of an insect shall be applied to the style of the same length in another plant, and thus there is a triple chance of the maximum of fertility.

THE STRUGGLE FOR EXISTENCE

But we must pass on from these seductive subjects to give some indication of the numerous branches of inquiry of which we have the results given us in the *Origin of Species*, but which have not yet been published in detail. The observations and experiments on the relations of species in a state of nature, on checks to increase and on the struggle for existence, were probably as numerous and exhaustive as those on domesticated animals and plants. As examples of this we find indications of careful experiments on seedling plants, and weeds to determine what proportion of them were destroyed by enemies before they came to maturity; while another set of observations determined the influence of the more robust in killing out the weaker plants with which they came into competition. The rare and delicate flower which we find in one field or hedgerow, while for miles around there is no trace of it, maintains itself there, not on account of any specialty of soil or aspect, or other physical conditions being directly favourable to itself, but because in that spot only there exists the exact combination of other plants and animals which alone is not incompatible with its wellbeing. Such considerations teach us that the varying combinations of plants characteristic of almost every separate field or bank, or hillside, or wood throughout our land, is the result of a most complex and delicate balance of organic forces—the final outcome for the time being of the constant struggle of plants and animals to maintain their existence.

GEOGRAPHICAL DISTRIBUTION AND DISPERSAL OF ORGANISMS

Another valuable set of experiments and observations are those bearing on the geographical distribution of animals and plants—a branch of natural history which, under the old idea of special creation, had no scientific existence. It is to Darwin that we owe the establishment of the distinction of oceanic from continental islands. By a laborious research into all the accounts of old voyages, he ascertained that none of the islands of the great oceans very remote from land possessed either land mammalia or amphibia when first visited, and on examination it is found that all these islands are either of volcanic origin or consist of coral reefs, and are therefore presumably of comparatively recent independent origin, not portions of submerged continents, as they were formerly supposed to be. Yet these same islands are fairly stocked with plants, insects, land-shells, birds, and often with reptiles, more particularly lizards, usually of peculiar species, and it thus becomes important to ascertain how these organisms originally reached the islands, and the comparative powers different groups of plants and animals possess of traversing a wide extent of ocean.

With this view he made numerous observations and some ingenious experiments. He endeavored to ascertain how long different kinds of seeds will resist the action of salt water without losing their vitality, and the result showed that a large number of seeds will float a month without injury, while some few survived an immersion of one hundred and thirty-seven days. Seeds might easily be carried 1000 miles, and in very exceptional cases even 3000 miles, and still grow. Seeds that have passed through the bodies of birds germinate freely, and thus birds may carry plants from island to island. It was also found that small portions of aquatic plants were often entangled in the feet of birds, and to these as well as to the feet themselves, molluscs or their eggs were found to be attached, furnishing a mode of distribution for such organisms.

Our space will not permit us to do more than advert to the numerous explanations and suggestions with which the *Origin of Species* abounds, such as, for example, the strange fact of so many of the beetles of Madeira being wingless, while the same species, or their near allies on the continent of Europe, have full power of flight, and that this is not due to any direct action of climate or physical conditions is proved by the equally curious fact that such species of insects as have wings in Madeira, have them rather larger than usual.

THE DESCENT OF MAN AND LATER WORKS

We must, however, pass on to the great and important work, *The Descent of Man and on Selection in Relation to Sex,* which abounds in strange facts and suggestive explanations. None of Darwin's works has excited greater interest or more bitter controversy than that on man.

Observation and experiment were the delight and relaxation of Darwin's life and he now continued to supplement those numerous researches on plants we have already referred to. A new edition of an earlier work on the *Movements of Climbing Plants* appeared in 1875, a thick volume on *Insectivorous Plants* in the same year; *Cross and Self-Fertilization* in 1876; the *Forms of Flowers* in 1877, the *Movements of Plants* in 1880, and his remarkable little book on *Earthworms* in 1881. This last work is highly characteristic of the author. For more than forty years this subject was kept in view, experiments were made, in one case involving the keeping of a field untouched for thirty years.

None but the greatest geologists have produced more instructive works than the two volumes of *Geological Observations,* and the profound and original essay "On the Structure and Distribution of Coral Reefs"; the most distinguished zoologists and anatomists might be proud of the elaborate "Monograph of the Cirripedia." Yet these works, great as is each of them separately, and taken together, amazing as the production of one man, sink into insignificance as compared with the vast body of research and of thought of which the *Origin of Species* is the brief epitome, and with which alone the name of Darwin is associated by the mass of educated men.

So long as men believed that every species was the immediate handiwork of the Creator, and was therefore absolutely perfect, they remained altogether blind to the meaning of the countless variations and adaptations of the parts and organs of plants and animals. They were content to pass over whole classes of facts as inexplicable, and to ignore countless details of structure under vague notions of a general plan, or of variety and beauty being ends in themselves; while he whose teachings were at first stigmatised as degrading or even atheistical, was enabled to bring to light innumerable hidden adaptations, and to prove that the most insignificant parts of the meanest living things had a use and a purpose, were worthy of our earnest study, and fitted to excite our highest and most intelligent admiration.

QUESTIONS

1. What was the feeling of most of the scientists in regard to the doctrine of special creation in the years preceding Darwin's work?
2. What seemed to be the main occupation of scientists before Darwin's time?
3. How did Darwin's *Origin of Species* change their habits of thought and work?
4. For about how many years did Darwin work on his theory of evolution before publishing it?
5. What principle did Darwin formulate to explain the appearance of stripes on mules?
6. Give an example of the effect of the use and disuse principle.
7. Discuss the problem of adaptation in the orchids.
8. What seems to be the main reason why certain plants and animals are associated together?
9. What was Darwin's main concern in regard to Oceanic Islands? What was his answer to the problem?
10. Give the title of three works of Darwin other than the *Origin of Species*.

Sir Gavin de Beer

The Darwin-Wallace Centenary

Reprinted by permission from Endeavour **17**: (66), April 1958.

FROM SPECIAL CREATION TO TRANSFORMISM

Only one hundred years have gone by since the concept of evolution was brought to the attention of thinking men in a manner which has compelled its acceptance. The demonstration that the members of the plant and animal kingdoms are as they are because they have become what they are, and that change, not immutability, is the rule of living things, is one of the most important contributions ever made to knowledge, and its effects have been felt in every field of human thought. Some naturalists, including Linnaeus himself in his later years, adopted a compromise, allowing that species could have descended with modification from genera, but that genera were immutable.

THE FACT OF EVOLUTION

When Darwin started on the voyage of the *Beagle* in 1831, he had no reason to doubt the immutability of species. The speculations of his grandfather Erasmus counted for nothing with him, because they were not supported by evidence. Those of Lamarck on the causes of evolution had the additional demerit of bringing the subject into disrepute by their fanciful nature. It must be added that in Lyell's "Principles of Geology," to which Darwin owed so much because of the general background of uniformitarianism in place of catastrophism that it advocated, the possibility of evolution was firmly rejected.

Three sets of observations started Darwin's revolt against the immutability of species. The first was occasioned by his studies of the fauna of the Galápagos Islands, where he found that species of finches differed slightly from island to island, while showing general resemblances not only to each other but to the finches on the adjacent mainland of South America. If these species had been separately created, why should there have been such a prodigal expenditure of "creations" to resemble each other so closely; why, in spite of the similarity in physical conditions between the islands of the Galápagos Archipelago and the Cape Verde Islands, are there faunas totally different, the former resembling that of South America while the fauna of the latter resembles that of Africa?

The second set of observations related to the fact that as he traveled over South America he noticed that the species occupying a particular niche in some regions were replaced in neighboring regions by other species that were different, yet closely similar.

The third set of observations was concerned with the fact that in the pampas he found fossil remains of large mammals covered with armor like that of the armadillos now living on that continent. Why were these extinct animals built on the same plan as those now living?

On the view that species were immutable and had not changed since they were severally created, there was no rational answer to any of these questions. On the other hand, if species, like varieties, were subject to modification during descent and to divergence into different lines of descent, all these questions could be satisfactorily and simply answered.

In possession of a working hypothesis that species have undergone evolution and succesive origination by descent, with modification, from ancestral species shared in common with other species, Darwin next proceeded to search the whole field of botanical and zoological knowledge for evidence bearing on his hypothesis. He realized that no general principle that explained the evolution of animals was acceptable unless it also applied to plants. The result was one of the most remarkable attacks on a problem ever made by the inductive method of searching for facts, whatever their import might be.

In the first place, in cultivated plants and domestic animals such as the dahlia, the potato, the pigeon, and the rabbit, a large number of varieties have in each case been produced from a single original stock. Descent with modification and divergence into several lines is therefore certainly possible within the species.

Comparative anatomy reveals the existence of similar plans of structure in large groups of organisms. Plants may have vegetative leaves, and in some cases these are modified into parts of flowers. Vertebrate animals have forelimbs that may be used for walking, running, swimming, or flying, but in which the various parts of the skeleton correspond, bone for bone, from the upper arm to the last joints of the fingers, whether the animal is a frog, a lizard, a turtle, a bird, a rabbit, a seal, a bat, or a man. This is what is meant by saying that such structures are homologous, and these correspondences are inexplicable unless the animals are descended from a common ancestor. Fundamental resemblance is therefore evidence of genetic affinity.

Embryology reveals remarkable similarity in structure between young embryos of animals which in the adult stage are as different as fish, lizard, fowl, and man. This similarity even extends to such details as the manner in which the blood vessels run from the heart to the dorsal aorta, a plan which is of obvious significance in the case of the fish that breathes by means of gills, but not so obvious in that of lizard, chick, or man, where gill pouches are formed in the embryo but soon become transformed into different structures, and breathing is carried out by other means. This similarity between embryos is explained by the affinity and descent from a common ancestor of the groups to which they belong.

Embryology also provides evidence of vestiges of structures which once performed important functions in the ancestors but now either perform different functions or none at all. Examples of such organs are the teeth of whalebone whales, the limbs of snakes, the wings of ostriches and penguins, and the flowers of the feather-hyacinth.

Knowledge of the fossil record in Darwin's time was so imperfect that nothing was then available in the way of series illustrating the course of evolution. Nevertheless, he noticed that in Tertiary strata the lower the horizon the fewer fossils there were belonging to species alive today. Paleontology therefore showed that new species had appeared and old species become extinct, not all at the same time, but in succession and gradually.

Darwin also investigated the problem of interspecific sterility and saw that it was by no means absolute, because numerous examples can be found of different species that produce hybrids, and in some cases these hybrids are themselves fertile. From the point of view of breeding, therefore, such species behave like varieties. Why, then, can species not have originated as varieties, by descent and modification from other species?

From the evidence provided by all these sources Darwin built up an irrefutable argument that species have changed and originated from other species and that evolution has occurred. That he should have been able to do so from such few data is a mark of genius, for at the time when he worked out his conclusions, none of the cases had been discovered which would now be used as the most striking examples with which to illustrate the fact and the course of evolution. Chief among these are the beautiful series of fossils which reveal the evolution of the ammonites or of the horses, step by step, and those which represent the precursors of the various classes and groups of vertebrates such as *Archaeopteryx* or *Pithecanthropus*.

The main steps in Darwin's proof of the fact of evolution were established by 1842, when he committed them to paper in the form of a Sketch which he expanded into an Essay in 1844, though neither was published by him. Soon after this, another naturalist, Alfred Russel Wallace, was led to explore similar lines of research.

Wallace's observations were based on the facts, first, that large systematic groups such as classes and orders are usually distributed over the whole of the earth, whereas groups of low systematic value such as families, genera, and species frequently have a very small localized distribution, Second, "When a group is confined to one district, and is rich in species, it is almost invariably the case that the most closely allied species are found in the same locality or in closely adjoining localities, and that therefore the natural sequence of the species by affinity is also geographical." Third, in the fossil record large groups extend through several geological formations, and "No group or species has come into existence twice."

The conclusion which Wallace drew from these observations was that "Every species has come into existence coincident both in space and time with a pre-existing closely allied species."

So much of the credit for the establishment of the fact of evolution has, rightly, been accorded to Darwin that it is only just that Wallace's contribution to this problem should be recognized and honored.

THE MECHANISM OF NATURAL SELECTION

Although Darwin already knew in 1837 that evolution was an inescapable conclusion to be drawn from the evidence, he did not allow himself to proceed any further with his discovery until he had found an explanation of the fact of adaptation. In a general way, all plants and animals are adapted to their environment, for otherwise they could not live. A man drowns in the sea; a fish dies out of water. But there are some structures which show a particularly intimate relationship between the organism and its conditions of life. Mistletoe is a parasite that requires a tree of certain species to live on, a particular insect to pollinate its flowers, and a thrush to eat its berries and deposit its seeds on branches of the same species of tree. A woodpecker has two of its toes turned backward with which it grips the bark of trees; it has stiff tail feathers with which it props itself against the tree; it has a very stout beak with which it bores holes in the tree trunk; and it has an abnormally long tongue with which it takes the grubs at the bottom of the holes. Other plants than mistletoe and other birds than woodpeckers do not have all these adaptations, and therefore, if evolution has occurred, it is necessary to give an objective explanation of how these adaptations arose.

Darwin was then able to formulate a complete theory providing a rational explanation of the causes as well as of the fact of evolution in plants and animals. It is formally based on four propositions which he already knew to be true, and three deductions which are now also known to be true. They may be enumerated as follows:

1. Organisms produce a far greater number of reproductive cells than ever give rise to mature individuals.
2. The numbers of individuals in species remain more or less constant.
3. Therefore there must be a high rate of mortality.
4. The individuals in a species are not all identical, but show variation in all characters.
5. Therefore some variants will succeed better and others less well in the competition for survival, and the parents of the next generation will be naturally selected from among those members of the species that show variation in the direction of more effective adaptation to the conditions of their environment.
6. Hereditary resemblance between parent and offspring is a fact.
7. Therefore subsequent generations will by gradual change maintain and improve on the degree of adaptation realized by their parents.

This is the formal theory of evolution by natural selection, first announced jointly on July 1, 1958, by Darwin and Alfred Russel Wallace, who had, again independently, come to the identical conclusion. It represents a step in knowledge comparable to Newton's discovery of the law of gravitation.

THE INTEGRATION OF MENDELIAN GENETICS WITH SELECTION

When Darwin wrote, nothing whatever was known about the laws of heredity, and all that he had to go on was the vague notion that offspring tended to strike an average between the characters of their parents. This supposition went by the name of "blending inheritance," and it occasioned for Darwin the greatest difficulty with which he had to contend in formulating his theory. In the first place, if blending inheritance were true, it would mean that any new variation which appeared, even if heritable, would be rapidly diluted by "swamping," and in about 10 generations would have been obliterated. To compensate for this it would be necessary to suppose that new variations were extremely frequent. This problem of the supply of variation was a difficulty which Darwin felt so acutely that it even led him to look for a source of this supply in the supposed hereditary effects of use and disuse.

This reliance on the effects of use and disuse as a source of variation, without any effect on his main argument, is the only part of Darwin's demonstration that has had to be abandoned, and he would have welcomed the reasons for it.

The Mendelian theory of the gene was worked out by T. H. Morgan and his colleagues. It has established, as firmly as Newton's laws of motion or the atomic theory, that hereditary resemblances are determined by discrete particles, the genes, situated in the chromosomes of the cells, which are transmitted to offspring in accordance with the mechanism of germ-cell formation and fertilization, and conform to distributional patterns known as Mendelian inheritance.

The genes preserve their separate identity; they collaborate in the production of the characters of the individual that possesses them, but they never contaminate each other; they remain constant for long periods, but from time to time they undergo a change, known as mutation, which involves a change in the characters which they control; after this they remain constant in their new condition until they mutate again. It has been conclusively proved that the theory of the gene applies to all plants and all animals investigated, and that the mutation of genes is the only known way in which heritable variation arises.

The Mendelian geneticists had to learn two lessons. On the one hand they discovered that although individual genes are associated with particular characters, their control of those characters is also affected by all the other genes, which constitute an organized gene complex. As a result of previous mutations, gene complexes of plants and animals in nature contain many genes, and these are sorted out and recombined at fertilization in astronomically numerous possibilities of permutations. The recombinations have been shown to bring about gradual and continuous changes in the characters under the major control of individual genes.

The second lesson that Mendelian geneticists had to learn was that although the effects of the mutations which they first observed appeared to be clear-cut, they were already the results of past gene complexes. For these mutations have occurred before, and the gene complexes have become adjusted to them.

It is therefore clear that mutations and recombinations of genes provide the supply of variation on which selection acts to cause evolution exactly in the way Darwin's theory requires.

THE SIGNIFICANCE OF PARTICULATE INHERITANCE IN EVOLUTION

The particulate theory of inheritance which Mendelian genetics has established involves a number of consequences of fundamental importance for the problem of evolution. In the first place, the substitution of this quantitative and deterministic science for the vague and baseless notion of "blending inheritance" completely disposes of the difficulty under which Darwin labored to account for the necessary supply of variation on which natural selection could act. The most characteristic feature of the Mendelian gene is that it never blends, but retains its identity and properties intact for long periods of time until it mutates, after which it remains intact in its new condition until it eventually mutates again. This means that the amount of variation, or variance, present in a population resulting from previous mutations, is not only conserved through generation after generation, but is actually increased as a result of the recombinations of the gene complexes in their innumerable possible permutations.

Mutations are chemical changes in the gene molecule, and since chemical stability is not absolute, the puzzle about mutations is not so much that they occur as that they occur so infrequently. This ignorance of the causes which determine the directions in which mutations take place, if such causes indeed exist, is, strange to relate, no handicap to the understanding of the mechanism of evolution, because it is emphatically selection, not mutation, that determines the direction of evolution. It has been estimated that if mutation were to stop now, there is already sufficient variation in the plant and animal kingdoms for evolution to continue for as long in the future as it has continued hitherto in the past.

NATURAL SELECTION, "IMPROBABILITY," AND "CHANCE"

An argument sometimes used against the efficacy of natural selection involves the claim that the initial stages in the evolution of complex structures or functions could not have been favored by natural selection until such structures or functions had reached a certain level of perfection. Like all other arguments of the *non possumus* type, this one melts away before the progress of knowledge. A case in point is that of the electric organs of fish, developed out of muscles which are capable of discharges strong enough to catch prey and defend the fish against its enemies. These organs are clearly adaptive and confer survival value on their possessors, but the question arises what functions they could perform in the initial stages of their evolution, when it must be supposed that their power was too weak to kill prey or to deter predators. The discovery by H. W. Lissmann that weak electric discharges given off by certain fish function in a manner analogous to those of radar equipment, and serve to convey information of the proximity of objects in the water. Electric organs can therefore be adaptive even when they are too weak to kill prey or deter predators.

It has also been objected that natural selection is a difficult concept to apply to the evolution of very complex adaptations involving co-ordinated variations either in one and the same organism, or even in two different organisms. It is not necessary to go far afield to find examples of this, for in all animals with separate sexes and internal fertilization there has been a separate yet harmonious evolution of the reproductive organs in the two sexes. It has been supposed that such situations argued so high a degree of "mathematical improbability" that they could not be explained as a result of natural selection, which was, very erroneously, called "chance."

Those who invoke mathematical improbability against natural selection can be refuted out of their own mouths. Muller has estimated that on the existing knowledge of the percentage of mutations that are beneficial, and a reasoned estimate of the number of mutations that would be necessary to convert an amoeba into a horse, based on the average magnitude of the effects of mutations, the number of mutations required on the basis of chance alone, if there were no natural selection, would be of the order of one thousand raised to the power of one million. This impossible and meaningless figure serves to illustrate the power of natural selection in collecting favorable mutations and minimizing waste of variation, for horses do exist and they have evolved.

From the undoubted fact that

many of the products of the plant and animal kingdom convey to man the aesthetic quality of beauty, it has been supposed that beauty is an end in itself to which the criterion of usefulness and survival value could not be applied, and therefore that it could not be imagined as a product of evolution. To this argument Wallace opposed the demonstration that if the quality of beauty were an exception to the principle of evolution by natural selection, it would be necessary to find an explanation for the existence of so much in plants and animals that is positively ugly.

Darwin showed it to be an invariable rule that "When a flower is fertilised by the wind it never has a gaily-coloured corolla." The beauty of flowers has been gradually achieved because of the survival value of cross fertilization (consequent upon the attraction of insects to such flowers) conferred on plants possessing them. The beautiful colors and structures of birds and some other animals have resulted from the survival value conferred on successful competitors in sexual selection.

NATURAL SELECTION IN ACTION

Natural selection can be seen to be at work here and now in directing evolution. An example of this type of research is that of H. B. D. Kettlewell on "industrial melanism" in moths. Up to 1850 the British peppered moth existed in its typical gray form known as *Biston betularia,* which is remarkably well adapted to resemble the lichens on the bark of trees. From that date a dark melanic variety appeared, known as *carbonaria,* which is extremely conspicuous against the natural bark of trees. The melanic variation is controlled by a single dominant Mendelian gene and is slightly more vigorous than the normal gray type. Nevertheless, because of its conspicuous color the *carbonaria* variety was constantly eliminated, and this variety persisted in the populations of the peppered moth only because the same mutation kept on occurring again and again. The industrial revolution brought about a marked change in the environment, since the pollution of the air by increasing quantities of carbon dust killed the lichens on the trees and rendered their trunks and branches black. Under these conditions it is the *carbonaria* variety which is favored and the *betularia* penalized. This has been proved by direct observation of the feeding of birds, and by measurement of the survival rates of the different forms in the different environments. The dark *carbonaria* form survives 17 per cent less well in an unpolluted area and 10 per cent better in a polluted area. One hundred years ago the dark variety of the peppered moth formed less than 1 per cent of the population; today in industrial areas it forms 99 per cent, and selection has made it more intensively black than when it first appeared.

The case of melanism in the peppered moth also introduces a principle to which L. Cuénot drew attention and gave the name of "preadaptation." The melanic form of the peppered moth happened to be "preadapted" to conditions which were only subsequently realized, or in other words, if the industrial revolution had not taken place, the melanic variety would never have become adaptive at all, and would have suffered the same fate as the countless other mutations resulting in variations which, whether "preadapted" or not, have been eliminated because they fell short of the requirements imposed by natural selection.

While the overriding importance of the effects of selection is now generally realized, it has been suggested that when populations are split up into very small isolated colonies, changes in the relative frequencies of different genes might result from the errors of random sampling in the formation of the germ cells and their fertilization, without involving selection. This concept, advanced by Sewall Wright and known as "random genetic drift," has been invoked as a possible cause of nonselective, nonadaptive evolution. It has, however, been invalidated by the results of experimental studies in the field such as those of Fisher and Ford on moths, which have shown that selective factors are much more important than casual nonadaptive factors in determining the relative frequency of genes and in bringing about close adaptation to local environmental conditions.

THE NEW SYSTEMATICS AND THE ORIGIN OF SPECIES

The researches on industrial melanism in the peppered moth, banding and color of snails, mimicry in butterflies, local adaptation in moths, and sickle cell in man are examples of new techniques of experimental study of evolution in the field. Nobody would have welcomed these developments of biological science more than Darwin himself, as a glance at the last few pages of "The Origin of Species" will show. It is therefore appropriate to return to the problem with which this article began. As is now certain, species are not immutable but have undergone change, and many examples have been given above. Evolution can take place up to a point without the production of new species, but if this process continues the time must come when new species can be seen originating, and it is legitimate to ask whether modern research has revealed any evidence of this. The answer is that new species can be seen originating in nature here and now, and new species have been artificially produced in the laboratory.

As E. Mayr has shown, some form of biological isolation between portions of populations is a necessary condition for divergence leading to the formation of new species and higher groups.

Among the kinds of isolation that are chiefly responsible for the origination of species, geographical isolation is the most important; it involves physical barriers such as oceans, mountain ranges, or deserts which separate whole populations. Geographical races are the chief raw materials from which new species are formed, and it was the different finches on the different Galápagos Islands which first suggested to Darwin that evolution had occurred.

Geographical isolation is important for the origin of species of plants as well as of animals, but there is another form of isolation which appears to be restricted to plants and involves the sudden erection of sterility barriers between individuals in the same population as a result of changes in the chromosome mechanism. This is known as genetic isolation. When *Primula verticillata* is crossed with *Primula floribunda*, hybrid offspring are produced, but they are sterile because the chromosomes of one parent species are incompatible with those of the other, and the intricate machinery involved in the formation of germ cells is thrown out of gear. Occasionally, however, the hybrid plant undergoes doubling of its chromosomes, a condition known as polyploidy, and when that has occurred the hybrid is able to breed with hybrids similar to itself because all the chromosomes have compatible partners, but it is sterile in respect to both parent species. Furthermore, the hybrid is not only true breeding but is different in structure and in habit from each of its parent species. It therefore fulfills all the criteria of a species and has been called *Primula kewensis.* Many other new species have originated by intentional hybridization and accidental polyploidy in this way. Some of these artificially produced species have been found to be identical with, and to breed with, wild species, and this is the proof that this method of species formation occurs in nature.

THE CENTENARY OF EVOLUTION BY NATURAL SELECTION

In conclusion, it may be said that during the hundred years that have elapsed since Darwin and Wallace first published their theory, the fact of organic evolution is now universally accepted and its mechanism has been formally explained.

The alternative to evolution is so naive that it comes as a shock to realize that as recently as one hundred years ago, ideas such as called for the following questions could still be current: "Do they really believe that at innumerable periods in the earth's history certain elemental atoms have been commanded suddenly to flash into living tissues? Do they believe that at each supposed act of creation one individual or many were produced? Were all the infinitely numerous kinds of animals and plants created as eggs or seeds, or as full grown? And in the case of mammals, were they created bearing the false marks of nourishment from the mother's womb?" Darwin might well allow himself to ask these questions, for he and Wallace had found the answer to them.

So soundly was the theory of evolution by natural selection grounded that research does nothing but confirm the links in its chain of evidence and the inferences to be drawn from them. Its field has extended from the explanation of the production of plants and animals to every aspect of the intellectual life of man, and it would be imprudent to doubt that its greatest triumph may yet lie in the highest aspect of that life. Only a genius could have discovered a key of such simplicity to so great a problem. Only ignorance, neglect of truth, or prejudice could actuate those who, in the present state of knowledge, without discovering new facts in the laboratory or in the field, seek to impugn the scientific evidence for evolution.

QUESTIONS

1. What three main observations did Darwin make on his voyage which stimulated his thinking about the immutability of species?

2. What are the evidences of evolution from: a. domestic plants and animals, b. comparative anatomy, c. embryology, d. paleontology?

3. Briefly discuss the relationship of Darwin's ideas on evolution to those of Wallace.

4. Outline Darwin's Theory of Natural Selection.

5. What part does "blending" inheritance play in modern evolutionary theory? Explain.

6. What are some of the objections to natural selection?

7. Discuss the moth in England as a proof of evolution. Does this prove evolution, the immutability of species, or both?

Harold C. Bold

Development of Plants in Time

Reprinted with the permission of the author and publisher from Chapter 10 of The plant kingdom. Englewood Cliffs, New Jersey, Prentice-Hall, Inc., 1960.

Current classifications of the plant kingdom are natural or phylogenetic in that they attempt to group organisms in categories which indicate real, genetic relationships. Now that we have surveyed representative types of plants, we can discuss the possible relationships of currently living plant groups to each other and to extinct members of the plant kingdom, the latter known to us only as fossils. Phylogenetic systems of classification, as indicative of real relationships of higher taxa such as families, orders, classes, and divisions, are speculative, necessarily the more so, the higher the category. This is in contrast to evidences of evolutionary change in individuals and species in the study of which an experimental procedure is possible. Thus, X-rays, chemicals such as nitrogen mustard gas, and other agents produce changes or *mutations* in individuals which may be transmitted to their offspring, a direct and incontrovertible evidence of change and relationship by descent. The occurrence of such mutations in nature and their segregation and recombination in sexual reproduction are undoubtedly responsible for changes in individuals, populations, and species. These are effected by natural selection.

From such evidence, we assume that the operation of similar mechanisms over millions of years, together with natural selection, which has resulted in the extinction of individuals and species, have brought about the diversity now apparent in our extant flora and fauna. No experimental evidence is available to test relationships among plants of the past and their supposed descendants now living. The evidences which support speculations regarding the origin and putative relationships among the groups of plants in our present flora and those of the past reside in comparative morphology of living plants, their comparative biochemistry, and the study of extinct plants are revealed by the fossil record. A few examples of these several lines of evidence will be presented in the following paragraphs.

The comparative study of plants (and animals) reveals certain common attributes. Among these are similarity in cellular organization, metabolism, reproductive phenomena (including sexuality, meiosis, and life cycles), inheritance, and the capacity for adaptation. The occurrence of the same active, photosynthetic pigment, chlorophyll *a*, throughout the plant kingdom (except in fungi) and of the storage product, starch, in a great majority of green plants, are examples of significant, common attributes. The production of archegonia, all consisting of venter and neck, however modified in liverworts, mosses, vascular cryptogams, cycads, and conifers is another example of a widely distributed characteristic. In a word, there is a series of attributes common to species, to genera, families, orders, classes, and, finally, to divisions of plants—both living and fossil—which indicate continuity. These are most satisfactorily explained on the basis of kinship.

The fossil record presents us with important information regarding the course of evolution and the relationship of various forms of plant life. As the original, igneous rocks of the earth's crust weathered, particles were washed away and deposited as sediments in bodies of water. Among these particles, various organisms were deposited. Later, when compression transformed these mixed sediments into rocks, the organic remains sometimes were preserved as fossils. These are of various types and differ in the perfection of their preservation. The most perfectly preserved are *petrifactions,* in which details of microscopic structure are remarkably clear upon sectioning.

The older strata of sedimentary rocks obviously contain fossil remains of the most ancient organisms, while strata deposited subsequently contain a series of increasingly more recent organic remains, culminating in those of extant (now living) plants. Although this "record of rocks" is remarkably long and uninterrupted in such localities as the Grand Canyon, there are few places where such a great series of strata is exposed. Paleobotanists are forced to rely on exposure of fossil-bearing strata by landslides, washouts, road and rail construction, and, especially, by mining and drilling operations.

In spite of the incompleteness of the fossil record, considerable information has been obtained about plants of the past. Paleobotany has not shed direct light on the origin of life itself, but indirect evidences of its existence, such as calcareous (limestones) sediments and iron ores, are available in strata approximately 1½ billion years old. The oldest organisms were aquatic, algal, fungal, and probably bacterial. Many calcareous (lime-encrusted) algae occurred in the lower (Ordovician) strata of the Paleozoic. The Silurian and Devonian strata of the Paleozoic are strikingly different from earlier ones in that they contain abundant remains of truly terrestrial plants. Here are represented as fossils primitive precursors of all the vascular plants except the flowering plants. This gradual development of terrestrial plants with vascular tissues indicates a correlation between the migration of plant life to land and the evolution of xylem and phloem. In spite of the rise of the land plants, aquatic algae and fungi have continued to flourish, apparently with little change, until the present.

Sedimentary rocks, of non-marine origin, of the late Paleozoic (Mississippian and Pennsylvanian) contain a wealth of fossils. An indirect evidence of the abundance of photosynthetic plants in the Pennsylvanian is the occurrence of extensive deposits of coal in that period. The Pennsylvanian often is called the "age of ferns" because of the abundance of fossilized fern leaves in its strata. Some of these, however, were seed ferns, sometimes considered to be the precursors of the flowering plants. In addition, giant, tree-size *Equisetum*-like plants and others of similar stature, resembling somewhat our modern *Lycopodium* and *Selaginella*, flourished in the swamps in Pennsylvanian times. Mosses, liverworts, and the remains of tree-like gymnosperms (in addition to seed ferns) are preserved in Pennsylvanian strata. Most of these are still well represented as fossils in Mesozoic strata, but in the Jurassic and Cretaceous periods, especially the latter, the angiosperms appeared and became dominant as the number and diversity of other fossils waned.

Several important generalizations may be made on the basis of this brief survey of the fossil record.

(1) Indirect and direct evidence indicates that algae, fungi, and bacteria are probably among the most ancient plants, their presence on the earth extending back into the Pre-Cambrian, 1½ billion years ago and possibly even longer. Similar organisms, with slight modification, are represented in our flora at the present time.

(2) Land plants, probably derived from algae which gradually colonized muddy shores and finally drier habitats, had evolved by the Silurian and became more abundant in the Devonian (275 million years ago).

(3) The widespread occurrence of vascular tissues (xylem and phloem) coincided with colonization of the land.

(4) Successively more recent strata reveal an apparent orderliness of development of representative divisions of plants, the order being, from ancient to recent, algae, bacteria, and fungi, other cryptogams and phanerogams. Of the latter, the flowering plants are the most recent.

(5) A number of organisms prominent in ancient floras are no longer present in our current floras. In most cases, the reasons for their extinction are not clear.

Plant fossils, then, indicate that our present flora is changed in composition as compared with floras of earlier periods of the earth's history. Since we know that living organisms are descendants of other living precursors, we conclude from the fossil record that our present plants (and animals, of course) are the modified descendants of more ancient ones. This, in essence, is what is meant by evolution. All modern biologists accept this point of view. When individual biologists attempt to outline the *course* of evolution and thus to draw up the actual phylogenetic lines of descent, especially among the taxa more comprehensive than genera, they often disagree, because individuals interpret evidences differently.

One who surveys the comparative morphology of living plants in the light of the paleobotanical record usually becomes convinced that terrestrial plants have evolved from aquatic algal precursors, and that the primitive, spore-bearing cryptogams which grew upon the earth from the Devonian through the late Paleozoic periods have now themselves been crowded into near oblivion by the flowering plants that have been dominant since the Cretaceous. What will occur in plant life in the millions of years ahead is open to speculation. The changes are occurring at present, inexorably, but the framework of our human life span clouds our perception of the long-range events yet to transpire in the evolutionary process.

QUESTIONS

1. With what degree of certainty may we regard phylogenetic schemes of classification in contrast to evolution under experimental conditions?

2. What significance can be attached to the fact that similar structures and functions are found in diverse groups of plants?

3. What are some of the oldest known organisms?

4. Discuss the possible connection between (1) xylem and phloem, and (2) the development of the terrestrial habit.

5. What are angiosperms and when do they first make their appearance in the rock strata?

PART EIGHTEEN

SCIENCE

Science can be said to be the search for knowledge in the physical and biological sciences, and knowledge includes facts and the interrelationships of the facts. Observation and experimentation are the primary tools of the investigator, aided and abetted by such instruments as have been invented to aid sensory data. Deduction is frequently employed, a process which goes beyond the data and serves as a stimulus for further empirical work. Much has been written about pure versus applied research. Like the old controversy regarding the importance of heredity and environment, the excitement has died down. Most scientists agree that pure and applied research are opposite ends of the spectrum, that they merge in the middle of the band, and that both are very important in the total scientific endeavor.

Science has its faults, as Dr. Weaver points out. As a group, scientists are honest and broad-minded, and they would be the first to admit that science has some imperfections. This is a very healthy attitude because unless scientists are willing to evaluate criticism, no real progress can be made.

Ralph W. Gerard

The Role of Pure Science

Reprinted with the permission of the author from The American Institute Monthly 2(5): 8–15, 1938.

One anecdote has it that when Gladstone, shown the electromagnetic motor, asked, "What good is it?" Faraday replied, "What good is a baby?" The same question might be asked about science itself, the last great offspring of civilization sired by intelligence. If no longer a baby, it is at least an obstreperous child, already playing mischievous pranks on its staid mother, and fearsomely regarded by many as irrevocably headed towards a wayward youth and a criminal maturity. Some babies are best unborn, is this such a one? Science, we hear, has warmed our homes but not our hearts, increased our longevity but not our charity, raised our speed but not our hopes, brightened our night but not our spirit; in short, that it has comforted our flesh but destroyed our soul. Society is sick and science must be poisoning it, for it has been taking great mouthfuls of the bitter stuff; and is it not always something just eaten that is responsible for any ache?

As a physician, I know that a generous portion of spirit of peppermint, applied outside or in, neither brings on nor wards off a renal colic; and as a scientist I demand better evidence than "post hoc ergo propter hoc," before agreeing that the social organism is suffering from scientific dyspepsia. But let us clearly understand one another before proceeding.

"Science," as Conklin, retired president of the American Association for the Advancement of Science, said, "is organized knowledge, and knowledge itself is neither good nor bad but only true or false." Pure science is concerned only with understanding, not with using; it might be denounced as valueless, never as harmful. But, comes the cry, this is sophistry; for are not scientists incessantly prating their wares and asking society to buy of them; do they not ask to have their researches subsidized and promise a manifold return on the investment; is there any demarcation between pure science and applied technology, which most assuredly does us knowledge for weal or woe? Let me answer in reverse sequence.

Pure science is not distinguished from applied by method, which is identical for both; often not by content, which may overlap in each; but by intent alone. The technologist endeavors to solve a problem with a view to immediate utilization—whether for individual or general ends; the scientist, only to know the solution. His immediate gain is the selfish satisfaction of the climber struggling to the summit, of the poet rounding his rhyme or, if you will, of the successful cross-word puzzler.

Or, again, there is the story of the three hod carriers. On being asked, "What are you doing?" the first replied, "carrying bricks"; the second, "earning a dollar an hour"; the third, "building a cathedral." The last represents pure science.

True, few scientists would justify their labors on such a basis, even to themselves, let alone to society. That may be the reason they wish to do research, not the one that makes them think they should do it, and be aided in the doing. There is, besides, the conviction that the fruits of discovery will benefit all mankind—not at once but soon or late, and riper and more luscious for the waiting. They point out to themselves and the world, correctly, case upon case of the "purest" scientific advances that have risen rocket-like into the intellectual sky only to burst and scatter mankind with riches; induced electricity and the motor, electrons and radio or what you will, hormones and the relief of disease, structural formulae and modern creative chemistry. But, then, pure science is simply long range application; and motors and radios do make noise, and chemistry creates explosives and tough steel from which to shoot them, and science is daubed with the same paint as technology.

From my viewpoint, science has another far more valuable contribution to make to mankind than that of upholstering his physical comfort; a vital contribution to his mental climate. And this is at least tacitly recognized by modern educators who include ever more scientific subjects in the curricula. Surely none is so fatuous as to believe that a few semesters of dabbling in physics, chemistry and biology at the high school or college level will prepare the students to build or even repair their autos and radios, let alone to improve upon them. It takes no great erudition to be a handy man about the house, and radio repair men do quite well without having heard of the Schott effect or the uncertainty principle. In biology, where the gulf between common experience and the more esoteric expert knowledge has not yet opened so widely, some practical returns may result from even a casual acquaintance with the latter. It may be useful to know, for example, that spinach is not especially rich in iron, that cathartics do more harm than good, that yeast has no magic dietary virtues, and that patent medicines are, almost without exception, expensive packages of common chemicals and more often harmful than efficacious.

Education has two major aspects: utilitarian, vocational training to enable one to live effectively in society, to do; and aesthetic, avocational training to enable one to live with himself, to be. The former includes the preschool shaping into the major molds of civilized behavior, with the aid of the few "do's" and the many "don'ts"; the use of language and number taught in elementary school; and such technical information and skill as are acquired in appropriate trade or professional schools. It is reasonably tangible and on the whole this education achieves its goal. The aesthetic education—the word is not satisfactory, for it should embrace more; yet I would prefer it to ethical and so emphasize beauty over good; better is the Greek, Kalos, which includes the good, the true, and the beautiful—the aesthetic education is the general education which Hutchins has expounded. It is the appropriate nucleus of high school and college, although not university, training; the very portion of the curriculum which is being enriched with science courses.

This phase of education is confused because its ends are so intangible and the progress towards them so difficult to evaluate. But it is incomparably more important than vocational training for it shapes the man and so eventually the society. I hasten to add that aesthetic education is not purveyed only in college class rooms at so much a course—it is acquired by steady accretion from family and other social groups. What, then should this training for self include?

I submit that it must deal with values and with judgment, must help to establish individual standards and to display materials of worth. Let me be more specific An ear tuned solely to such strident rhythms as "Yankee Doodle" will not at once respond to Beethoven's softer cadences, melodic though they be; nor will the magnificent panorama of celestial and animate evolution have any appeal to the intelligence that has never soared from a bookkeeper's desk. Man is the highest animal only in the sense that he has the possibility of a greater variety of experience than have others, and the "higher" type of man can savor adventures of the spirit to which the lesser one is insensate. In this sense, then, one may speak of establishing standards of and a taste for the worthy and good—a task of aesthetic education.

Besides implanting an urge for the good, the true, and the beautiful, this phase of education should offer examples of them and, even more, acquaint the student with their sources in library, laboratory and museum, and encourage him to explore them. Facts and ideas, no less than poems and pictures, may have their beauty. I shall never forget the state of exaltation in which I left the chemistry lecture room after hearing, in the even slightly monotonous voice of Julius Stieglitz, the story of the brilliant logic and inspired experimentation with which Emil Fischer built and identified the unknown but theoretically anticipated kinds of sugar molecules. To one without the requisite background, the lecture would be a tedious mistake. The painter finds much in a picture overlooked by others, the chess-player alone can rhapsodize over a scholarly mate, the scientist can see in the starry sky or the human body beauties invisible even to the lover's eyes. Science, like art, contains the beautiful and offers ever more riches to him who penetrates its terrain from the frontier of dilettante interest to the hinterland of research advance.

The avocational part of education must include, besides the aesthetic, still other elements which are of no less importance to the individual and of the gravest import to society. These have to do with truth and judgment, are primarily at the intellectual level, and are quite particularly related to science. To the extent that man acts rationally, he makes progress in the battle with chaos, and he and his society become more integrated and more complex. Irrational behavior, directed by emotion when intelligence is uninformed or in abeyance, is sooner or later retrogressive.

What are some earmarks of intelligent behavior? First, the absence of superstition, the emancipation from fear of nature and the here-and-now prejudices of the group. Think of the aboriginal Gods—lurking in animals and trees, in earth, winds and waters; cruel, demanding, all-powerful; quick to destroy, difficult to propitiate; rendering the future insecure and the present restricted—that peopled the primitive imagination. Recall the native, taught by missionaries to plow deep, who, alone in his tribe, grew grain despite a drought and whose torn off limbs were scattered on the field to repel the Evil One. Think of our own recent history—the heretics tortured, the were-wolves burned and witches drowned, the sick exorcised; largely in good faith. The Koran was only recently printed in Islam, for it was blasphemy to touch the word "Allah" with pig bristles.

Second, intelligent behavior is marked by tolerance. The new is neither fatuously accepted nor blindly damned. Decisions are reached after due instruction in and evaluation of the facts, pro and con; and action, while not always correct, is rational in the light of the evidence and, since action generates new evidence, it is automatically self-corrective.

Third, intelligent behavior does not confuse the symbol with the thing. This requires some explanation. Man tries to understand nature, for his pleasure and profit. But nature is a blooming buzzing confusion of semi-discrete units and systems in a great continuity. Analysis cannot proceed until this is ordered into classes—for logic and science deal with the uniqueness of the individual.

I have said that education for truth, for a rational behavior, engenders freedom from superstition and prejudice, inculcates tolerance and the open mind, and brings discrimination of the symbol from the symbolized. I credit science, pure science, with such progress as civilization has made in this direction and maintain that in its charge lies further advance. On what grounds is so much claimed for science? Conklin has summed the case up admirably, ". . . as an educational discipline there are no other studies [than science] that distinguish so sharply truth from error, evidence from opinion, reason from emotion; none that teach a greater reverence for truth nor inspire more laborious and persistent search for it. Great is philosophy, for it is the synthesis of all knowledge, but if it is true philosophy it must be built upon science, which is tested knowledge."

If our sacred cows of belief and convention cannot stand the light of reason they are sickly animals. Do you maintain that science has undermined the foundations of ethics, I reply, "Only of false ethics." There is no conflict between the true and the good any more than between the true and the beautiful. Whichever idols have crumbled with the growth of science were made of clay, and it is well to have cleaned out the debris. Religion is struggling to establish new ethical values; surely science, which has faith in truth and honesty, in patience and order, strains at her side. Perhaps, even, the new ethics will stem from science directly.

Many of you, I am certain, are now about at the bursting point of indignation with my elegiac mood. "Man, alive," you would say, "stop talking like an evangelical Pollyanna and look at some facts yourself. Science has been taught in increasing intensity for a century or two and you have already admitted that we still are clouded in prejudice, intolerant to an extreme degree, and regularly misled by words. And you can't wriggle out of it by saying that science has not adequately reached the masses for we know any number of scientists who are as egregious asses as the rest of us when they dare to emerge from their narrow specialties, which by the way, they rarely do."

Yes, I know. Much that passes for science is utterly trivial and many of its supposed devotees are dull followers of a trade. Don't you, my friendly challenger, make another error and mistake the work for the thing. If you define "science" as the produce of departments of physics, geology, botany, etc.; and "scientists" as the men who people them; we are not talking quite the same language.

Yet I must admit there is something to your position. Scientists today fall far short, on the average, of what one might expect from them. It is, perhaps, possible to trace the reasons. A century and more ago, science was an esoteric pursuit. The men who followed its call were amateurs, usually wealthy or patronized. They worked largely as individuals at an avocation or hobby, like philatelists today, because they enjoyed it. They were eddies in the social stream, amusing or ludicrous to the serious-minded of the time but not important. One cultivated science as one cultivates a garden, without ulterior motive beyond the satisfaction of watching its lovely flowers unfold. Not so today. Science became useful, its flowers yielded expensive perfumes and healing drugs, and it was taken up by the best society. Departments of science crowded into and multiplied within universities, even high schools; research institutes sprang up; industry sprouted laboratories or subsidized technical schools and plants; great foundations pumped nourishment into all of these, aided here and there by government. Technology spread everywhere, new industries based upon it grew into gigantic stature. And men were needed.

There is a cycle in education which might be benign but is still vicious. Bad teachers teach students badly so that they in turn become bad teachers. Ignorance, like syphilis, would be eliminated if we could only make it spare one generation. What a stride forward humanity would take if just one crop of youngsters was put through the hands of really good teachers! This is just pleasant day dreaming, we have not enough good teachers nor prompt means of developing them. Yet the situation is not hopeless and civilization has always had to pull itself up by its bootstraps.

There is one more point to make about teaching scientists and educators in general, especially in this country. Let me say it quickly and have it over for it is rather shameful. The truth is that those in social and financial power—donors, governments, founders—have so little confidence in professors that they do not trust them to run themselves, let alone others. Almost without exception, a separate body—of trustees, president, deans, and other administrative officers—runs our universities and the faculty pretty much does what it is told. Administration is often enough excellent, and academic freedom is jealously guarded in any university worthy of the name, but the fact remains that our institutions of higher learning are painfully different from a Republic of scholars.

Is it any wonder, then, that science has made no greater impress on the mind of man and that scientists are so often found wanting? They have nearly all been taught badly, except in some limited field of proficiency; they have been debased by the rapid and incompletely assimilated influx of opportunists; they are little prized, except for their technical skill; of course they are oblivious to or prejudiced about most problems of society.

Knowledge is cumulative in time, generation building on generation, while emotion is not. Perhaps cerebral control is increasing. Modern psychiatry is finding the hidden springs of behavior and modifying their flow. Men will probably always want more than their share, but it may be that it will not always be of the same things. The mass desideratum now is money, yet large groups of men have completely renounced this end for another; for example, fame. As man learns more of himself, his neural mechanisms, the hormones that modify them, the drives they generate, and the personal and social consequences of his acts, much control will undoubtedly be possible. And this knowledge will be deposited only by the stream of science. I am perhaps not overly guileless in believing that reason will sufficiently dominate emotion to keep a functioning civilization from perishing. Some emotion is needed, but the future of society is a direct challenge to the cerebrum of man and to its tool for rational advance—Pure Science.

QUESTIONS

1. What is Dr. Conklin's definition of Science? Do you agree with it?
2. What is a good distinction between applied science and pure science?
3. Which type of education does Dr. Gerard favor—vocational or avocational? Why?
4. What are some of the earmarks of intelligent behavior?
5. What does Dr. Gerard mean when he says that science has made progress in clearing the pea-soup fog of the past?
6. What are the steps in the scientific method?
7. Does science eliminate ethics? Explain.
8. Can a man (or woman) know the facts, theories and techniques of a science and not be a scientist? If so, what do these people lack?
9. Can the scientific method aid in the solution of our social problems?

L. A. DuBridge

The Inquiring Mind

Reprinted from Engineering and Science Magazine, October 1954, with the permission of the author and publisher, the California Institute and Technology.

In 1798 a monk by the name of Thomas Robert Malthus published a paper with a long and complex title which attempted to analyze man's future on this planet. Examining past experience and bringing to bear on this experience the brilliant logic of an analytical mind, he came to some rather dire conclusions about the future. It was quite obvious to him that men had to eat; that the only major source of food was the arable land; that the area of such land was limited. Therefore, there was a limit to the potential food supply, and hence to the population that could exist on the earth.

On the other hand, he noted that the human population tended to grow at an ever-increasing rate. Any sort of voluntary birth control, it seemed to him, would be either unnatural or immoral. Therefore, the only possible future was one in which the population eventually outgrew the food supply, and thereafter death by starvation, disease and war would take over to balance a birth rate which knew no control.

Clearly, a world in which most of the people would assuredly die of one of these causes was not a very pleasant one to contemplate.

However, here we are 156 years after the Malthusian prediction, and the portion of the world that we live in does not face the Malthusian death sentence. Our population is expanding at a rate never dreamed of in Malthus' time. There are four times as many people on the earth now as then. At the same time, here in the United States at least, we have far more trouble with food surplus than with shortage. We buy potatoes and dye them blue, butter and let it spoil, wheat and give it away, in our desperate effort to avoid the economic consequences of growing more food than we can eat.

Surely Malthus was the most mistaken man in history. Or was he?

Actually, as Harrison Brown points out in his recent book (from which I shall now borrow heavily), *The Challenge of Man's Future*, Malthus' reasoning and logic were entirely correct. His only misfortune was that his observations and assumptions were later rendered obsolete by unforeseeable new developments. What were these new developments? They were of two kinds—technological and social. On the technological side men learned how to raise more pounds of food to the acre, learned to get more nutritive value to the pound, and learned how to transport food quickly from areas of surplus to areas of shortage. On the social side, great segments of the human race came to regard voluntary birth control not as a sin but as a virtue.

Now I think it is quite evident that without this latter factor—voluntary population control—the Malthusian disaster can be only postponed, and not finally prevented, by any advances in technology. We must admit that the supply of land is limited, that the productivity of land can *not* be expanded beyond all limit. But population, if not controlled, does expand without limit, and sooner or later—in 50, 250, 500 or 5000 years—a population which is doubling every 75 years or so is bound to outrun any given food supply.

This makes it clear that the primary need of the world is to insure that in all parts of it the population recognizes the need for growth that is controlled by voluntary action rather than through starvation. Clearly, this is not primarily a job for science and technology, but rather for education.

But science and technology do have some terribly important tasks to perform in this field. First, there is the task of improving the technology of producing, processing and preserving food so that the food supply will keep pace with population for the 25, 50 or 100 years required to complete the educational job. Second, there is the task of improving standards of living over a larger part of the world—for increased education goes only with increased living standards and increased disposable wealth. Finally, science and technology have the task of providing the necessary tools so that any segment of the population that has overcome the starvation limit can then proceed to help men and women lead happier and richer lives.

Now I claim that these constitute quite substantial and immensely challenging tasks. Another way of expressing them is to say simply that if men are to attain those social, moral and spiritual goals which we of the Christian nations believe desirable, then science and technology must provide the physical tools to make their attainment feasible.

This being about as important a goal as I can think of, it behooves those of us who are working in the fields of science and technology to ask ourselves how we are doing. Have we properly visualized our task and our goals? Have we properly analyzed and evaluated the steps which need to be taken, the prerequisites for progress? Are we putting first things first and do we know which things *are* first? Are we creating within science and technology itself, and within the community at large, the conditions most likely to nurture progress and success?

THE GOALS WE SEEK

It seems to me obvious from the way in which I have stated the problem that it is important that we keep in mind the goals we seek. As I have suggested, these goals are not merely more food, more products, more gadgets. Our goal in the last analysis is a moral goal—more happiness for individual human beings, expressed in whatever terms their own philosophy of life dictates.

I emphasize and repeat this matter of ultimate goals precisely because it is so obvious to us that it is often forgotten. We become so absorbed in our gadgets, our machines, our new foods, new medicines, our new weapons, that only too often we think of them as ends in themselves—forgetting what they are *for*.

Now if we ourselves—if we scientists—forget the ends in our absorption with the means, that is bad enough; for then our work loses its meaning. But it is even more dangerous if we let the public believe that our machines and our mechanisms are ends in themselves. For then our work, which in the end depends upon public support, will surely be destroyed. And it will be destroyed by the public even though the public itself, rather than the scientists, would be the principal losers.

Let us bring this closer home. It is a paradoxical fact that, in these days of the mid-20th century, science and technology are being simultaneously praised to the skies and damned with religious fervor; they are being handsomely supported and heartily kicked. Scientists are publicly acclaimed as a group and privately slugged as individuals.

Why is this?

Clearly, we have not told our story adequately. Our physical achievements are evident. But, because they are physical, we are accused of being materialists. Because the tools of science are powerful, their power is feared and those with the power are suspected of evil motives. Because weapons have been produced to help men fight in their own defense, it is assumed that they also make men *want* to fight. So we see that as we brag about our knowledge but are silent about our aims, then the public will come to ignore our knowledge and denounce our aims.

WHAT SCIENTISTS WORK FOR

So my first plea is that scientists shall throw off their reticence in speaking of their feelings and come out boldly and unashamedly to say, "We are working for the betterment and happiness of human beings—nothing less and nothing more."

But, in spite of the romanticism of the poet, we know full well that for most human beings *happiness* is not attained solely by sitting under a tree with a loaf of bread and a jug of wine. And even if it were, someone has to bake the bread and bottle the wine. The poet was right in suggesting that the essential elements of happiness consist of food, shelter, companionship and leisure. He only forgot to mention that these must be achieved by effort, and that the effort itself may bring happiness, too.

In any case, we are forced at once to consider how human effort can be most effectively employed to provide the physical elements for happiness and also the leisure to enjoy them. Nor are we content—as were those of medieval and ancient times—to have *many* people exert the effort and a few people enjoy the leisure. We have proved that *all* may work and *all* may play.

Now what is it that has made it possible for us today to think of a modest amount of happiness coupled with a reasonable amount of work as a possible goal for *all* people, rather than just a few? The answer is, clearly, that a series of *intellectual achievements* have enabled men to enlarge, to expand, and to dream of achieving a moral goal.

What are the intellectual achievements?

I think it is fair to say that the essential cause of the difference in the physical and the moral outlook of the western world in the 20th century, as compared to the 10th is simply that, along some time between those dates, men invented a new process of thinking.

Men had, of course, always thought, always observed, always speculated, always wondered, always asked questions, always explored. But along about 1700 men began to do these things in a new way. Men began to realize that by making observations carefully and analyzing them quantitatively, it could be shown that nature behaved in a regular manner and that these regularities could be discovered, reduced to mathematical form and used to predict future events.

This was an astonishing discovery. And as this new concept, outlined by Francis Bacon, was pursued—first by Galileo, then by Newton, then many others—a new world of understanding was opened to men's minds. Nature was partly comprehensible, not wholly mysterious and capricious. The falling stone and the moving planets became suddenly not only understandable but miraculously and simply related. Men couldn't *affect* the motion of the planets, but they *could* control the motion of the stone and of other objects.

And so, machines were invented, the concept of energy emerged, steam was put to work—and suddenly, after thousands of years of doing work only with the muscles of men and animals, men found that a piece of burning wood or coal could take the place of many slaves or horses or oxen.

From that time on, happiness and leisure for all men became a possible goal, not a crazy dream.

A LIMITLESS QUEST

But that was only the beginning. The scientific method led from physics to astronomy to chemistry to biology. A beachhead on the shores of ignorance became a vast area of knowledge and understanding. Yet, as the frontiers of knowledge advanced, the area of ignorance also seemed to enlarge. Nature was not simple after all. A literal eternity of new frontier was opened up. The quest for understanding, we now see, will, for finite man, be limitless.

I would like to direct your attention to the conditions that are required for knowledge and understanding to grow and to spread. Intellectual advancement does not come about automatically and without attention. There have been throughout human history only a few places and a few periods in which there have been great advances in knowledge. Only under certain special conditions does the inquiring mind develop and function effectively. Can we identify these conditions? Certainly we must try.

The first condition, of course, is that at least a few people must recognize the value of the inquiring mind. Here we all take for granted that new advances in understanding come only from the acts of creative thinking on the part of individual human beings. We know that, and we respect and admire the men who have shown the ability to think creatively. But we mustn't get the idea that our admiration for original thought is shared by all people.

Even in this country, the man who thinks differently is more often despised than admired. If he confines his new thoughts to the realms of abstruse theoretical physics or astronomy, he may not be molested. For then he will be speaking only to those who understand him. But if he wanders into biology or medicine, into psychology or sociology or politics, then he should beware.

Now in recognizing the virtues of thinking differently, we do not mean that we must encourage the idiot, the criminal or the traitor. Honest, truly intellectual inquiry is perfectly easily recognizable by those who have some training in the field. But just here we run into difficulty. Those who are incompetent to judge may nevertheless render judgment and pass sentence on those with whom they disagree, or whom they fear.

One of the great unsolved problems of a democracy is how to insure that, in intellectual matters, judgments are left to those who are competent, and the people will respect that competence. But when uneducated fanatics presume to choose and to censor textbooks, when government officials impose tests of political conformity on the scholars that may leave or enter a country, and when the editors of a popular magazine set themselves up to judge who had the proper opinions of nuclear physics, then the inquiring mind finds itself in an atmosphere not exactly conducive to maximum productivity.

THE NEEDS OF THE INQUIRING MIND

But physical conditions are not enough. Big, beautiful laboratories do not themselves produce research—only the men in them can think. And if conditions are such as not to attract men who think or such as to impede their thinking, then the laboratory is sterile. Such laboratories, as you well know, do exist. There is no use storming and raging at the perverseness of scientists who refuse to work when conditions are not just to their liking. We don't call a rose bush perverse if it fails to bloom when deprived of proper water and soil. A community or a nation which wishes to enjoy the benefits that flow from active inquiring minds needs to recognize that the inquiring mind is a delicate flower, and if we want it to flourish we are only wasting our time if we do not create those conditions most conducive to flowering. The cost of doing so will be well repaid.

The inquiring mind then needs, first of all, some degree of understanding and sympathy within the community. And if there are those who cannot understand, then at least they must be insulated by those who do, so that they do the least harm. As someone has said, we can stand having a few idiots in each community as long as we don't put them on the school board.

As I have already suggested, it is not enough for the scholar or the scientist to wring his hands and wish that there were fewer idiots or that they had less influence. He must also, to the extent of his ability, explain to those who can understand what he is doing and why. We now see that an intelligent and informed segment of public understanding is essential to the progress of scholarly endeavor.

SCIENTIST AND GOVERNMENT

This leads me to another subject which has become timely to the scientist and to the citizen in recent years; that is, the relation of the scientist and the government. This is obviously a very large subject which I cannot attempt to explore here. But as the scholar needs an informed community to support him, so he owes an obligation to that community.

The prime obligation of the scholar, of course, is to pursue scholarship. That is, he must seek answers to important questions, observe carefully, analyze accurately, test rigidly, explain imaginatively, and test and test again. Then he must publish his results, fully, fearlessly, objectively, and defend them enthusiastically unless or until the facts prove him wrong. Through such intellectual struggle does the truth emerge.

But in these days the results of science impinge so heavily on public affairs that the public—in particular the government—needs the scientist's help in so many ways. Obviously, the government needs the direct services of thousands of scientists and engineers to carry on work in public health, standards of measurement, agriculture, conservation of resources and in military weapons, to name a few.

But when there is developed a new weapon, a new treatment for a disease, a new way of using public resources, does the scientist's responsibility end there? I think not. There are so many ways in which important matters of public policy are affected by these new scientific achievements that scientists must stand by as advisers at least to interpret, explain, criticize and suggest on policy matters.

SCIENTIFIC ADVICE

We would not think, of course, of allowing a new law affecting public health to be passed without asking a physician's advice on whether it is wisely conceived. Yet I am sure state and federal legislatures *have* thought of it—in the various antivivisection bills, for example. Fortunately (for this purpose at least), the medical profession has great influence and can make its opinions heard. And most of the public respects its doctors.

But when national security matters are being discussed which involve the nation's strength in atomic weapons, it is clear that those in charge of forming policy will need to have much help on questions of what atomic weapons really are, what they do individually, and what would be the effects of setting off the whole stock pile. I am not saying that such scientific advice is not sought (though I think it is not always adequately used). But I do say that scientists need to be ready to help. Yes, they may need to be ready to intrude with their advice even if it is not asked for.

This problem has, of course, caused much recent trouble and misunderstanding. Many prominent citizens, including many politicians and editors, apparently feel that scientists should stick to the laboratory and let public policy matters be handled by others. Now no one argues that *decisions* on public matters must be made by the properly constituted responsible officials. But *advice* and *information* on scientific aspects of the problem is often essential and must come from scientists.

I fervently believe that the world has been remade the past century—remade physically, socially, and spiritually—by the work of the inquiring scholars. These scholars have sought new knowledge and new understanding; they have sought to use this understanding to produce those things that men needed—or thought they needed—to improve their health, their comfort, their happiness, their security.

Scholars will continue these activities and the world will continue to change. Their efforts must be aided; for though what they do may yield dangers, the dangers are far greater if they do less. And since what they do affects the world, affects you and me and our community and our country, we should have these inquiring and active minds around all the time to direct their attention to the most difficult of all problems—how to help men make better use, in their relations with each other, of the great new areas of knowledge which can yield so much to make men happier and better.

QUESTIONS

1. Do you think the Malthusian Death Sentence threatens the world today? Explain.
2. Which one, if any, of the following is the ultimate goal of mankind: adequate food for all, a healthy world, improved transportation or a warless world?
3. What effects did scientific thinking have on world progress?
4. Refute this statement: "Original thinkers are universally admired."
5. Does Dr. DuBridge believe that scientists should remain divorced from political matters involving scientific discoveries and applications?

Warren Weaver

The Imperfections of Science

Reprinted with the permission of the author and publisher from Proceedings American Philosophical Society, **CIV** (5), October 17, 1960.

I propose to consider two questions. First, why does science command the respect, prestige, and admiration which it obviously possesses? Second, does science really deserve the reputation which is often, if not usually, given to it by scientists and public alike; and is it not possible to take a more restrained, more candid, and, I believe, more accurate attitude toward science which honestly concedes certain limitations?

It may seem surprising, and even trivial, to ask why science has so great a reputation. We are, in the modern world, completely surrounded by science and by the technological achievements which science makes possible. By this powerful partnership we are warmed and cooled, clothed and fed, protected, cured, transported, and entertained. Science has made possible color television and jets, dial telephones across the continent and shortwave radio across the oceans, polio serum, hi-fi and stereo, heart, lung and kidney-function machines which substitute temporarily for our own damaged internal parts, electronic computers that play chess and compose music, satellites about the earth and rockets to the moon, automatization and microminiaturization, machines that think and which learn from experience (which is more than some people do), nuclear energy, and G.L. 76 in toothpaste. If we have not yet conquered cancer, cardiac disorders, and the degenerative diseases of later life; if we are uncertain about the genetic effects of long continued low doses of radiation; if we miss recovering a nose-cone now and then; if we are a little puzzled about psychology and psychiatry and are not yet sure whether the mind is in the head; if we still have cavities in our teeth, aches in our joints, and clocks that won't run in our automobiles—well, surely these are minor gaps which will soon be filled in by science.

Indeed, there is a good deal of evidence that if science once chooses to drive a path out into the wilderness of ignorance, then, no matter where that path is headed, there seems to be no inherent limitation to the distance science can penetrate, no limit to the amount of experience that can be explained and brought under control by the methods of science. In our modern physical laboratories we transmute the elements, and change mass to energy and *vice versa*. We experiment with fantastic entities ludicrously called elementary particles—the most evanescent of which exist for less than one one-hundred-thousandth of a billionth of a second. We create an electrical disturbance in the recently discovered radiation belt thousands of miles above the surface of our earth; and, sure enough, auroral lights appear at another and far distant location on our planet, just at the time theoretically predicted.

Yes, the triumphs of the physical scientists are impressive enough to explain why science has a great reputation. But the triumphs of those parts of science which are concerned with living nature are, in many ways, to be interpreted even more seriously. For it seems, on the whole, reasonable and proper for man to analyze his physical environment. But the mysteries of life —perhaps they are intended to *remain* mysteries.

The age-long history of man's learning about plants and about the lower animals contributed to the good reputation of science without creating any large counter-feeling of apprehension. But when the first brave anatomists invaded the human body, and the early physiologists began to analyze man's own parts in mechanical terms, then the philosophers and humanists and theologians were convinced that they could hear the distant footsteps of an all-conquering science monster.

When experiments show that the normal mothering behavior of an animay—the concern to feed and clean and protect the very young offspring— is destroyed by leaving a metallic trace element out of the diet; when the modern biochemist can explore inside the mitochondria within a cell and analyze the enzyme systems there; when the microbiologist can take a virus apart into chemically identifiable and wholly "dead" pieces and then can reconstitute these pieces into an organism which can reproduce itself— then indeed science begins to earn a reputation which is in many senses great, but which is also in some senses frightening.

So science has, it seems, been so successful that it has inevitably earned a great and strange reputation. If it has never yet been defeated, presumably it is all-powerful. Since science is, after all, the work of scientists—for one seldom encounters disembodied science —then presumably these scientists are both so clever and so wise that *they* can do anything. Perhaps we should turn the world over to this superbreed. Perhaps they could, if properly supported, really liberated, and put in charge—perhaps they could solve all problems of human relations, of economic stability, of international peace, and of the good life. Perhaps they should design not only the churches, but the creeds also. Perhaps the best music and the loveliest poetry *will*, in a short time, come out of a machine.

The sad fact is that some scientists themselves appear to believe precisely this. And this arrogant attitude quite naturally irritates, or even angers, the social scientists, the humanists, the moralists, and the creative artists.

To advance to our second question, does science deserve either the favorable or the unfavorable parts of its reputation? Can science not be given a more true, more realistic, and more constructive interpretation? I think that the favorable part of the present reputation of science is often significantly misunderstood; and I think that the unfavorable part is largely if not wholly false.

To deal with these questions we must start with pretty basic considerations. When man—scientific man—confronts any object he has a deep craving to *understand*. The difference between the state of *not understanding* and of *understanding* is a complex and subtle matter which has several aspects, of differing importance to different persons.

For a scientist, a phenomenon is *understood* provided he possesses a satisfactory *theory* for this phenomenon. But this statement is not very illuminating until one goes on to say what a satisfactory scientific theory is, how it operates, and in what senses it is useful or interesting or both.

The theory, in refined cases and in the physical sciences, is likely to consist of a body of mathematical equations. These equations state the interdependence of a few or several quantities, represented simply by letters in the equations. If you point to one of the letters and ask, "What is this: what physical thing does this represent?" then the answer, at least from the group here being described, is that you have asked an irrelevant and improper question.

For associated with this body of equations is a set of procedural rules. You are told: "Perform such and such observations, either in a laboratory experiment set up thus and so, or directly upon nature in such and such a way. Take the numbers which result from those observations, and put them into these equations, substituting the numbers for certain specified letters. Then solve the equations, thus obtaining numerical values for certain other letters. Now go back to your experiment (or another similar one), or go back to nature and make certain further observations. This will provide you with a new set of numbers: and if you have a sound theory, these new numbers will coincide (with certain probabilistic error which need not confuse us at the moment) with the numbers which were previously solved out of the equations."

The procedure sounds complicated —and often it is in fact exceedingly complicated. And how can this procedure possibly bring about *understanding?*

Let us, therefore, drop this line of attack for a moment, and consider a more friendly, more understandable sort of understanding. A person says, "I don't understand genetics at all. I don't understand genes and chromosomes." He is told, "Well, a chromosome (in every cell of your body, incidentally) is sort of like a string of beads, each bead being a gene. And each gene determines, or helps to determine, one of your characteristics, such as your blue eyes, or your attached earlobes, or, for that matter, your sex." And the person thinks, "Well, this is something like it; I am beginning to understand."

With these extreme examples before us—of a very abstract and formal theory on the one hand, and of a friendly, loose, incomplete, but nevertheless useful analogy on the other hand, we can now contrast two extreme concepts of understanding.

One of these, the friendly, man-in-the-street variety, attempts to explain by describing an unfamiliar phenomenon in terms of its similarity to a familiar phenomenon. The fact that this kind of explanation by analogy is comforting, that it satisfies the listener, is, if you stop to think about it, rather surprising. For logically and philosophically this procedure is a complete fraud. The unfamiliar is explained in terms of the familiar. But the *familiar*, if one examines the situation honestly and in detail, is itself simply *not understood*.

The other, formal, types of procedure is, again, clearly *not an explanation*, in any normal sense of that word. In fact it baldly states that the scientist has no business to ask, "What is the real nature of physical phenomena"; or to ask, "Are there really precise deterministic laws behind the statistical data which I observe"; or to ask, "How *can* light be both a wave motion and a beam of particles"; or to ask, "What sense does it make for a particle to have electric charge but zero mass?"

These are, to the one who accepts the formal procedure, senseless assortments of words. For the formal procedure makes no pretense whatsoever of "explaining." The formal procedure, in fact, says "It is impossible to explain phenomena, and it is in fact senseless to try. All you can do—and this is a triumph of great dimensions—is to *deal successfully* with phenomena.

The equations, or more generally the theory, are a sort of "black box." You can feed one set of numbers into this black box, turn the crank, and out comes a second set of numbers. If this second set correlates properly with numbers which can be determined, following given rules, from nature, then you have a successful theory.

This idea of *not explaining*, but of *dealing successfully* with phenomena deserves a few further words. What, to the scientists, constitutes a really satisfactory sort of success for a theory?

The answer lies largely in the words *generality*, *elegance*, *control*, and *prediction*. If one single theory—one black box—is capable of grinding out results that relate to a wide range and a large apparent diversity of experience, then the theory has the obvious practical advantage of *generality*. If in addition the theory is stated in compact form, then it possesses the illusive but lovely trait which the scientist calls "elegance."

Suppose that the black box of our theory has certain dials on one of its faces, and that we set these dials, before inserting input data, to values which are characteristic of the particular experiment in question. Then the numbers ground out by our black box will depend not only on the numbers we insert, but also on our dial settings. And then by changing these dial settings one can answer such a question as "How will the result change if I vary one or more of the circumstances of the experiment?" Under useful circumstances such as these, the theory has brought the phenomenon under *control*. You know just what to do in order to modify the result in the desired way.

Finally, the black box, if it is a really good one, must be able to grind out numbers which will prove to correlate properly with numbers which you will obtain in an experiment or observation *not yet made*. That is to say, the theory should be able to *predict*.

We can now state in more compact summary what the modern scientist calls a good theory. It is a theory which is *general* and *elegant*, which puts us in *control* of the phenomena in question, and which can *predict*. But notice that I have not said one single word about *explaining*. The advocates of abstract theories have to agree that the scientist *understands* a phenomenon when he can *control* and *predict* it, and that as a product of his creative imagination he appreciates and admires the theory the more, the more *general* and *elegant* it is.

It is essential to my general argument to point out at once that many scientists enthusiastically disagree with this position.

The general and popular reputation of science rests largely on its success at *control*, and to a lesser degree upon its ability to *predict*. Unfortunately, only scientists themselves, and a few others who make a real effort, achieve the knowledge that makes *generality* important, and *elegance* lovely.

When we restrict attention to moderate-scale phenomena, involving, say, objects above electron-microscopic size, and if we stay away from such phenomena as the toss of a single coin or the decisions of a single mind, then science can often offer "explanation by analogy," this being useful, interesting, and curiously comforting. But this kind of explanation is, fundamentally, a complete illusion: and at the other extreme the strict and formal abstract type of a scientific theory contains nothing whatsoever that constitutes, in any sense, explanation.

This is a rather shocking thing to say—that science does not furnish any really ultimate or satisfying explanation. And this imperfection leads at once to the question: Does science have other important imperfections?

Without claiming completeness, I want to speak here of a total of five imperfections. You will not be surprised, I think, to have me say that these are not, actually, so much imperfections in science as imperfection in the views that are held by some concerning science. Science is amazingly successful at the surface, so to speak. But at its logical and philosophical and artistic core, it has, at least in my view, a number of limitations which can be viewed as imperfections. These are the blemishes that make science a human and endurable enterprise.

For example, the fact that science is superbly successful at dealing with phenomena, but that it possesses the inherent defect (which I assume it shares with many other fields of thought) that it cannot furnish ultimate explanation, is, in my own view, really not a defect at all, but rather an example of the honesty and clarity that comes with maturity. And again, this defect has the virtue that it *joins* science to the rest of life, rather than separating it off in cold perfection.

Second, it is an obvious imperfection that scientists themselves do not, and apparently cannot, agree about certain of the deepest and most central aspects of science.

This imperfection of science I find a most attractice one; for it reflects the fact that science is not monstrous and monolithic, but is a very human enterprise, exhibiting the same lively and useful diversity which one finds in philosophy, art, music, etc.

Thirdly, you are all aware of the nineteenth-century fear that science was in the process of imposing purely mechanistic and deterministic interpretations upon all phenomena, including ultimately the individual decisions of an individual person. And you are all aware—for this has been widely publicized—that science has itself now abandoned the view. Science recognizes that the individual events, down at the level of electron, protons, photons, mesons, etc., are all probabilistic in character, and individually simply not predictable. Since all large-scale events—the falling of a stone, say —are ultimately composed of individual events, the large-scale events are themselves, strictly speaking, probabilistic also. But the large-scale phenomena are nevertheless dependable. And this is simply because this large-scale event is the net result of so incredibly vast a number of small-scale events that the eccentricities always average out.

So it is an imperfection of science, if you choose so to name it, that it is essentially statistical in nature. This means, for example, that perfect accuracy is unattainable in any measurement, that certainty is impossible in any prediction.

My fourth defect is related to the fact that there are those who say, "I will admit that science is no doubt more strictly *logical* than any other field of intellectual activity, but logic is a cold and relentless master, and I am not so sure that I want my life dominated by it."

Logic is indeed an integral and central part of science. But logic, although a vastly useful mental tool, does not now have the reputation which it was once supposed to deserve.

There are two main types of logic: deductive and inductive. In the former, one starts by making a certain number of pure assumptions—technically speaking, he adopts the postulates of the system under examination. Then with the addition of a certain accepted vocabulary of signs, certain assumed formation rules for combining the signs, and certain assumed transformation rules for deriving new formulas from old ones—with this assumed machinery one then proceeds to—to do what?

Of course, all he can possibly do is to unroll, in all its lovely and unsuspected complexity, the truths—or more properly, the formally correct relationships—which were inherent in what he originally assumed. This procedure is, of course, quite powerless to create truths—it can only reveal what has been previously and unconsciously assumed.

But apart from this inherent limitation on deductive logic, which has of course been long recognized, there have rather recently been discovered, by Gödel, wholly unsuspected and startling imperfections in any system of deductive logic. Gödel has obtained two main results. He proved that it is impossible—theoretically impossible, not just unreasonably difficult—to prove the consistency of any set of postulates which is so to speak, rich enough in content to be interesting. The question, "Is there an inner flaw in this system?" is a question which is simply unanswerable.

He also proved that any such deductive logical system inevitably has a further great limitation. Such a system is essentially incomplete. Within the system it is always possible to ask questions which are undecidable.

If deductive logic has these vital and built-in limitations, how about inductive logic, the branch of reasoning which examines all the observed cases recorded in the evidence, and seeks to induce therefore general laws. To quote from my previous paper on this subject:

> Over 200 years ago David Hume bluntly denied the propriety of inductive logic. Ever since, certain skeptics have urged the necessity of practicing induction without pretending that it has any rational foundation; certain deductionists have vainly tried to prove Hume wrong; certain philosophers have optimistically hoped that a mild and friendly attitude towards such words as "rational" and "reasonable" could of itself sanction their application to statements referring to future and hence unexamined cases; and certain scientists have felt that it is vaguely sensible to suppose that future phenomena would conform to past regularities.

Deep and troublesome questions are involved here. Consider, just for a moment, the question: When and why does a single piece of past evidence give useful information about a future situation? If one takes a single piece of copper and determines that it conducts electricity, then it seems sensible to suppose that other future pieces of copper will also conduct electricity. But if we pick out a man at random and determine that his name is John, this does not at all lend credence to the idea that all other men are named John. The first of these seems to lead to a "lawlike statement," and the second to an "unlawlike" one; but no one, so far as I know, has ever been able to give workable form to this distinction.

In fact, in spite of many attempts to make induction intellectually tolerable, the matter remains a mess.

As the fifth imperfection in science I come to a topic which, because of its depth and subtlety, deserves a far more extensive and far more competent summary than I can give. This particular element of imperfection has to do with the supposed *objectivity* of science.

Careful thinkers have for long been skeptical about the supposed objectivity of so-called scientific facts. In the translator's preface to one of the master works of Poincaré, George Bruce Halsted said a half-century ago,

> What is called "a knowledge of the facts" is usually merely a subjective realization that the old hypotheses are still sufficiently elastic to serve in some domain; that is, with a sufficiency of conscious or unconscious omissions and doctorings and fudgings more or less wilful.

We have spoken thus far of five imperfect aspects of science. Let us summarize the view necessitated by these five points.

Science has, as a tool for dealing with nature, proved to be superbly successful. With respect to physical nature, and at all moderate scales of space or time—say larger than an atom and smaller than a galaxy, say more persistent than 10^{-10} seconds and less than a billion years—science seems to have unlimited ability. With the extremely small or the extremely large, with inconceivably brief or extended phenomena, science has a difficult time. It is by no means clear that our present concepts or even our existing language is suitable for these ranges. In the realm of animate matter, science has made wonderful, but more limited, progress. And we can, at the present, see no fixed barriers to further progress.

But if one looks deeply within this system, instead of encountering a harder and harder inner core, instead of meeting more and more dependable precision, more and more rigidity, compulsion, and finality, instead of finally reaching permanence and perfection, what does one find?

He finds unresolved and apparently unresolvable disagreement among scientists concerning the relationship of scientific thought to reality—and concerning the nature and meaning of reality itself. He finds that the explanations of science have utility, but that they do in sober fact not explain. He finds the old external appearance of inevitability completely vanished, for he discovers a charming capriciousness in all the individual events. He finds that logic, so generally supposed to be infallible and unassailable, is in fact shaky and incomplete. He finds that the whole concept of objective truth is a will-o-the-wisp.

For those who have been deluded, by external appearances and by partial understanding, into thinking of science as a relentless, all-conquering intellectual force, armed with finality and perfection, the limitations treated here would have to be considered as damaging imperfections. You will have realized, however, from the pride and enthusiasm with which I have exhibited these points, that I do not myself think of them as unpleasant imperfections, but rather as the blemishes which make our mistress all the more endearing.

And this remark leads at once to the final point—the fault which I do in fact consider a serious imperfection. This is not a weakness which is inherent in the nature of science, but one which has been created by the attitude of scientists and non-scientists alike.

I refer to the fact that many scientists—and the public which they have over-falsely impressed—have created a horrid and dangerous gap between science and the rest of life. This is the tragedy of the "Two Cultures," which have been so brilliantly discussed by C. P. Snow. "I believe," says this scientist who is a distinguished essayist and novelist, "the intellectual life of the whole of western society is increasingly being split into two polar groups."

The two cultures referred to by Snow are formed, on the one hand, of the scientist and the very few non-scientists who have bothered to understand science and its role in modern life, and on the other hand, of the literary intellectuals, the artists—in a broad sense the humanists. Snow comments that "thirty years ago the cultures had long ceased to speak to each other: but at least they managed a kind of frozen smile across the gulf. Now the politeness is gone, and they just make faces."

What we must do—scientists and non-scientists alike—is close the gap. We must bring science back into life as a human enterprise, an enterprise that has at its core the uncertainty, the flexibility, the subjectivity, the sweet unreasonableness, the dependence upon creativity and faith which permit it, when properly understood, to take its place as a friendly and understanding companion to all the rest of life.

QUESTIONS

1. List ten areas of accomplishment by science and technology which are cause for respect and admiration.
2. List the five imperfections of science as given by Dr. Weaver.
3. Discuss the explaining and understanding roles of science.
4. Which type of logic is superior—deductive or inductive? Explain.
5. Discuss the four requirements for a good theory.
6. What is the relationship of statistical theory to reality?
7. What is meant by "The Two Cultures"?